AIR POLLUTION
CONTROL

AIR POLLUTION CONTROL

CLARK C. HAVIGHURST

Editor

OCEANA PUBLICATIONS, INC.

Dobbs Ferry, New York

1969

Originally published as the Spring 1968 issue

of

LAW AND CONTEMPORARY PROBLEMS

DUKE UNIVERSITY SCHOOL OF LAW

CONTENTS

FOREWORD

Recent years have seen accelerating efforts to organize government's response to air pollution. The federal Air Quality Act of 1967 has now defined the general shape and direction of the federal effort and, in so doing, has focused renewed and additional attention on present and future regulation at the interstate, state, and local levels. Because it has appeared to the editors that a plateau has been reached from which it is possible to look both backward and forward, this symposium undertakes to provide a review of the current state of thinking and action on air pollution control.

In addition to the interest necessarily attached to any new challenge to man's capacity to avoid self-destruction, the subject has interest as a practical problem of government. The most fascinating central difficulty is that of legislating and regulating with seriously imperfect scientific understanding and within the constraints of inadequate but fast-changing technology. Another matter of overriding interest is the Air Quality Act's allocation of control responsibility, subject to federal oversight, to "air quality regions," which are federally defined areas, transcending municipal and state boundaries, in which the affected states are to administer a coordinated control program. Both of these aspects of air pollution control—the need for regulation in relative ignorance and the federal experiment in "functional regionalism"—hold significance for future efforts toward dealing with other problems of an increasingly complex society.

Pollution pours from many sources, including motor vehicles and aircraft, but stationary sources pose most of the outstanding problems. Pollution from stationary sources is currently dealt with mainly through statutes, ordinances, or administrative regulations setting absolute limits on the pollutant emissions allowable; zoning-type "variances" are available in hardship cases. These laws, and especially the variance provisions, could probably be adapted by conscientious administrators to permit the weighing of both the benefits and the costs of pollution abatement as factors in determining whether to require it in a particular case. Still, a new generation of state and local air pollution control legislation may be the preferable means of replacing arbitrary emission standards with more sophisticated regulation. A possible advantage of the federal act's allocation of ultimate responsibility to air quality regions is that it permits experimentation with regulatory approaches. Thus, one can hope that out of the "laboratories" carved out by federal law mechanisms will emerge that are finely tuned both to accomplishing abatement effectively and to maximizing the return on each dollar required to be spent.

Whether innovations in pollution control will emerge under the federal act depends in part upon the flexibility with which the Department of Health, Education, and Welfare exercises its power to approve state control programs. The act appears already to have confined states to the use of emission standards rather than a system of effluent fees, which many economists have favored. HEW must at least allow to the states some freedom in granting variances, not confining their availability to cases where an unconstitutional "taking" of private property would otherwise occur. For example, variances might be made available in any case where the costs of abatement would exceed the damage reduction attributable to it; a desirable refinement would require a fee to be paid for the variance on a unit-of-pollution basis, a sort of effluent fee. Flexibility must also characterize HEW's use of its forthcoming "air quality criteria," which, being formulated without regard to abatement costs, should not be made a mandatory goal of every pollution control program. And, finally, the states should probably be allowed to select their own methods of dealing with the many subsidiary problems, such as those associated with controlling combinations of pollutants having synergistic effects.

These reflections on the problems of air pollution control should convey the nature of the challenge. The ultimate problems are many and difficult, including those inherent in (1) creating new regulatory institutions to "internalize" costs classed by economists as "external"—that is, imposed on others without compensation because of the inadequacies of the market and the legal system; (2) regulating an important industrial activity under conditions of extreme uncertainty about every aspect of the problem except the need to control it; (3) spurring efforts to find cheap technological answers and protecting the public health and interest until they are forthcoming; (4) incorporating sophisticated analytical and simulation techniques in a regulatory program; (5) regulating on a regional basis under intergovernmental arrangements yet to be developed; (6) dealing with vested economic and community interests and the pressures they generate; (7) attempting to limit pre-existing uses of private property without incurring a constitutional obligation to pay compensation for a "taking"; and (8) meeting standards of procedural due process, particularly in satisfying judges on evidentiary sufficiency where understanding is so limited.

The war against air pollution proceeds on many fronts—scientific, technological, economic, and legal—even as the strategy is still being mapped. This symposium should assist both tacticians and grand strategists in confronting an enemy that, while newly arisen, promises to be a permanent concern.

CLARK C. HAVIGHURST.

November 1, 1968

THE HEALTH EFFECTS OF AIR POLLUTION AND THEIR IMPLICATIONS FOR CONTROL*

Eric J. Cassell†

Introduction

Air pollution is particularly interesting, not only in and of itself, but because it is the prototype of problems to come.

It is the prototype because it is intimately linked with the texture, problems, and activity of modern urban life. Where previously we sought the health effects of air pollution by attempting to pin them to the effects of individual pollutants acting separately, we are coming to realize that in a problem of this sort there is no one villain that can be pinpointed, discovered, eliminated, and the problem solved.

We are no longer as much in search of one substance in the atmosphere to account for the health effects of air pollution as we are in search of an understanding of the complex chemistry occurring in our dynamic atmosphere and the results of that chemistry on our health. But simultaneously we have become aware that we are no longer seeking one disease for which air pollution is solely responsible. Rather, there are numerous diseases in part caused by infection, by allergy, by cigarette smoking, by hereditary predisposition, by aging, to which air pollution may be only an added insult in the final outcome—a chain of events initiated by our birth, furthered by our habits, and inexorably linked to the design of our industrial society. The luxury of previous public health research—looking for one cause, one disease—is finally lost to us. And, I believe, with that loss we are ready to progress further in understanding the unquestioned health effects of air pollution and how to control it.

The legal basis for the control of air pollution has progressed from nuisance law to the statutory regulation of specific substances as the sophistication of the sciences involved progressed. But if the multifactorial nature of the problem has stymied the previous research approach, it may stymie legislation based on that research; where simplistic research approaches have failed, so too may simplistic legal remedies. The statutory control of air pollution by pursuing air pollutants one by one as evidence accumulates seems clearly inadequate to a technology producing new pollutants or sources of pollution at an almost geometric rate. Progress in control may require a return to nuisance law, perhaps more broadly based and sophisticated than formerly but still effective in achieving needed abatement.

As a basis for understanding the health effects of air pollution, ensuing sections

* This article is supported in part by the Health Research Council of the City of New York (Contract U-1155), and the Division of Air Pollution, U.S. Public Health Service (Grant No. AP-00266-01).

† Associate Professor of Community Medicine, Mount Sinai School of Medicine, New York, N.Y.

of this article deal with the nature of the research problem as well as the lines of evidence that have accumulated.

To maintain a manageable size I have confined myself primarily to air pollution as it occurs in the industrial atmospheres and is typified by the sulfur oxides. This is not to minimize the great importance of the other pollutants and the automobile, but I believe the conclusions that arise from a consideration of one type are applicable to the others.

I

NATURE OF THE PROBLEM

At the outset, let us review the nature of the biological research problem that is posed by air pollution. As John Goldsmith[1] clearly stated several years ago, this is a problem in toxicology, determining for man in his natural setting (now increasingly urban) the relationship between the dose of the noxious agent in the atmosphere and the biological response in man. Classically the toxicologist works in the laboratory and is able to present the dose of the pure toxic agent over such a wide range that he is assured of going from no effect to the most severe effects and can reliably assess the noxious capability of the substance in question. But in air pollution studies that occur in the natural setting, almost none of the ideals of the toxicology experiment are met; conversely, in laboratory studies of the effects of pollutants on man or animals, almost none of the realities of the urban setting are approximated.

What complicates these studies? For simplicity the examples that follow are based primarily on sulfur dioxide, but the problems are almost the same for all the common pollutants.

First, the dose, the sulfur dioxide, except under the most bizarre and rare circumstances, is present in the urban atmosphere in very low concentrations and over a very narrow range. The peaks are rarely ten times the daily averages. The peaks themselves are usually not above one part per million (ppm). One ppm is about the bottom of the range frequently used in the laboratory. The highest levels to which populations are exposed, therefore, are so low that they are seldom used in the laboratory. New York City levels average around 0.15 ppm.[2]

Second, sulfur dioxide does not exist alone in the atmosphere. When it is present, almost invariably, numerous other substances which may or may not have an effect on man are also present. Because of atmospheric conditions, concentrations of the other substances will be increased at the same time as the sulfur compounds are increased. It is difficult, therefore, for the scientist to know whether an effect he has observed was caused by the sulfur compounds, or by the other materials present—

---

[1] Personal communication from John Goldsmith, 1961.

[2] J.R. McCarroll & E.J. Cassell, unpublished data, Christodora Monitoring Station, New York City, 1962-65.

whether, in other words, the sulfur compounds are merely "markers" of the presence of other, more toxic materials.

The third and related complication of such studies is that all the various substances do not co-exist without interaction. The atmosphere is often naively pictured as a large pot in which things are dumped and in which they stay unchanged. But in reality the atmosphere is a dynamically active chemical retort in which substances change themselves and react with other materials to produce new and sometimes unknown substances, with this atmospheric chemical factory variously affected by the wind, sun, humidity, and other weather factors. The meaning of this dynamic chemistry for the Los Angeles oxidant type of air pollution was well demonstrated by Dr. Haagen-Smit and others;[3] but we have avoided this same conclusion, that the problems faced in the predominantly sulfur oxide pollution of the northern industrial cities may also derive from the complex interaction of pollutants and weather.

Fourth, how do we know what is really in the atmosphere? Frequently, knowledge is a function of technology. We know about sulfur dioxide because we have instruments to measure it, and have had for some time. But there are substances in the atmosphere of whose nature and presence we know nothing, and the number of such substances is probably increasing as our technology expands. For example, what happens to a plastic bag when it is incinerated; and what is the effect in the atmosphere of gasoline additives?

The fifth complicating feature of the natural experiment is the meaning of what the pollution-measuring instruments say. When a research study reports that the population was exposed to, for example, 0.25 ppm of sulfur dioxide, what does that mean? Generally the instrument did not even really measure sulfur dioxide. If it was of the conductivity type commonly in use, this instrument only reflects sulfur dioxide when that gas exists alone—but as has been pointed out, that ideal is rarely met in the atmosphere. The measurement is interfered with in numerous ways that cast serious doubt on any interpretation of experimental results that are presented as though the exposure was really to sulfur dioxide. In our studies, at one point, we had two instruments side by side, one measuring "true" SO_2 and the other employing the conductivity method commonly in use; not infrequently their readings bore no relationship to each other. In our papers we carefully use the words "whatever is represented by the measurement of sulfur dioxide";[4] but when we are quoted that important note of caution is left out or forgotten. Similarly, in some studies, the average sulfur dioxide of one area is compared to that of another and then the research findings are causally related to sulfur dioxide. However, sulfur dioxide levels are associated with many things: the weather, type of fuel used in home heating, degree of industrialization, socioeconomic level of population, crowding,

---

[3] Katz, *Physical and Chemical Aspects*, in AIR POLLUTION 97, 149 (World Health Organization 1961).
[4] *E.g.*, McCarroll *et al.*, *Health and the Urban Environment*, 14 ARCH. ENVIRON. HEALTH 178 (1967).

and probably a host of other factors, all of which have a bearing on disease. Many attempts, some successful (notably the elegant studies of Winkelstein),[5] have been made to dissociate these related factors from the effects of the pollutants, but in a number of studies these confounding factors are ignored. Legislation of the type which proposes a numerical standard for SO_2 does not deal with "whatever is represented by the measurement of sulfur dioxide"; it deals with the *gas, sulfur dioxide*.

Finally, the effect of pollutants on man is further complicated by the effect of the atmosphere itself. Temperature and humidity have an unquestioned and well known effect on health quite apart from the effect they may have on the pollutants in the atmosphere. The most sharply defined mortality peaks in New York City between 1962 and 1965 occurred during heat waves in two successive summers; and in that three year period there were more than a dozen air pollution episodes.[6]

These additional factors that influence the dose of pollutants appear to be inordinately complicating; but they cannot be dismissed because they are inconvenient. An understanding of them must underlie future approaches to the control of pollution as well as other, similar, public health problems.

The problems that beset the epidemiologist concerned with the dose of the noxious agent in his natural toxicology experiment are no more than the difficulties he confronts in looking for the effect of the pollutants on man.

Briefly stated, there have been no responses in man or animals thus far discovered which are unique to, or solely caused by, exposure to the oxides of sulfur, except perhaps odor. Secondly, there has been no way thus far to get experimental populations who are alike in all respects except their exposure to the oxides of sulfur.

I would like to amplify somewhat on these two points because they lead to an important conclusion. The effects of the oxides of sulfur on man and animals appear to be a consequence of irritation of the mucus membranes. (And to produce this irritation in the laboratory has required levels of SO_2 generally well above those found in the atmosphere.) Cough, airway constriction, increased sputum or mucus are all secondary to the irritant effect of the noxious agent on the sensitive mucus membranes. But these symptoms and research findings are also produced by cigarettes or other irritants, allergy, infections, other pollutants, emotional factors, and so on. Diseases which are, at least in part, contributed to by air pollution are also clearly influenced by other factors. Thus one of the major research tools is denied us, a marker by which we can clearly define an effect of a pollutant on the study population, uncomplicated by any other effects.

The "control population" is dear to the heart of science: a population the same

<hr>

[5] Winkelstein *et al.*, *The Relationship of Air Pollution and Economic Status to Total Mortality and Selected Respiratory System Mortality in Men*, *id.* at 162.

[6] E.J. Cassell *et al.*, Reconsiderations of Mortality as a Useful Index of the Relationship of Environmental Factors to Health, a paper presented at the American Public Health Association meeting, Miami, Fla., Oct. 1967.

in all respects except its exposure to the agent in question. But this too is denied us. Air pollution is so ubiquitous that one can never find an urban group that has no pollution. There are such great differences between life in the city and country, besides exposure to air pollution, that it is difficult, if not impossible, to disentangle these factors with any more ease than we can disentangle the differences in the same population between days of high and low pollution.

The problem becomes, therefore, not one of simply deciding on an acceptable numerical level of pollution, but of deciding how to handle a situation of this type where numbers appear to be necessary and where real meaningful conflict exists over the choice of those numbers.

II

LINES OF EVIDENCE

A. The Disasters

Certainly the most dramatic, convincing, and undeniable evidence of the deleterious effects of air pollution on humans has come from the several air pollution disasters. Although the list is not long (Meuse Valley, Belgium, 1930; Donora, Pennsylvania, 1948; London, 1952 and 1962; and Poza Rica, Mexico, 1950) the effects of these unplanned exposures were startling and impressive. The Meuse Valley, Donora and London disasters all have much in common with air pollution episodes which are quite frequent but do not cause the great mortality or morbidity. Considerable knowledge can be gleaned from a careful review of the circumstances involved.

Occurring almost universally in the autumn or early winter, they all have the same meteorologic conditions: the stable air mass of a prolonged anti-cyclonic high pressure system with secondary inversion. The inversion (in which a layer of warm air sits above a layer of cold air, the reverse of the usual situation in which the air gets colder the higher one goes) serves to act as an effective lid retaining below it all the substances that are dumped into the atmosphere and thus preventing their effective dissemination. Fog has been an invariable ingredient of every air pollution disaster.

The Donora, Pennsylvania, episode[7] occurred in October 1948. Donora is a small town with a population of 14,000 situated on a bend in the Monongahela River about thirty miles south of Pittsburgh. Donora lies in the center of an area of heavy industrial production; there are steel mills, a wire plant, a zinc smelter, and coke plants, all in the immediate vicinity. Also, the hills rise sharply behind Donora to the west and on the other side of the river to the east.

The inhabitants were long accustomed to dirty air but had never experienced a

---

[7] See generally H. SCHRENK et al., AIR POLLUTION IN DONORA, PENNSYLVANIA, EPIDEMIOLOGY OF THE UNUSUAL SMOG EPISODE OF OCTOBER, 1948 (Federal Security Agency, Public Health Bull. No. 306, 1949); Ciocco & Thompson, A Follow-Up of Donora Ten Years After, 51 AM. J. PUB. HEALTH 155 (1961).

smog like the one which began on October 26, 1948. On Monday, October 25, a stable layer of air formed in the valley area. From then until the smog was broken by rain on Sunday, October 31, this layer acted like a lid clamped over the valley, allowing the build-up of atmospheric pollutants.

✕ Two days after it started, the air was thick and heavy, and visibility was markedly reduced. Although a few persons started to feel ill on Wednesday, October 27, it was on Thursday, October 28, that large numbers became affected.✕Just as in the other disasters, shortness of breath and cough were the most prominent symptoms, although sore throat, headache, lacrimation, eye irritation, nausea, and even vomiting and diarrhea occurred in some. Between 6:00 p.m. and midnight on Thursday, forty per cent of the affected people reported the onset of their illness. By Friday, October 29, almost every person who became ill during the episode was already ill; seventeen of the total twenty deaths occurred that day. By the end of the episode, a total of 5,910 persons, 42.7 per cent of all persons living in the area, were affected to some degree by the smog.✕As in the other disasters, the elderly and those with pre-existing heart and lung disease were the most severely affected, although persons in all age groups were affected as well.

In December 1952, a temperature inversion and fog lay over most of southern England, particularly from December 5 through December 9.[8] It was especially heavy in the Thames Valley, where London is situated. Because the fog occurred in winter, sulfur dioxide and soot from soft coal used in home heating contributed heavily to the usual industrial emissions. By examining the mortality records, it was noted that an increased number of deaths occurred during the episode and in the following weeks. There were approximately 4,000 excess deaths attributed to air pollution. As in the other disasters, the majority of deaths and the greatest number of illnesses occurred in the elderly and those with previous heart and lung disease. However, increased mortality was experienced in every age group and in almost every diagnostic category. It must be emphasized that the assumption that all of these deaths were due to the air pollution episode comes from the coincidence in time of the excess mortality and the increased pollution.

Although most of the attention has been focused on the 1952 London episode, there is also evidence that there have been other similar occurrences in London prior to and since that time. As is so often the case in an acute air pollution episode, the extent of the episode and the amount of illness are often not appreciated at the time of its occurrence. In December 1962 another severe episode of markedly increased levels of pollution was noted in London. On this occasion the excess mortality was estimated to be about 600.

There has been much discussion of the reasons for the differences in mortality between the two episodes. The Donora and London 1952 disasters focused attention

<hr/>

[8] See generally MINISTRY OF HEALTH, MORTALITY AND MORBIDITY: THE LONDON FOG OF 1952 (No. 95, London, 1954).

on sulfur dioxide as the causative agent, and were in part responsible for the large volume of research into the health effects of sulfur dioxide. However, reconsideration of these episodes themselves has helped show that for effects to be manifest, more must be present in the atmosphere than sulfur dioxide alone.

In London in 1952 the highest concentration of sulfur dioxide was 1.34 ppm. In London in 1962 with fewer excess deaths, there was a higher hourly concentration of sulfur dioxide (1.98 ppm) but a considerably lower level of particulate matter or soot than in the 1952 episode. At the same time that London was experiencing the 1962 episode, the Netherlands was visited by similar weather conditions and had, as a consequence, markedly increased levels of both sulfur dioxide and particulate matter.[9] Little increased illness or mortality was reported. In general, sulfur dioxide levels were slightly lower than the English values but the amount of particulate matter was very much lower in the Netherlands.

The interrelationship between SO_2 and particulate becomes more manifest the more closely the disasters and episodes are examined. As will be seen later, this interrelationship of one pollutant to another is crucial to understanding the problem and, I think, developing a control philosophy.

That a high concentration of a specific common pollutant alone is probably not sufficient to cause increased mortality is clear from the fact that while there have been few air pollution disasters (periods of high mortality) there have been many episodes during which concentrations of air pollutants reached very high levels.

Several authors have investigated a number of episodes in New York City and have come to the conclusion that there was an increase in mortality during those periods of increased pollution. Greenburg[10] and his group have stated that increased mortality was present during episodes in New York City in 1953, 1963, and more recently in 1966. McCarroll and Bradley[11] have commented upon increased mortality occurring during several periods of increased pollution in New York City. However, more critical examination of mortality statistics and air pollution levels in New York City by the author and his colleagues[12] has thrown considerable doubt on the previous observations. What is apparent is that, if on occasion increased mortality is associated with increased air pollution, those occasions are considerably less frequent than increased air pollution without attendant changes in mortality. This latter note of caution does not detract from the fact that air pollution episodes have un-

[9] *See generally* Tesch, *Air Pollution in the Netherlands*, 57 PROCEEDINGS OF THE ROYAL SOC'Y OF MEDICINE 997 (1964).

[10] Greenburg *et al.*, *Report of an Air Pollution Episode in New York City, Nov. 1953*, 77 PUB. HEALTH REP. 7 (1962); Greenburg *et al.*, *Intermittent Air Pollution Episode in New York City, 1962*, 78 PUB. HEALTH REP. 1061 (1963); Greenburg *et al.*, *Air Pollution, Influenza, and Mortality in New York City*, 15 ARCH. ENVIRON. HEALTH 430 (1967).

[11] McCarroll & Bradley, *Excess Mortality as an Indicator of Health Effects of Air Pollution*, 56 AM. J. PUB. HEALTH 1933 (1966).

[12] E.J. Cassell *et al.*, *supra* note 6.

questionably occurred during which there was increased illness and death. As Lawther has noted in the past, "the mortal results of high concentrations of urban pollution are recognized though much work still needs to be done to elucidate the mechanism by which it exerts its effects."[13]

The basic requirement for a potential air pollution episode, the concentration of numerous and active sources of smoke and gas, is not unique to Donora, London, or even New York. This requirement is met by many of our cities and industrial areas. The meteorologic conditions necessary to produce an episode also are not unique to these areas but are found in many cities and encompass many regions of this country. The meteorologic conditions necessary to produce an episode cannot be prevented although they can usually be predicted. While there may be considerable argument about the need to control this or that specific pollutant, there is no question about the need to prevent the occurrence of air pollution episodes. All the technology necessary to accomplish this exists today. The ability to predict the occurrence and duration of the meteorologic conditions that promote air pollution episodes has made possible effective episode control. In addition, it is possible to cut back the emission of pollution from major sources. An increasing number of cities have episode control mechanisms already in force and in some areas they have been written into law.

B. Laboratory Studies

As noted earlier, determining the health effects of air pollution is a problem in toxicology, and toxicology is classically a laboratory science. Many studies on the health effects of specific pollutants have been carried out over the years. Generally speaking, these investigations have been used to determine the following things: basic physiologic response to specific pollutants; the dose-response relationship; factors within the host which modify the response; factors affecting the pollutant which modify the response. As mentioned earlier, laboratory studies are generally unable to approximate the realities of the urban situation. It is often difficult to know the degree to which laboratory results apply to the real setting. The most striking difference between most laboratory studies and "real life" is the use of animals rather than man to determine the effects of the pollutant involved. Although there are very real ethical and medical limitations to the use of man as an experimental animal in determining the effect of air pollutants, there have been a number of studies utilizing man as well as studies utilizing animals. The footnote references include studies involving other pollutants, but the discussion here will deal primarily with the oxides of sulfur.

Reid exposed rats to sulfur dioxide at a level of 400 ppm and was able to produce

---

[13] Lawther, *Symposium on Air Pollution—Summary*, 57 PROCEEDINGS OF THE ROYAL SOC'Y OF MEDICINE 1040 (1964).

a secretion of mucus analogous to that found in human bronchitis.[14] Earlier, Dalhamm had shown that an exposure to high concentrations of sulfur dioxide effectively stopped the ciliary activity (which is part of the mechanism for removal of foreign particulate matter introduced to the lung) within the tracheo-bronchial tree.[15] Humans are intolerant to atmospheres containing 400 ppm of sulfur dioxide.

Over the last number of years, Amdur and her colleagues have carried out a series of experiments on guinea pigs in an attempt to determine the mechanism of effect of sulfur dioxide.[16] It was early shown that sulfur dioxide in sufficient concentration was able to increase airway resistance. This broncho-constriction is a feature of chronic bronchitis and other chronic diseases of the lung. While the effect in guinea pigs required concentrations of sulfur dioxide considerably above those found in ambient atmosphere, Amdur found that the addition of an inert particle (sodium chloride) seemed to produce a synergistic effect; an increase in airway resistance greater than could be accounted for by the sulfur dioxide or the sodium chloride particles alone. In the ensuing years, the group has used particles which are not in themselves inert, but interact with the sulfur dioxide to produce sulfuric acid or sulfur trioxide. With these more active particles the dose of sulfur dioxide required to produce a physiologic effect has more nearly approached the levels that might be found in urban air. Amdur has reported some effects in men exposed to relatively low (one to eight ppm) concentrations of sulfur dioxide.[17] Frank, in experiments on healthy humans,[18] was generally unable to show any change in airway resistance (the most sensitive indicator of effect at hand) at concentrations of sulfur dioxide below five ppm. However, in his experiments one individual responded to the range one to two ppm. In studies over many years, Lawther has been unable to demonstrate any effects in man of realistic concentrations of sulfur dioxide although an occasional experimental subject has reacted in a more sensitive manner.[19] Sim and Pattle, while showing similar lack of response to the usual ambient concentrations, also demonstrated the phenomenon of the sensitive individual.[20] If such "sensitive" individuals exist in large numbers in the population, then ambient concentrations of sulfur dioxide, thought now to be harmless, might represent a greater threat.

[14] Reid, *An Experimental Study of Hypersecretion of Mucus in the Bronchial Tree*, 44 BRIT. J. EXPERIMENTAL PATHOLOGY 437 (1963).

[15] Dalhamm, *Mucous Flow and Ciliary Activity in the Trachea of Healthy Rats and Rats Exposed to Respiratory Irritant Gases*, 36 ACTA PHYSIOLOGICA SCAND., 123 SUPPLEMENTUM (1956).

[16] Amdur, *The Effect of Aerosols on the Response to Irritant Gases*, in INHALED GASES AND PARTICLES (C. Davies ed. 1961).

[17] Amdur, Melvin & Drinker, *Effects of Inhalation of Sulfur Dioxide by Man*, [1953] 2 THE LANCET 758.

[18] Frank & Speizer, *Uptake and Release of SO_2 by the Human Nose*, 7 THE PHYSIOLOGIST 132 (1964).

[19] Lawther, *Effects of Inhalation of Sulfur Dioxide on Respiration and Pulse-Rate in Normal Subjects*, [1955] 2 THE LANCET 745.

[20] Sim & Pattle, *Effects of Possible Smog Irritants on Human Subjects*, 165 J.A.M.A. 1908 (1957).

Initially, studies by Frank,[21] Dalhamm and Strandberg,[22] and others showed that almost none of the sulfur dioxide that is inhaled enters the deepest reaches of the lung; that it is virtually completely removed by absorption in the nose or pharynx. Nadel, trying to explain why the sulfur dioxide should cause broncho-constriction if it did not reach the lower lung passages, demonstrated that the effect was a reflex from irritation in the upper airways.[23]

More recent studies by Amdur have resolved some of the conflict by showing that the higher the concentration of inhaled sulfur dioxide the higher the percentage absorption in the upper airways.[24] At very low concentrations of inhaled SO_2 (0.16 ppm) very little is absorbed in the upper airways and almost all reaches the lung itself. In addition, the absorbed sulfur dioxide has been shown to enter the blood stream.

The use of sulfuric acid mists in experiments similar to those quoted above has shown this substance to be a potent irritant of the respiratory tract. Here again, concentrations larger than those experienced in the worst air pollution have been required to produce an effect. However, sulfuric acid mist is not a gas but rather a particle. In appropriate particle sizes as much as sixty to eighty per cent of the inhaled particulate reaches the alveoli.

Once a solid particle reaches the small airways and alveoli, its residence time is measured in weeks, months, or years. The effects of some particles are well known; the occupational disease silicosis results from the long-term inhalation of silica containing particles.

The studies of Johnstone over many years have demonstrated that the inter-action of the gas sulfur dioxide with catalyzing particles such as manganese, iron, vanadium, and titanium, for example, can result in the formation of sulfuric acid in the presence of the particle.[25] While it is only speculation, it appears likely that under certain conditions where both sulfur dioxide and catalyzing particle nuclei are present in the same atmosphere, the gas will be adsorbed onto the particle and sulfuric acid will be produced. In the proper size range such particles can be inhaled and retained in the lung. Under those circumstances one would be in-haling what is, in essence, a tiny sulfuric acid manufacturing plant.

Such catalytic particles are a common constituent of urban atmospheres. They result from the burning of fuel oil and coal, and they are increasingly used as gasoline additives. The kinds of particles and the type of catalyst may vary widely from region to region. The "London particle" is different from the "New York

---

[21] Frank & Speizer, *supra* note 18.

[22] Dalhamm & Strandberg, *Acute Effect of Sulfur Dioxide on the Rate of Ciliary Beat in the Rabbit*, 4 INT'L J. AIR & WATER POLLUTION 154 (1961).

[23] Nadel *et al.*, *Mechanism of Bronchoconstriction*, 10 ARCH. ENVIRON. HEALTH 175 (1965).

[24] Amdur, *Respiratory Absorption Data and SO_2 Dose-Response Curves*, 12 ARCH. ENVIRON. HEALTH 729 (1966).

[25] Johnstone, *Properties of Aerosols Related to the Effects of Inhaled Particles and Vapors*, in INHALED GASES AND PARTICLES 95 (C. Davies ed. 1961).

particle." It is intriguing to speculate whether these particle differences may play a role in the apparent differences between the effects of air pollution in London and, for example, New York. Differences in weather are also likely to contribute to differences in the reactive chemical retort that is now the urban atmosphere.

The laboratory has provided evidence that the common constituents of air pollution are capable of producing adverse effects in both man and animals. Such a demonstration of adverse effect has also been made for virtually all the common pollutants, including those in the oxidant atmospheres, such as that of Los Angeles.[26] In general it has required amounts of pollutants far above those generally found in the atmosphere to produce effects. Again, one is forced to conclude that because of the multiplicity of factors at work, the whole is greater than the sum of its parts.

C. Chronic Pulmonary Disease

Even a cursory perusal of morbidity and mortality data shows that chronic bronchitis is more commonly found in large towns than in sparsely populated areas of Great Britain. In Great Britain it is a common disease, accounting for a significant percentage of the total mortality and morbidity. The apparently obvious association between the urban situation and chronic bronchitis led to great interest in its study as a means of demonstrating the health effects of air pollution. The interest was widened by the increasing prevalence of chronic respiratory diseases in the United States and Europe. The studies of Reid and others seemed initially to incriminate sulfur dioxide as a causative factor in the production of chronic bronchitis.[27] As sophistication increased in the study of this disease it became clear that the problem was not so simple. One of the first victims of the increasing sophistication was the definition of the disease. Investigators in the United States were talking about a different thing than the British when they used the words chronic bronchitis. After many years the definition has become standardized and studies that are comparable have now been done on an international scale. It is now called non-specific lung disease, chronic obstructive pulmonary disease, chronic respiratory disease, and several other names, but all of these names are descriptive of an illness which is characterized by cough, the production of variable amounts of phlegm, and broncho-constriction (an obstruction to the easy passage of air through the bronchial tubes). The relationship of this disease to emphysema is unclear except that while emphysema is a disease in which cough and phlegm may not be present, several of the physiologic features are shared by both. The end state in either is a respiratory cripple.

Within limited and climatically fairly homogeneous areas, for example in London, the distribution of bronchitis mortality has been shown to reflect the varying

---

[26] See, e.g., 1 AIR POLLUTION passim (2d ed. A. Stern 1968).
[27] E.g., Reid & Fairbairn, The Natural History of Chronic Bronchitis, [1958] 1 THE LANCET 1147.

concentrations of smoke and sulfur dioxide in the local atmosphere. A marked gradient exists between country districts and urban areas which correlates well with local pollution levels. However, as noted above, elevated levels of sulfur dioxide and smoke are more than indicators of air pollution. Therefore, it may be un- warranted to assume a cause and effect relationship between air pollution and bronchitis. Sophisticated techniques, however, have been used to show that there is a positive correlation between local air pollution levels and bronchitis death rates that are independent of such social characteristics as population density and over- crowding. Other approaches are possible to delineate the various factors in the production of the disease. The investigation of industrial cohorts has been widely used. Reid, in England, studied postmen,[28] and Cornwall and Raffle, in England, studied bus employees.[29] These studies, done on occupational groups where job and pay are uniform throughout the area, have demonstrated an excess in bronchitis morbidity in the most heavily polluted districts. Postal employees working much out of doors, for example, have a higher bronchitis morbidity than postal employees who work inside.

Investigations using the same techniques as those used in England have been carried out in the United States.[30] The greater frequency of chronic respiratory disease in Britain as compared to the United States that was indicated by the reported death rates was confirmed in these studies of respiratory symptoms. The results also confirmed previous indications of more serious respiratory disease in British cities than rural areas of that country. In addition, although there was a smaller urban- rural difference in the United States, the prevalence of chronic respiratory disease was not as high in the United States as in England, and even more significantly, did not vary greatly from New York to San Francisco or Los Angeles. The most im- portant finding of these studies, however, is that the overwhelming factor that cor- relates with chronic bronchitis is cigarette smoking. The contribution of the cigarette to this disease appears to be so great, that at least in its production it is difficult to indict another agent. However, even differences in smoking do not appear to account for the differences in prevalence of chronic bronchitis between the United States and England. It may be significant that although there are sev- eral areas (which were included in the studies) in the United States which have sulfur dioxide levels as high as those occurring in London, the amount of suspended particulate matter is almost invariably very much less.

There may be some question about the role of air pollution in the production of chronic respiratory disease, but there can be no question that it is a factor in

---

[28] Reid, *General Epidemiology of Chronic Bronchitis*, 49 PROCEEDINGS OF THE ROYAL SOC'Y OF MEDI- CINE 767 (1956).

[29] Cornwall & Raffle, *Bronchitis Sickness Absence in London Transport*, 18 BRIT. J. INDUSTRIAL MEDICINE 24 (1961).

[30] E.g., Holland *et al.*, *Respiratory Disease in England and the United States*, 10 ARCH. ENVIRON. HEALTH 338 (1965).

the aggravation of pre-existing symptoms or disease. Dr. Lawther and his group in England have studied the problem extensively and have shown fluctuations in the state of well-being of a group of patients with chronic pulmonary disease that are clearly associated with changes in air pollution.[31] C. M. Fletcher's group in London came to the same conclusion while following an industrial population, the majority of whom had some evidence of chronic bronchitis.[32] Spicer used advanced techniques for evaluating day-to-day variations in pulmonary function in a group, some of whom had chronic obstructive pulmonary disease and others of whom were normal.[33] While he was unable to demonstrate that the observed variations were due to any particular pollutant or meteorologic variable, it was clear that the group tended to react together and therefore appeared to be responding to some common, presumably environmental, stimulus.

In addition to what other factors may contribute to the production or exacerbation of chronic pulmonary disease, occupation may be important. Enterline's studies on the prevalence of chronic pulmonary disease in miners[34] has shown distinct variations from mining community to mining community although the evidence seems to indicate that coal miners in general have a far higher prevalence of chronic lung disease than the "normal" population in the United States.

From all the data we must conclude, with Professor Reid, that although air pollution is "certainly not the only cause, nor perhaps even the major initiating cause, it is almost certainly a promoting or aggravating factor in the evolution of serious chronic lung disease."[35]

For the purposes of this discussion, consideration of chronic pulmonary disease should bring sharply into focus the multifactorial nature of the public health problem before us. What appeared at first to be a simple direct cause and effect association between air pollution and an easily identifiable disease soon lost that attractive simplicity. The disease itself turned out to be more complex than was thought at first. The association of cigarette smoking, so clear and undeniable; the role of infection in worsening the course; the effect of air pollution in producing exacerbations; the greater prevalence among lower socioeconomic groups; and the real differences in the disease between the United States and Britain make chronic respiratory disease a model for the concept of the complex interplay of factors in diseases associated with air pollution.

[31] Lawther, *Climate, Air Pollution and Chronic Bronchitis*, 51 PROCEEDINGS OF THE ROYAL SOC'Y OF MEDICINE 262 (1958).

[32] Angel, Fletcher *et al.*, *Respiratory Illness in Factory and Office Workers*, 59 BRIT. J. DIS. CHEST 66 (1965).

[33] Spicer & Kerr, *Variation of Respiratory Function: Studies on Patients and Normal Subjects*, 12 ARCH. ENVIRON. HEALTH 217 (1966).

[34] Enterline, *The Effects of Occupation on Chronic Respiratory Disease*, 14 ARCH. ENVIRON. HEALTH 189 (1967).

[35] Reid, *Air Pollution as a Cause of Chronic Bronchitis*, 57 PROCEEDINGS OF THE ROYAL SOC'Y OF MEDICINE 965 (1964).

D. Epidemiology of Air Pollution in Normal Populations

It is in normal populations that the importance of the health impact of air pollution on the general population must be sought. The finding of a meaningful effect on the health of normal citizens would provide greater impetus in the control of air pollution. On the other hand, studies in normal populations should also make it clear whether the effects found are the result, in so far as can be determined, of one pollutant or of the total complex.

The type of investigation used has varied from the crudest search for differences in mortality between polluted and less polluted areas to repeated surveys of normal populations using the most sensitive physiologic measurements of lung function. The early hope that a survey of mortality patterns in the United States would clearly show a difference that might be attributed to air pollution was not sustained by the evidence.[36] More recently, and with considerable elegance, the studies of Hammond on a large population in California have not shown differences in mortality that could be attributed to air pollution.[37] What has repeatedly shown itself in all such surveys is an urban-rural difference which is now acquiring the popular label, "the urban factor."

Some studies in special populations have been mentioned earlier in the section on chronic bronchitis. There it was noted that the examination of special industrial populations in England had clearly demonstrated a difference in the prevalence of chronic bronchitis which was thought to be associated with the air pollution of the region of employment. Less satisfactory correlations have resulted from the similar studies in the United States. An earlier study established a positive correlation between respiratory absenteeism and the sulfation levels of a number of cities in which one large company had employees.[38]

Because young children can be expected not to smoke and to have relatively normal pulmonary function, free from the effect of long-term disease or aging, they would appear to be ideal populations in which to determine a difference between those living in polluted and non-polluted atmospheres. Several studies employing such populations of children have been conducted in the United States and abroad. Toyama and Tomono studied the pulmonary ventilatory capacity of primary school children in Kawasaki.[39] They compared 245 students aged ten to eleven in a polluted area with 163 students of the same age in a school located in a clean air area of the same city. They were able to show that the average pulmonary function

---

[36] *See* Prindle, *Some Considerations in the Interpretation of Air Pollution Effect Data*, 9 J. AIR POLLUTION CONTROL ASS'N 12 (1959).

[37] C. Hammond, Epidemiological Evidence on the Effects of Air Pollution, a paper presented at the Annual Meeting of the Air Pollution Control Association, Cleveland, Ohio, June 1967.

[38] Dohan *et al.*, *Variations in Air Pollution and the Incidence of Respiratory Disease*, 12 J. AIR POLLUTION CONTROL ASS'N 418 (1962).

[39] Toyama & Tomono, *Pulmonary Ventilatory Capacity of School Children in a Heavily Polluted Area*, 8 J. JAPANESE SOC'Y OF PUB. HEALTH 659 (1961).

measurements fluctuated with a striking parallelism to the monthly dustfall in the children in the school in the polluted area. The pulmonary function of students in the school in the cleaner environment was invariably better than that of the children in the school in the polluted area. A questionnaire survey of the same children confirmed the differences with symptoms such as coughing and expectoration occurring in greater numbers in those children in the more highly polluted area. Similar results were reported by Watanabe from Osaka where again it was shown that students attending two schools in a polluted industrial area in Osaka had worse pulmonary function values than students attending a school in a rural area with little pollution.[40] There was in both of these studies, of course, a large effect of weather and season. In neither study was it possible to separate the effects of sulfur oxides from those of particulate matter of other pollutants.

Lunn and his group reported on a group of 819 infant school children living in areas of Sheffield, England, with widely ranging air pollution levels.[41] Upper respiratory tract illness and lower respiratory tract illness showed differences between the areas which were attributed to differences in pollution exposure. When several other socioeconomic factors were accounted for, the difference remained. Therefore, from the studies cited, it would appear that in children there is a distinct difference in the illness experience and certain pulmonary functions which appears to be related to the degree of pollution in the area in which they reside or go to school.

The ideal epidemiologic experiment would be one in which two populations the same in all respects except for their air pollution exposure could be compared to determine the effects of the air pollution. Such a "natural" experiment was studied by Prindle and his associates in the Public Health Service.[42] Seward and New Florence, Pennsylvania, are towns only a few miles apart. Their inhabitants are similar but, because of the prevailing winds, a power plant situated between them unloads most of its effluent onto Seward. Seward has three times as great a dustfall, six times as much sulfation but almost equivalent amounts of suspended particulate (the size range that is breathed deep into the lungs). Studies of pulmonary function, chest x-rays, and surveys of bronchitis failed to show major differences between these two towns that might be attributed to air pollution. There did seem to be a greater frequency of increased airway resistance in Seward, the dirtier town, than in New Florence. However, other extremely important factors which bear on this difference, such as smoking habits, and occupational differences, were not taken into account in the original conclusions. Subsequent examination of the data has failed to support a marked difference in illness experience between the polluted and

[40] Watanabe et al., *Effects of Air Pollution on Health*, 26 OSAKA CITY INSTITUTE OF HYGIENE 32 (1968).

[41] Lunn et al., *Patterns of Respiratory Illness in Sheffield Infant School Children*, 21 BRIT. J. OF PREV. & SOCIAL MED. 7 (1967).

[42] Prindle et al., *Comparison of Pulmonary Function and Other Parameters in Two Communities with Widely Different Air Pollution Levels*, 53 AM. J. PUB. HEALTH 200 (1963).

non-polluted atmosphere. The inability to clearly demonstrate a health effect of air pollution in such a setting is somewhat disappointing. However, what appeared to be markedly different levels of pollution are, on closer inspection, not as dissimilar as one might have believed. The small-sized, respirable particulate matter is sufficiently the same so that if, as there is reason to suspect from other evidence, it is the interaction of particle and other substances which produces the effect, then the difference between the two towns may be illusory.

Ferris and Anderson carried out a similar but more extensive survey of two widely dissimilar towns.[43] The first, Berlin, New Hampshire, is a relatively polluted industrial town. The contrasting area was Chilliwack, British Columbia, in which there is no major pollutant-producing industry. The town is bypassed by large highways and therefore not much exposed to motor car exhausts; it could be classified as a rural community. Utilizing the internationally accepted questionnaire method for determining chronic bronchitis as well as pulmonary function studies of several types, the population in the two towns was similarly surveyed. In the section related to Berlin, New Hampshire, it was clearly shown by the authors that the smoking habits of the population were an important factor in the causation of chronic non-specific respiratory disease. In Berlin, New Hampshire, they could not demonstrate any significant difference in the prevalence of chronic non-specific respiratory disease in residents of different areas of the town exposed to different levels of air pollution. Between the two areas, however, while men had the same rate of chronic respiratory disease in Berlin and Chilliwack, there was a higher rate of chronic respiratory disease among women in Berlin than in Chilliwack. Similarly, respiratory function was more impaired in Berlin than in the cleaner town of Chilliwack. These results can be interpreted to indicate an effect of the air pollutants in Berlin. On the other hand, the authors point out that ethnic differences might explain the finding.

An extensive air pollution and health study was conducted in Nashville, Tennessee, in the late 1950s by the Division of Air Pollution of the Public Health Service together with cooperating university and local agencies.[44] Nashville was selected because it was believed to have a chronic air pollution problem in large measure due to the combustion of coal. This study has been criticized on a number of counts, but it represents an extremely detailed attempt to show a relationship between air pollution and mortality, general and specific morbidity data, specific cardio-respiratory disease rates, asthma, and a number of other indices of health. There seems little question from the results that a number of these health indices were directly related to exposure to air pollution. The hypothesis that the oxides of

[43] Ferris & Anderson, *Epidemiological Studies Related to Air Pollution: A Comparison of Berlin, New Hampshire and Chilliwack, British Columbia,* 57 PROCEEDINGS OF THE ROYAL SOC'Y OF MEDICINE 979 (1964).

[44] Kenline & Contee, *Nashville Air Pollution and Health Study—A Summary,* 82 PUB. HEALTH REP. 17 (1967).

sulfur were the direct cause rather than indicators of the specific cause is not supported by the data. In this study, as in others, the socioeconomic determinants of disease had to be controlled to demonstrate an air pollution effect.

Winkelstein in a series of very careful epidemiologic studies has demonstrated a positive association between air pollution level and total mortality among a group of men aged fifty to sixty-nine when economic factors were controlled.[45] The same pattern was evident among women. For chronic respiratory disease a similar positive association was found in men. No association was found between air pollution and cancer of the lung although there was an inverse relationship between socioeconomic status and lung cancer.

As an attempt to overcome the frustrations involved in demonstrating a meaningful relationship between usual urban levels of air pollution and illness in urban populations the Cornell Family Illness Study was set up in 1961.[46] The population studied was a reasonable cross-section of New York City residents and was comprised of 1,800 persons living in one-half square mile of reasonably homogeneous air pollution. A daily record of the appearance of each of twenty-one symptoms of disease as well as much other health information was obtained by weekly interview. The participants remained in the study for an average of forty-six weeks each. Generally speaking, the results have shown no striking correlations between any of the symptoms and any specific measurement of pollution. However, analyzed in a number of different ways there has been a consistently demonstrable association between certain respiratory symptoms and a combination of pollutants and weather variables. In other words, while no correlation could be made which indicted a single pollutant as the cause of these symptoms, when combined with other pollutants and weather, then the environment appeared to contribute to the symptom burden of the population. More recent analyses of the data are beginning to reveal more clearly the complex interrelationships and how they vary from season to season and symptom to symptom.[47]

Again, a demonstration has been made of an association between health indices and air pollution as a generality. The ability to provide positive evidence of the effect of air pollution in the natural setting disappears when individual pollutants are looked to as the direct cause of the expression of illness or mortality.

[45] Winkelstein et al., supra note 5.

[46] McCarroll et al., Air Pollution and Family Illness, 10 ARCH. ENVIRON. HEALTH 357 (1965); Cassell et al., Two Acute Air Pollution Episodes in New York City, id. at 367.

[47] See E.J. Cassell et al., Air Pollution, Weather and Illness in Children and Adults in a New York Population, a paper presented at the Ninth Annual Air Pollution Medical Research Conference, Denver, Colo., July 22, 1968.

III

Implications

From the foregoing, the following conclusions seem reasonable. First, under certain meteorologic conditions air pollution may increase to such degree as to cause widespread illness and even death. Second, individuals with chronic bronchitis or other similar diseases of the lung may be affected by air pollution at the levels experienced in the industrialized urban center. Third, there are present in urban air substances that can cause irritation of the mucus membranes, increased airway resistance and other specific changes in man and experimental animals, but to produce these changes in the laboratory requires pollutants in amounts that are virtually never found in our air even during air pollution episodes. Fourth, in normal populations of all ages there is little question that air pollution contributes to the symptom, illness, and physiologic burden in the urban setting. Finally, and perhaps most important in considering the legal aspects of the control of air pollution, to produce these effects the whole is greater than the sum of its parts, with interactions between particles and gases, pollutants, and weather all necessary to produce the noxious effect.

In the last few years, while the sciences involved in understanding the health effects of air pollution have gradually moved from the naive search for single villains to an increasing appreciation and understanding of the multifactorial nature of the problem, the society has also moved forward. There is more and more evidence of an increasing desire of the population for improvement in the total environment as the right of man in an affluent state.

This drive to a cleaner environment is not an original trend in our time. In England during the 1830s, largely as the result of the efforts of Edwin Chadwick who was a lawyer, not a physician, the Sanitary Movement was founded. The Sanitarians, without benefit of scientific evidence, became intolerant of the grossly filthy environment that characterized English cities at the time: sewage running in the streets, foul water, unbridled dirt and smell. As a matter of fact, originally they held against the germ theory of disease in favor of the miasmatic theory which stated that all smell was disease. By their work they effected, in essence, a sanitary revolution whose benefits we still actively enjoy. It may be that we are in the beginning of what Dr. Prindle has called "The Era of Sanitary Reawakening," similar in magnitude to the Sanitary Movement of the nineteenth century.

But despite the fact that the science has moved towards an understanding of the complex relationships involved and the society has become increasingly intolerant of its atmosphere, we are still employing old concepts in the control of air pollution. Despite the fact it bears little relationship to the nature of the problem, the concept of a fixed numerical standard is difficult to exorcise since it seems so logical. Air pollution standards imply that below a certain set level we are all safe and above a set level we are in danger. But health is a continuum, and we expect to be better off as the continuum of pollution approaches zero. It is an old public health philosophy that a clean environment is a healthy environment and a cleaner environment a healthier one. While apparently moral in tone, the philosophy is really a recognition of the totality of the contribution of environmental influences to health or, conversely, to disease. It is interesting that the Public Health Service, so long an advocate of that philosophy, has become entrapped in the policy of pursuing pollutants one at a time. The recent Public Health Service publication, *Air Quality Criteria for Sulfur Oxides*,[48] has virtually no merit as an attempt to prove the specific effects of the oxides of sulfur. It is a much better document viewed as a compilation of the available data indicating that air pollution, as a totality, has a deleterious effect on health.

It is interesting, but not surprising, that as a result of increasing understanding of the problem we should have come full swing to the point where, based on hard scientific evidence, air pollution control measures might better be those which are more general rather than more specific. In the move from control based on law against nuisance to statutory regulation of specific pollutants we may have moved to control measures inappropriate to the problem and the scientific evidence. We may be forced to return to more sophisticated use of basic public health law.

Jonsson has discussed some of the health research implications of the use of nuisance legislation in Sweden.[49] I have attempted to find some control concept that is sound both in relation to the health effects evidence and the way pollutants are produced. Those requirements are met, I believe, by *the control of emissions to the greatest extent feasible, employing the maximum technological capability*. While seemingly simplistic, the concept fits the growing body of knowledge indicating the complex totality of air pollution in its effects. In addition, determining feasibility and technological capability, although difficult, is vastly easier than determining the level in the atmosphere at which a pollutant may be safe or unsafe. In essence this is process control rather than individual pollutant control. Process control recognizes the fact that any avoidable soiling of the environment from a process that produces emissions is undesirable. What is avoidable or not avoidable, in practical terms, is determined by feasibility and technological capability.

There is no reason why research directed towards understanding the specific mechanisms by which air pollution produces disease should be stopped. There is increasing need for the time-consuming expensive research that is required to understand the long-term effects of low levels of pollutants on normal populations. If, however, each regulation must await specific evidence of health effects prior to enactment, the situation is hopeless. The number of substances indiscriminately added to the air increases all the time. Gasoline additives contain copper, nickel, vanadium, titanium, boron, barium, and numerous other catalytic metals. Plastic

---

[48] U.S. PUBLIC HEALTH SERVICE, DEP'T OF HEALTH, EDUCATION, AND WELFARE, AIR QUALITY CRITERIA FOR SULPHUR OXIDES (1967).

[49] Jonsson, *Nuisance from External Environmental Factors and Norms for Their Evaluation*, 44 NORDISK HYGIENISK TIDSKRIFT 69-84 (1963).

bags contain trace metals of endless variety. Transistor batteries contain large amounts of mercury and other toxic metals. Food packaging, clothing, building materials, rubber, asbestos, and endless other substances end their lives in the air and become part of the respiratory intake of every urban individual. They end their lives in the air because they end their lives in industrial or commercial incinerators. It is inconceivable that effective regulation of these potential hazards will come about by fixed standards.

What makes air pollution a prototype public health problem is its complexity because the interaction of multiple social, individual, and technical factors in the production of disease is by no means unique to air pollution. Noise, poverty, nutrition, medical care, automobile accidents, to name a few, are all public health problems of similar type.

There is nothing new in the concept of many factors playing a part in the origin of a disease. What is different is that often in these problems no one factor is so dominant, that by its removal or control alone, the problem to which it contributes will be solved. Where one factor is so dominant (the automobile in automobile accidents) its role in the society is so pervasive that its removal is not feasible. In a sense these dominant factors *are* the urban industrialized society, and they cannot be completely removed except at the cost of the society as it is. The persistence of the attempt to regulate SO_2 as an individual pollutant down to "clean" levels has a tint of nostalgic past-pointing: of returning to less complicated times. We cannot go back to less complicated problems but we can go forward to better methods of dealing with the problems we have.

For science this demands new or improved analytic and research tools for understanding the quantitative relationships of the involved components. For the law it requires a better understanding of science and its implications for the society.

CONCLUSION

A brief review of the health effects of air pollution has been presented. The nature of the biological problem itself and evidence from various lines of inquiry indicate that while many of the pollutants in urban atmospheres have demonstrable effects on health, the effects of air pollution as a whole are not explained by the individual constituents acting separately. Because of the multifactorial nature of air pollution and its effects, control based primarily on standards for individual pollutants may be inadequate to the problem. The proliferation of pollutant and manufacturing or other process changes makes fixed standards seem as inappropriate to the sources of pollution as they are to the health effects. Evidence is presented for a return to more broadly based control concepts.

The need for re-examination of control concepts is enhanced by the fact that air pollution is a prototype problem, typical of the complex interrelationships of public health problems in a modern industrialized urban society.

AIR POLLUTION CONTROL TECHNOLOGY: RESEARCH AND DEVELOPMENT ON NEW AND IMPROVED SYSTEMS

JOHN H. LUDWIG[*]

INTRODUCTION

It is one of the great ironies of the twentieth century that we should be threatened by a cloud of pollution created by our own technological progress—and we are challenged to use our ingenuity to eliminate the production of pollutants that destroy property, damage plant life, endanger human health, and rob us of our enjoyment of natural beauty in our urban areas. Unfortunately, the job of control is not an easy one. There are as many potential sources of air pollution as there are manufacturing operations, motor vehicles, home heaters, power plants, and incinerators, to list some of the major sources.

Every year the number of possible sources increases sharply with the accelerating trends of population growth, urbanization, industrialization, increased affluence, and greater mobility. It has been estimated that total passenger car registration will reach 120 million by 1985. There were 75 million cars in 1965. And in 1985 there will be another 20 million trucks and buses.

In the decade between 1966 and 1976 it has been estimated that emissions of sulfur dioxide from combustion and industrial processes will increase from about 23 million tons per year to about 40 million tons per year even though a severe but realistic control program is effected. The volume of solid wastes will increase from 170 million to 230 million tons per year during this same decade, and most importantly, the percentage of these wastes that will have to be incinerated will increase at a much greater rate as the space available for landfill becomes even more scarce.

Just to maintain present air quality we will have to make great progress in pollution control; to effectively clean up the air will require increased application of control procedures already available as well as adoption of new techniques, which are only now under development, as soon as these are reduced to reasonable practice.

The need for a vigorous control program has been recognized by President Johnson[1] and by the Congress[2] and is reflected in the Air Quality Act of 1967,[3] which goes far beyond previous legislation in providing the administrative procedures and

---

[*] B.S. 1934, University of California (Berkeley); M.S. 1941, University of Colorado; M.S. 1956, Sc.D. 1958, Harvard University. Associate Director, National Center for Air Pollution Control, U.S. Public Health Service, Department of Health, Education, and Welfare.

[1] *E.g.*, PRESIDENT OF THE UNITED STATES, MESSAGE ON AIR POLLUTION, H.R. Doc. No. 47, 90th Cong., 1st Sess. (1967).

[2] *E.g.*, H.R. REP. No. 728, 90th Cong., 1st Sess. (1967); S. REP. No. 403, 90th Cong., 1st Sess. (1967); H.R. REP. No. 916, 90th Cong., 1st Sess. (1967) (conference report).

[3] 81 Stat. 485, *amending* 42 U.S.C. §§ 1857 to 1857*l* (1964).

financial backing for an effective program. One of the requirements of this act is that the Department of Health, Education, and Welfare develop and publish information on techniques for preventing and controlling air pollution, including cost-effectiveness of alternative methods.[4] Reports on control of specific pollutants are to be published concurrently with the Department's air quality criteria describing the effect of these pollutants on people and on property.[5] The first reports on sulfur oxides and particulates are expected to be published during the latter part of 1968, and will be followed by reports on carbon monoxide and other pollutants.

The Air Quality Act also provides for a substantially accelerated research effort—an effort which for the first time is commensurate with the magnitude of the air pollution control problem.[6] Special emphasis is being placed on finding new and improved ways of dealing with the complex problems associated with combustion of fuels, especially those fuels containing a high percentage of sulfur and those used in motor vehicles.[7]

In response to the need to develop new and more efficient methods for combatting pollution from a multitude of sources, the National Center for Air Pollution Control has expanded research and development in its own facilities and in those of other federal departments and agencies. But more significantly, the Center will utilize the technological resources of the entire nation. Private industry is especially capable of contributing to the search for practical solutions to the various technical problems involved in controlling air pollution; the federal program is already moving in this direction. The language of the Air Quality Act clearly reveals the intent of Congress that there shall be the closest kind of cooperation, not only between the Center and state, municipal, and county governments in control programs for enforcing regulations on pollution control, but also between the federal government and all segments of the private sector to assist, both technically and financially, in the development of new or improved technology.[8]

In some areas of control technology we have begun to make considerable progress, but there is much yet to be done. In this article I shall attempt to indicate the present status of control technology and the direction of future research and development.

I

THE CONTROL OF POLLUTION FROM STATIONARY SOURCES

If smoke from many factory stacks is no longer black, this is due to the application of technology that has been available for some time—at some economic penalty, of course—for the removal of particulates from flue gas wastes. Many factories use electrostatic precipitators which trap particles by applying electrical charges to them.

[4] § 107(c), 81 Stat. 491 (1967).
[5] § 107(b), 81 Stat. 491 (1967); see H.R. REP. No. 728, 90th Cong., 1st Sess. 15-16, 33-34 (1967).
[6] § 103, 81 Stat. 486 (1967).
[7] § 104, 81 Stat. 487 (1967).
[8] E.g., § 102, 81 Stat. 485 (1967).

Others use scrubbers in which process exhausts are forced through a liquid spray, and still others employ filters of various types, or devices that utilize inertial properties of the particles for collection.

Particulate control, however, is not so complete or so economical as it needs to be to meet the need for removal of ever-increasing percentages of material from process effluents. Very small particles elude most equipment designed to control air pollution, and it is this portion of particulate pollution which remains suspended indefinitely in the atmosphere and which produces the greatest potential hazard to human health, or, for that matter, threatens to have long term effects on the earth's climate. Small particles can penetrate more deeply into the respiratory system, carrying on their surfaces traces of many chemicals. Such particles, when added to the atmosphere in increasing amounts, can result in a decrease in the earth's albedo and a cooling of the atmosphere.

Although private industry is responsible for the development of most of the control technology currently available for particulates, the National Center for Air Pollution Control (NCAPC) in the last several years has conducted research in its own laboratories to develop improved fabric filters (baghouses) capable of trapping tiny particles. The NCAPC has been experimenting with fabrics which can withstand the corrosive effects of gases at elevated temperatures, and with improved techniques for removing the accumulation of particulates on the filter bags.

At the present time, a major effort nationally is focused on the control of sulfur oxides from stationary sources by both private industry and the federal government—especially by the Government. Sulfur oxide pollution is largely created by the combustion of coal and fuel oils used in heating and in generation of power. The Air Quality Act of 1967 specifically authorizes appropriations of up to $35 million for fiscal year 1968 and $90 million for fiscal year 1969[9] for development of methods "having industry-wide application, for the prevention and control of air pollution resulting from combustion of fuels";[10] and so work is being rapidly accelerated on control of pollution emissions resulting from the use of fossil fuels in both vehicular and stationary sources.

A segment of the sulfur oxide control research is directed towards finding ways to remove sulfur from coal and heavy fuel oils before they are shipped to users, other research is aimed at developing processes for removing sulfur by the addition of sorbent materials to the combustion process itself, and still other research involves the removal of sulfur oxides from flue gases before they leave the smoke stacks.

The National Center for Air Pollution Control has supported studies at the Commercial Testing and Engineering Company of Chicago, the U.S. Bureau of Mines, and the Illinois Geological Survey to evaluate the cleanability of various coals produced in the United States; work is still underway by these groups. A coopera-

[9] § 104(c), 81 Stat. 488 (1967).
[10] § 104(a), 81 Stat. 487 (1967).

tive study by Bituminous Coal Research, Inc., has also been funded to investigate the removal of pyrite sulfur particles from fine coals. A pilot-scale facility for evaluating the efficiency of commercial methods for pyrite separation and concentration has been operating since February 1968.

Studies by Arthur D. Little, Dorr-Oliver, and Bechtel are currently being conducted under NCAPC sponorship to determine the technical feasibility and economics of proved commercial processes capable of converting pyrite-coal refuse material into valuable byproducts.

The petroleum industry has been in the forefront in the development of methods for the desulfurization of high-sulfur residual fuel oils, and presently there are under construction a number of refineries using proprietary processes.

The NCAPC has been supporting a major program to remove sulfur during the combustion process itself which may be especially useful for the control of sulfur oxide pollution from power plants. Industry also has been active in this area, and one industrial concern markets equipment effective in removal of sulfur oxides during combustion. One process under extensive development by private and public efforts involves injecting ground limestone or dolomite sorbent materials into a furnace during firing. Sulfur oxide pollutants are collected on the surfaces of the sorbent particles and are thus removed from flue gases by collecting the particles together with the flyash in a dry or wet-type collecting device. Studies are underway for the utilization of the collected flyash-reacted limestone mixture to produce a useful byproduct such as brick or building block. To advance this process the NCAPC is supporting at several laboratories an intensive program for testing samples of limestone and dolomite obtained from quarries around the country. It is important that many sorbents be evaluated to determine the optimum properties, both chemical and physical, for use by power plants in different parts of the United States. This program is a cooperative one involving studies also supported by the coal and electric utilities industries.

The design of a prototype dry injection process to be installed on two TVA power plants has been started. These units are scheduled to begin operation in mid-1969 and will be operated under a comprehensive test program for approximately eighteen months.

To generate additional fundamental data needed to improve the application of the limestone process, five fundamental and applied research contracts were negotiated during 1967. These are two industrial contracts with Babcock and Wilcox and with Esso Research and Engineering to study process kinetics and to screen limestone reactants; a contract with West Virginia University's Coal Research Bureau to explore the potential of using limestone-modified flyash; a contract with Battelle Memorial Institute to investigate reaction and process kinetics of the limestone-sulfur dioxide reaction; and support to the Tennessee Valley Authority to investigate the effect of physical properties of limestone and for conceptual design studies of limestone processes.

A process that involves the treatment of flue gases—the one that has been most extensively developed for American application—involves the use of alkalized alumina absorbent. Work conducted since 1957 by the Bureau of Mines for the NCAPC indicates that alkalized alumina is a promising sulfur oxide sorbent that can be regenerated to yield a sulfur-rich gas which can be converted to elemental sulfur. The Bureau of Mines has under test a semi-pilot plant to develop information required for pilot plant trials. The Central Electricity Generating Board (CEGB) has also developed data for pilot application in England. In the last year NCAPC has stepped up its activities, heading towards early pilot plant trials in the United States. A high degree of cooperative exchange has been maintained between the CEGB and the NCAPC; and the National Center and the Electric Research Council in the United States are now negotiating with the British for joint support of their large prototype plant study. If an agreement can be reached, a saving of a year's time will be realized in the pilot demonstration in the United States.

An adjunct process being studied for removing sulfur oxides from flue gases after injection of powdered limestone or dolomite sorbents into the furnace involves the use of wet scrubbers before discharge out the stack. This process is now under engineering design for application to two power plants in the Midwest. For further improvement of this system contract studies are underway for prototype-scale limestone scrubber systems investigating the process kinetics of several scrubber types and defining and solving known engineering problems related to wet scrubbing of flue gas. These problems include corrosion and scaling, plume reheating (the flue gas must be reheated so that it will rise through the stack and will disperse high in the air instead of settling immediately to the ground), potential water pollution, and solid disposal.

To develop improved new processes for the control of sulfur oxides from fuel combustion, the NCAPC has under study by contract bench-scale studies involving a large number of new processes. These methods, termed second generation processes, are expected to be more economical and efficient than the first generation processes now under development for pilot scale trials.

Although the percentage of total sulfur oxide emissions from processes other than the combustion of fossil fuels is a relatively small proportion of the total burden of sulfur pollution, individual industrial plants may often become local problems, creating an unattractive, unpleasant, and sometimes unhealthy environment for the communities in which they exist. The National Center is, therefore, now in the process of planning a series of cooperative studies with industry to encourage more extensive control of sources such as primary smelters, pulp and paper mills, sulfuric acid plants, and coke plants. These studies will pinpoint many research and development needs.

In the immediate future the National Center for Air Pollution Control will expand research on pollutants from stationary sources other than particulates and sulfur oxides. An accelerated program involving control of nitrogen oxides is already being launched with a comprehensive systems engineering study which will evaluate the nitrogen oxides control problem in terms of the type, number, magnitude, and location of stationary sources of the pollutant now and through the year 2000, and the economics associated with control of these sources. From this systems study, a detailed plan will be formulated for a research and development program to make technology available for control of nitrogen oxides.

To date, most of the work on nitrogen oxide control from stationary sources has been conducted by industry and has involved combustion process modifications. Babcock and Wilcox, for instance, has developed two-stage combustion as a means of partial control for some designs of oil and gas-fired boilers. Combustion Engineering has done enough work to show that boiler design can affect the formation of nitrogen oxides. Esso Research and Engineering has also shown in the laboratory that nitrogen oxide emissions from oil-fired units can be reduced by changing fuel ratios.

Several organizations, including the Franklin Institute, Illinois Institute of Technology, University of California, and Chevron Research, have investigated catalytic decomposition as a possible approach to nitrogen oxides control; but most of these studies have been oriented towards application to the control of emissions from automobiles.

Current NCAPC projects on residential furnaces are giving first consideration to nitrogen oxides. A study supported by the National Center for Air Pollution Control at the U.S. Bureau of Mines is aimed at determining fundamental kinetic data on the formation of nitrogen oxides in gas flames.

As far as is possible, new and improved sulfur oxides control processes, such as the molten carbonate process (one of the second generation processes under consideration), will be evaluated for their nitrogen oxides control potential.

In addition to research on control of specific pollutants such as sulfur oxides and nitrogen oxides, NCAPC has initiated programs aimed at control of pollutants from a broad spectrum of industries and for the improvement of equipment that is generally applicable to pollutant removal. The smelter industry studies and fabric filters development, previously mentioned, are examples of these activities. In carrying out these studies, the systems engineering approach will be used to develop the needed programs which will then be conducted cooperatively with industrial groups. In this regard it is important that such studies be joint efforts to keep responsive to the needs of industry groups expected to utilize the processes and equipment developed.

In the future, work will also continue on the multiple pollution problems of solid waste disposal. Contract work already under way is directed towards control of air pollution created during municipal refuse disposal, since this constitutes a problem of concern at the present time. Control involves both improvement of incinerator designs and the application of better control devices. As with other programs, a series of systems studies will be launched by the National Center to define the over-all problem of air pollution from waste disposal and the research and development needed to control the problem. These systems studies are expected to result in a sizable contract program based on a modest effort of in-house research and development by the Center itself over the last nine years.

II

THE CONTROL OF POLLUTION FROM VEHICLES

Automobile manufacturers have been successful in meeting federal standards for reduction of hydrocarbon and carbon monoxide emissions required nationally for the 1968 model-year cars.[11] To meet the proposed standards for hydrocarbons and carbon monoxide for 1970 model-year cars, the motor vehicle industry will further optimize the two basic approaches utilized for 1968 model-year vehicles. The first involves, for the most part, injection of air into the exhaust manifold at the point of hottest exhaust gas temperature close to the exhaust valves in order to continue the combustion of the pollutants in the exhaust system. The second approach utilizes modifications in the engine induction and ignition systems.

Although these control techniques are resulting in considerable progress, the growth in vehicle population across the nation indicates that a further reduction of pollutant emission levels may be necessary. Systems studies to further define this need are now under way. At present, technology to achieve still lower emission levels has not been reduced to practice, although several promising systems are under intensive research and development, particularly by industry. One such system involves a high-temperature reactor to replace the exhaust manifold in the present engine configuration. The major problem today involves the development of alloys capable of resisting the high temperatures involved over the life of the vehicle and at a reasonable cost. The federal program in control device development is aimed towards assisting the automobile industry in such development and towards control of additional pollutants (such as nitrogen oxides and particulates) that are not specified for control at the present time. The NCAPC is also participating in cooperative research programs, jointly funded by the federal government and the Coordinating Research Council, an industry group jointly supported by the Automobile Manufacturers Association and the American Petroleum Institute. These studies are oriented toward further definition of the pollution problem from motor vehicles—involving either the automotive engine or the fuels used.

As previously mentioned, control of nitrogen oxide emissions is not yet required

---

[11] These standards are set forth in 45 C.F.R. §§ 85.1-.87 (1967). Proposed standards for 1970 model-year cars have been issued. 33 Fed. Reg. 8304 (1968).

by federal standards. However, considerable attention is being given by both industry and government to means by which nitrogen oxide emissions might be controlled without sacrifice to the control of hydrocarbon and carbon monoxide emissions.

One system, which has received rather wide attention in both university and industry research circles, involves the recirculation of a controlled amount of the total exhaust gas back through the engine intake system. By diluting the combustible mixture charge admitted to the engine cylinders, the peak temperatures are reduced—resulting in reduced formation of nitrogen oxides—though at some loss in engine performance.

While reduction in emissions will probably be met during the next decade by improving conventional reciprocating engines, serious attention will also be given to possible new approaches involving unconventional vehicle propulsion systems having inherently low emission characteristics. NCAPC is currently supporting systems studies defining the state-of-the-art of technology relating to electrically propelled vehicles (Arthur D. Little) and other types of unconventional combustion systems for vehicle propulsion (Battelle Memorial Institute).

Power systems such as turbines and steam engines are under study by a number of groups. Using updated technology, researchers have recently built vehicles powered by steam. Hydrocarbon and carbon monoxide levels discharged by these vehicles are quite low. These modern steam cars appear to have overcome many of the drawbacks of early "Stanley Steamer" type vehicles which were slow to warm up, consumed large amounts of water, and sometimes exploded. However, much remains to be done before comparable performance and economies of the present gasoline-powered vehicles are realized.

For the more distant future, the electric vehicle appears to offer considerable potential. Even now, electrically propelled vehicles using batteries are practical for limited application. Further advancement of battery or fuel-cell technology will, however, be required before an electric-powered family car of acceptable performance will become economically attractive.

III

AIR POLLUTION INSTRUMENTATION

Efficient, accurate, and easy-to-use instrumentation for measuring pollutants in the ambient air and in stacks and exhausts is vital to any air pollution control program. The complexity of instrumental requirements and the need for instrumentation to determine the quality and quantity of air pollutant emissions from stationary sources varies significantly, depending on the nature of the pollutant and the location of the measurement (within the stack, at the mouth of the stack, or in the plume downwind from the stack).

In-stack instrumentation is already available for measuring inorganic, gaseous emissions such as carbon dioxide, nitrogen oxides, and sulfur oxides resulting from fossil fuel combustion. But before the gas from a stack can be sampled, expensive scaffolding and a platform must be built on the stack and probe holes provided. Sampling then involves measuring the rate of flow of gas through the stack and extracting a sample of stack gas to be analyzed for the concentration of various pollutants.

It would be much more convenient to measure stack emissions from a distance. Through contracts the NCAPC has under development such instrumentation. A sulfur dioxide monitor utilizing infra-red technology to measure radiation from hot gases emitted from stacks has already been built by a contractor and is now being evaluated by the NCAPC. The Edison Electric Institute and NCAPC are jointly supporting the development of a remote monitor employing a laser system for measuring light transmission through stack plumes. Such measurement is related to the visual effects of particulates in the plume.

Compact, portable instruments that can be airborne are needed to sample the quality of air at different levels in the atmosphere and to measure dispersal of pollutants from plumes. Although such an instrument is already commercially available for sulfur oxides, similar instruments do not exist for nitrogen oxides and other pollutants. There is also a need for improved instruments for the NCAPC's nationwide Continuous Air Monitoring Network. The current array of instruments is essentially the same package adopted ten years ago. During the next several years it is expected that simplified and improved instruments will be developed which will constitute a significant improvement over existing instrumentation and will extend our abilities to pollutants not currently being measured.

Instrumentation for measuring vehicular emissions is generally adequate for testing vehicles in a well-equipped laboratory. If all vehicles are to be inspected at regular intervals during their use, however, instrumentation must be developed that will make testing simpler and less costly.

IV

METEOROLC

Because atmospheric properties control the transpor and dispersal of pollutants, they are intimately associated with the concentration levels of pollutants discharged into the atmosphere from various sources. Hence, a meteorology program is an essential input to a program for the control of atmospheric pollution. The NCAPC has utilized meteorology in its program since its inception in 1955.

Several urban diffusion models—mathematical models relating pollutant sources to atmospheric concentrations through mathematical simulation of meteorological processes—have been developed and applied to a variety of air pollution problems ranging from the interpretation of air quality data to experimental programs for forecasting pollutant concentrations within urban areas.

The culmination of meteorological research in air pollution is to provide air pollution control officials with a logical basis for initiating control measures to maintain air quality standards. The Air Pollution Potential Forecast Program was begun in 1960 and since that time ninety-two episodes of high air pollution potential have been forecast; many of these episodes were related to severe local pollution conditions. In July 1967, the routine operation of the Air Pollution Potential Forecast Program, developed by the NCAPC, was transferred to the Weather Bureau for machine operation. The responsibility for research and continued development of the program remains, however, with the NCAPC, and improved forecasting techniques are now being developed. Plans are now being implemented to produce and test quantitative forecasts, forecasts that indicate the relative dilution capacity of the atmosphere over the country.

CONCLUSION

In the area of control of pollution from stationary sources, major research and development is now concentrated on the control of sulfur oxides. In the future there will be expanded programs for other pollutants, especially nitrogen oxides.

Major emphasis on control of emissions from motor vehicles is now focused on reduction of carbon monoxide and hydrocarbons. Future efforts will focus on control of nitrogen oxides and particulates and on unconventional vehicles with low pollution potential, such as electric-powered and steam-powered cars.

Instruments and techniques are now available for measuring many pollutants, especially inorganic gases, but there is a need for automated, smaller-sized instruments both for stationary sampling stations and for airborne sampling of the atmosphere. There is also a need for remote-type monitors capable of measuring stack emissions from a distance.

In the area of meteorology, a number of urban diffusion models and an air pollution potential forecast program are now operational; improved models and quantitative forecasting methods are under development.

THE ECONOMICS OF AIR POLLUTION: CENTRAL PROBLEMS

HAROLD WOLOZIN*

INTRODUCTION

Afflicting damage and distress upon human, animal, and plant life, polluted air blankets most populated areas of the globe. The salient economic consequence of this is that pure or relatively unpolluted air is no longer a free good; it costs money to go where air is relatively cleaner, it costs money to trap pollutants before they escape into the air. Yet, by and large, those who are responsible for pollution do not bear the cost of the pollution they create; it is an "external" cost of production and consumption.

Born of this condition, the economics of air pollution is largely directed to two broad areas, both difficult assignments: (1) measuring the costs to individuals and society at large of the diffusive despoiling of the atmosphere (and the corresponding benefits of cleaning it up) and (2) determining economic measures to stimulate and/or coerce polluters to eliminate or at least cut down their emissions of destructive gases and particulate matter.

Air pollution—smoke and other airborne particles—has accompanied the growth of industrialization since its early days. However, in the last two decades overwhelming evidence has begun to accumulate that polluted air is a serious threat to the quality of life, even to man's continued existence itself; projections of economic growth and population expansion to the year 2000 pose the threat of a vast increase in the already high level of air pollution unless effective measures are taken to control it. It is in recognition of both the present and potential costs to society that increased importance has been given to the devising of means to detect, control and abate air pollution. It is also becoming clear that because of the damage to life and property, expenditures on air pollution control and abatement are as essential to society, if not to individual polluters, as investment in education, urban renewal, and other investment in social capital. In a basic sense, is not investment in air pollution control also investment in human resources?[1]

The primary purpose of this paper is to survey and evaluate the state of the art in the two broad areas of interest outlined above. I hope, in describing the nature of the difficulties and dilemmas that confront public and private efforts to devise

* A.B. 1942, Tufts University; Ph.D. 1955, Columbia University. Professor of Economics and Chairman, Department of Economics, University of Massachusetts at Boston. Editor, THE ECONOMICS OF AIR POLLUTION (1966).

[1] A decade ago Kenneth Galbraith's book, *The Affluent Society* (1958), argued tellingly for a broadening of the conventional definition of social capital to include investment in human resources. Thus far, it is principally in educational expenditure that this view has prevailed.

means and alternative techniques for coping with air pollution, to explore to what extent these very difficulties, when objectively evaluated, may bear within themselves the seeds of workable and practicable solutions to the problem. In this respect, we must recognize and include in our calculations the fact that air pollution is but one of several severe sources of an accelerated deterioration in the quality of the environment in which man works and lives. As we will see, the need for simultaneous solutions could result in certain savings, *i.e.*, "external economies," such as the lowering in air pollution which might result from expenditures on public mass transportation utilizing electricity.

I

MEASURING AIR POLLUTION COSTS AND BENEFITS

The singular characteristic of the extensive air pollution accompanying the rising levels of production and consumption in our society is its pervasiveness, a quality that makes especially difficult both its control and the measurement of its cost. Unlike water pollution, air pollution can be both a singularly local blight and a particularly wide-ranging one, limited only by the course of prevailing winds. It attacks man directly as well as his environment. Its damage to humans, animals, and crops can be both acute and chronic. The magnitude and implications of the latter are only beginning to be realized and are causing considerable concern, especially to agricultural and health specialists.

Air pollution cuts down visibility on airport runways and on our turnpikes. It dirties and decays buildings and works of art. A slow rise in the temperature of the earth has been attributed to air pollution; and it is suspected of altering genes of people, so that there may be a change in the inherited characteristics they pass on to their descendants as well as possible mutations.[2] The sources of air pollution are diverse and multitudinous, many resulting, paradoxically, from activities designed to alleviate other forms of pollution. Once released into the atmosphere, primary and secondary pollutants, unlike those in water or sewage, are untreatable, often unpredictable in their effects, and difficult to detect and measure.

It is, therefore, not surprising that to come to grips with the economic impact of air pollution is not a simple matter and poses a fundamental question: Can we presume with any confidence to measure the total economic costs of air pollution? What does the pervasiveness of air pollution imply in respect to our ability to measure its effects and for the scale of resources which would have to be allocated to obtain reliable national estimates of air pollution damage? The problem seems to be twofold: Economists who have specifically been concerned with the total measurement problems have cast serious doubts on the value and reliability of existing national

---

[2] Remarks of Dr. Haagen-Smit before the American Meteorological Society, reported in the Washington Post, Feb. 1, 1968, at 2, col. 6.

estimates of damage based on currently accepted definitions.[3] In the process they have understandably displayed some ambivalence; on the one hand, concern over the gravity of the pollution damage problem and, on the other hand, pessimism over what appears to be the exorbitantly costly as well as technically formidable task of arriving at defensible estimates of total damage and abatement costs. In view of the pervasive nature of air pollution, as we have briefly described it, this is under-standable. The author of one of the pioneering explorations along these lines, Ronald Ridker, for example, although recommending an intensification of efforts to gather more data "collected specifically for the purpose of air-pollution research," concludes on the basis of his investigations that "data collection is a very expensive process," and he is "not at all certain" about the "payoff."[4]

This ambivalence is also reflected in a paper delivered last year by Allen V. Kneese, who holds that estimates of national pollution costs are of a rather limited utility as an aid to decision-making, although, on balance, "they do have a certain usefulness."[5] It would, however, be hard to disagree with Kneese that those national estimates which are available are "indefensible," and "all guesses" worthy only of abandonment.[6] Kneese is not too concerned with the absence of reliable estimates; he reasons that "making improved decisions based on economic data does not *necessarily* require that we know the total costs and gains at all."[7] Fiscal planners at the national level might well question this position on the grounds that devising and implementing rational policies for control cost considerable sums of money and, hence, justify serious effort to obtain reliable estimates of the total cost of air pollution and its abatement. It is also possible that serious, adequately funded efforts to produce national totals can be more productive than either of the two authors cited above seems to believe. Both types of estimates are essential; the global sets the necessary priorities and framework for the partial estimates. This is im-plicit in Kneese's position, in the article cited above, that the relationship between incremental costs and damage on a national level can be useful as a guide to setting advisable levels of damage and control outlays. However, the truth of the matter is that to obtain these incremental costs (they are first derivatives), data on total costs and benefits must first be estimated.

One point which is of considerable importance is the nature of the total cost function defining the relationship between total costs of pollution and level of pollution. On the basis of what we already know, it is difficult to agree that the shapes of air pollution cost and abatement functions are linear, as implied by Kneese.

---

[3] Remarks of Linsky, in PROCEEDINGS: THE THIRD NATIONAL CONFERENCE ON AIR POLLUTION 539 (Public Health Service Pub. No. 1649, 1967) [hereinafter cited as PROCEEDINGS].

[4] Ridker, *Strategies for Measuring the Cost of Air Pollution*, in THE ECONOMICS OF AIR POLLUTION 87, 100 (H. Wolozin ed. 1966).

[5] Kneese, *How Much is Air Pollution Costing Us in the United States?*, in PROCEEDINGS, *supra* note 3, at 529.

[6] *See id.* at 530.

[7] *Id.* at 531.

Even on a priori grounds one might suspect that assuming linearity oversimplifies the problem. Perhaps we can demonstrate what nonlinearity could imply, utilizing as an example the functional relationship between the level of pollution and the magnitude of the costs of abatement. There are significant policy implications of such a nonlinear relationship. Figure 1 plots a hypothetical relationship, in an advanced industrial society, between various levels of pollution (measured by some composite index) and the total cost of abatement required to obtain each level of pollution measured on the horizontal axis. Two assumptions underlie this illustrative model: technology is assumed and the actual level of pollution at any given time is one point on the pollution scale. In other words, this is a static model depicting the inverse relationship between abatement costs and the level of pollution. What is under question is what happens as we move in either direction along the scale. If we go (Figure 1) from point "P" toward point "A," the recognition or minimum prob-

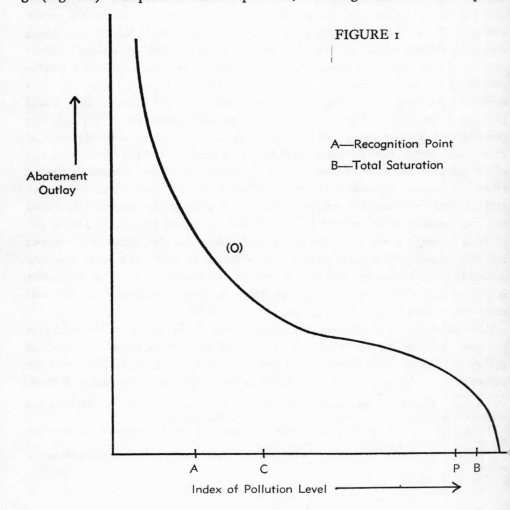

FIGURE 1

A—Recognition Point
B—Total Saturation

Abatement
Outlay

(O)

A   C   P   B

Index of Pollution Level ⟶

lem level—in other words, the point at which air pollution would be at a low level and just detectable—outlays for abatement would after a spell have to increase more rapidly as we reached successive and more difficult to obtain levels of cleaner air, and would soar as we approached "A." Contrariwise, if the alternative decision were to accept lower abatement outlays, then the choice would imply, correspondingly, an acceleration in damages. Such an abatement function, "O," would posit, initially, low returns to scale as abatement is initiated, near point "B," the saturation level on the pollution index. There would then be a rather long span over which returns to scale are increasing (between "P" and "C") and eventual entry into an area of diminishing returns to scale as the air is cleaned up. It is also possible that amounts of damage related to increases in pollution levels are nonlinear—an initial range of minimal damage, then a range of rapid rise in damage costs relative to pollution levels followed by a leveling off, even though this might not be reached except near the point of disaster. Such a damage function could be diagrammed as we have done for the abatement outlay function.

Even though the shapes of such functions could be quite different in real life than we have here posited, it should be clear that whatever their actual shape, knowledge of the fundamental relationships they depict could be of considerable importance, not to be dismissed as of marginal value. However, only systematic research can determine this. It should be pointed out that the cost function depicted in Figure 1 is based upon conventional assumptions in respect to returns to scale. If it were to turn out that the actual relationships were close to what we depict here, this would suggest some rather important conclusions. For example, on the basis of inspection alone it would follow that relatively modest increases in total abatement outlays would reduce the level of total damages more efficiently over one section of the range of pollution level than another part. This says somewhat more than the more conventional depiction of straight line incremental relationships assumed by Kneese in his representation of relevant benefits and cost concepts;[8] although, consistent with the calculus of cost-benefit analysis, one would theoretically want to reach equality of incremental costs and benefits of abatement outlays.

Furthermore, it is possible that cost and abatement curves are kinked. It would follow that the derived marginal curves would be discontinuous, which could introduce considerable uncertainty in the determination of "appropriate" levels of support for resources and research to reduce damage control costs and otherwise to control air pollution. On balance, these possibilities would seem to justify attaching considerable importance to research on total outlay and cost functions.

However, this in no way detracts from the importance of estimating damages and control costs at the "problem shed" level and certainly does not dispute Kneese's contention that it is at this regional level that it would be easier—"more feasible and

---

[8] *Id.* at 531. I am indebted to my colleagues Leonard Kirsch and Louis Esposito for helping to clarify my thinking on these relationships.

more relevant to decision-making"—to obtain "reasonably systematic analysis of damage and control costs."[9]

What should such estimates provide? On the damage side, the main categories of cost would include the effects of air pollution on life—human, animal, and plant—on materials, on maintenance and cleaning bills, and a wide range of indirect costs of smog. On the control cost side, pollution scientists would be concerned with the costs of abatement under existing technological possibilities as well as the savings in control costs which might be obtained from new technologies. This would include such things as new types of pollution-free transportation, new production techniques, new collection and treatment systems, and so on.

Given this qualitative difference in the problem, have the relatively few studies of air pollution damage at the "problem shed" level been more successful than those on the national level? The answer seems to be "No." In spite of their more limited scope and relatively greater appeal to the specialist, those few studies of direct damages that have been done at the problem shed level have been consistently poor. Kneese, Ridker, and this author, among others, have amply documented this point, so that further elaboration here is unnecessary.

However, it would be helpful to enumerate some of the difficulties which confront the researcher. First of all, even though it is ostensibly more manageable, the concept of the air shed is inherently vague. We have already alluded to the problem of the pervasiveness of air pollution to which this is related. Secondly, many categories of damage resist precise measurement, and where experimental approaches are utilized results are often misleading. Thirdly, chronic as opposed to acute effects of air pollution are often undetected and, hence, uncounted. Yet in the long run their effects, particularly on human health and agricultural crops and animals, may dwarf the immediately measurable damages.[10] Fourth, it is frequently difficult to isolate air pollution from other sources of damage. This problem is compounded when they interact and amplify each other. The questionable reliability of estimates of effects on property values is an easily demonstrated example of this. Yet, it is in this very area that some encouraging results have been obtained.[11] Such limitations extend to a wide spectrum such as cleaning costs and health. Even though the seriousness of the latter is causing increasing concern to public health officials, the suspected heavy costs of ill health stemming from air pollution are virtually unknown. Fifth, indirect costs of control may even go undetected let alone measured. Finally, the use of data gathered for other purposes often turns out to be grossly

---

[9] *Id.* at 531.

[10] As this author pointed out in an earlier article, the measurement of chronic effects has been seriously neglected. Wolozin & Landau, *Crop Damage from Sulphur Dioxide*, 48 J. FARM ECON. 394 (1966). An excellent study of problem shed agricultural damage can be found in E. Landau, The Public Control of Air Pollution: A Case Study (mimeo. 1966) (unpublished dissertation).

[11] *See* Kneese's reference to the work of Tom Crocker in PROCEEDINGS, *supra* note 3, at 534.

inadequate in isolating and measuring air pollution damage, especially where surrogates are relied upon.

Our ability to estimate the costs of alternative systems of pollution control at the problem shed level does not seem to be much better than it is in deriving national damage costs. Although there is a good deal of information on the costs of control utilizing specific processes and equipment, there are also basic disagreements such as in the case of automobile emission controls. And, as Kneese points out, when it comes to the questions of indirect effects and trade-offs between large-scale control measures involving location and alternative processes as opposed to conventional emissions controls, "information is nil."[12]

II

The Problem of Control—Alternative and Complementary Policies

The continuing debate among economists over air pollution control has centered on whether polluters of the air, be they businessmen engaged in activities which spew wastes into the air or consumers doing the same thing in driving automobiles or burning leaves, can be induced to take voluntary measures to eliminate or lessen their pollution in response to market incentives (or coercion), and how predictable the results would be; for under incentive systems there is the option not to be persuaded by the rewards. Specifically, market pressure would be exerted by imposing charges or effluent fees which would reflect the marginal costs of the pollution inflicted upon others. These effluent fees would be designed to bring the level of pollution down to tolerable and acceptable limits. The discussion in this paper will be confined to issues relating to the meaning and implications of the argument for resorting to primary reliance on the market mechanism to control air pollution.

Effluent fee schemes have been enthusiastically advanced as the logical alternative to direct governmental intervention through regulations stipulating standards and prohibiting certain pollution-creating activities. It should be pointed out that advocacy of effluent fee policy does not necessarily imply disagreement with parallel actions, such as subsidies of many sorts ranging from tax credits for air cleaning equipment and alternative processes to outright payment or reimbursement by government for control devices or relocation costs. (No such action as the latter has, to my knowledge, been seriously proposed.) Many proponents of effluent fees tend to minimize these other possibilities and suggest either implicitly or explicitly that effluent fees can do most of the job alone. The truth of the matter is, however, that with the emphasis placed by the Air Quality Act of 1967[13] on government enforcement of air standards and the designating of air quality control regions, the trend seems to be toward increasing governmental assumption of direct responsibility

---

[12] *Id.* at 534.
[13] 81 Stat. 485.

rather than any commitment to the indirect pressures operating through market incentives such as effluent fees. In a sense, the conceptual battle lines have been drawn.

A critical issue has been raised: to what extent can we reconcile the arguments for heavy reliance upon the market mechanism through the medium of emission or effluent charges with what appears to be the increasing evidence that air pollution is an externality which will require more than indirect coercion to control? To what extent should we consider seriously the advocacy of some experimentation with effluent fees. This has been advocated strongly by Crocker, Mills, and Vickrey. "Ideally," according to Crocker, "this charge would be levied upon the emitters at the level which would tend to equate the present value of receptor marginal damage costs to the present value of emitter marginal costs savings." Crocker would also reimburse those damaged, the "receptors."[14] However, these economists differ in the extent to which they would place reliance upon such schemes.

In one sense, the enthusiasm for effluent fees has been directly related to the degree of antipathy for direct regulation, most noticeably in the case of Mills and least so with Vickrey. While direct regulation and subsidy certainly affect the shape of economic decisions and activity, this is a subject for separate treatment. However, they do have certain policy implications which are germane to the subject of this paper. Moreover, it is likely that many of the problems, particularly technological, confronting the implementation of voluntary techniques would not disappear with direct regulation.

Let us now look briefly at the main thrust of the arguments supporting effluent fee schemes. Mills, the most positive proponent of principal reliance on effluent fee schemes, bases his advocacy "on practical, rather than theoretical, grounds." He lists several reasons:[15] (1) "If each discharger is faced with the same schedule of effluent fees, abatement is relatively cheap." "Complete flexibility" would be possible, if, in addition, it proved possible to confront dischargers with different effluent fee schedules according to the benefits to be derived from abatement. (2) Management rather than government officials are entrusted with the burden of investigation and decision-making. (3) "Dischargers" of effluents are provided continuous incentives to search for additional methods of abatement. (4) Any inability to measure the benefits and costs of abatement will show up "more quickly" with an effluent fee control program. Vickrey[16] contributes the following pertinent points to the debate on effluent fee abatement schemes: (1) effluent fees are "at

---

[14] T. Crocker, Some Economic Aspects of Air Pollution Control With Particular Reference to Polk County, Florida, U.S. Public Health Service Grant: AP-00389-02, Jan. 1968, at 282.

[15] Mills, *Federal Fiscal Policy in Air Pollution Control*, in PROCEEDINGS, *supra* note 3, at 574, 576-77. Mills discusses federal agencies' "dereliction of duty" in not adopting effluent fees. *Id.* at 577.

[16] Vickrey, Theoretical and Practical Possibilities and Limitations of a Market Mechanism Approach to Air Pollution Control, a paper presented at the annual meeting of the Air Pollution Control Association, Cleveland, Ohio, June 11, 1967.

least in principle" highly flexible because they can be varied with changing circumstances including changing weather conditions, (2) management, and their technicians, are "in the best position" to devise the best solutions for abatement, and effluent fee schemes will best insure their cooperation, (3) "necessary discriminations" which accompany regulatory control will be minimized if these controls are adjuncts to effluent fee systems, (4) at the local level, the revenues resulting from effluent fees can serve as a substitute for other taxes which are "quite injurious in their effects," and (5) effluent fees force the administrator "to bring the problem into perspective" and may restrain the "pure air enthusiast" who might "be inclined to impose standards" entailing "too high a cost relative to benefits."[17]

Discussions of effluent fee schemes have reflected grave reservations as to their efficacy and practicability and such points as those covered in the preceding discussion have been the subject of considerable disputation. There are several questions which might be raised, particularly the following: (1) The first, reflecting a degree of skepticism on the efficacy of effluent fee schemes, is on the nature of their assumptions about business behavior. To support the contention that externalities can be internalized through effluent fees, proponents generally fall back upon a conventional economic analysis of the nature of business behavior in the modern world, a model of business behavior which has been questioned seriously in the literature on the subject and one which very few economists adhere to rigorously in explaining the behavior of the firm or industry. (2) Directly related to this is the tenuous nature of current theories and knowledge about the formulation of investment decisions in business firms (pollution abatement requires investment). (3) Formidable detection and monitoring problems are implicit in effluent fee schemes, a problem compounded by the primitive state of technology in these areas. (4) Finally, there is a genuine concern that effluent fees discriminate against small firms. Let us look briefly at each of these.

In the first point, what is at issue is the state of the art in the economic theory of the firm and the economics of industrial organization, which includes the structure of competitive relationships in industry. It is generally agreed, as this author has pointed out in another paper,[18] that the neoclassical profit maximization model of business behavior ill fits the kind of business world in which effluent fee schemes would have to be imposed. One does not even have to replace the neoclassical model with a sociological analysis[19] as certain economists and statisticians have suggested. There are other economic models such as Baumol's sales maximization model which describe a good bit of reality in the business world. How determinative would

---

[17] *Id.* at 1, 2.

[18] Wolozin, Intransigent Economic Behavior in Air Pollution Control and Decision, a paper presented at the annual meeting of the Air Pollution Control Association, Cleveland, Ohio, June, 1966.

[19] For a brief discussion of such sociological analysis, *see* remarks of Wolozin in PROCEEDINGS, *supra* note 3, at 579-81. *See generally* H. Wolozin, Toward an Interdisciplinary Model for Air Pollution Control (mimeo.) (Washington, D.C., 1967).

effluent fee schemes be? In other words, how predictable would be their results under such models? The record of directly applicable tax research is also not encouraging.[20] One must not forget that no matter how coercive effluent fees might be in theory, compliance, requiring the installation of abatement equipment, alternative processes, or decisions to relocate, is voluntary. Furthermore, it should be noted that as unpredictable as compliance might be, the impact upon resource allocation is equally unpredictable.

The above leads to the second of our points: the complex and little known nature of the determinants of investment decisions in business firms. There is great dispute on the impact of investment credits, for example, as there is on the whole question of the effects on investment of the corporate income tax. Evidence to support the thesis that effluent fees will result in investment outlays on pollution abatement equipment is shaky. Uncertainty, the complex nature of capital markets, and other factors determining investment decisions would inject a good deal of indeterminateness into any attempt to predict responses to effluent fees. At a more personal level, this author has testimony from those close to the business world which casts further doubt on the efficacy of effluent fees. One former businessman writes me,

> True, if you would base pollution control on a system of incentives, you might be disappointed. The marginal dollar gained for pollution control is hardly as exciting as the marginal dollar gained in expanding sales, creating new products or improving technology. This type of income promises growth and future profits. I think that many, if not most businesses have a shortage of key personnel and they would rather use this resource to develop the mainspring of their profits than to maximize their pollution subsidies.[21]

Vickrey has presented an eloquent description of the difficulties of monitoring and metering with the present grossly imperfect state of our technology.

> The real problem which advocates of effluent charges must face is the problem of metering, or of estimating in some way the amount of effluent actually generated by various emitters. Here the problem of air pollution is seen to be a particularly difficult one in that the number of small emitters and of the emitters difficult to meter effectively is large and their contribution to the problem is too great to be ignored.[22]

Vickrey goes on at some length to catalogue difficulties of inspection, measurement, and the like. Given the immensity of the monitoring and metering problem, and we have not even spoken of personnel and recruiting problems, one might conclude that simplicity should be high on the list of criteria for air pollution policy. On this count, effluent fee schemes might well founder as opposed to more direct regulatory measures. For example, it might not be so impractical to require regular tuning

---

[20] Remarks of Wolozin, in PROCEEDINGS, *supra* note 3, at 580.

[21] Letter from Robert E. Kohn to Harold Wolozin, July 4, 1967.

[22] Vickrey, *supra* note 16, at 5.

of automobiles at the expense of the community. This would be tantamount to compensating the emitter for his expense but in a much simpler manner. The same reasoning, for example, might be applied to the providing of scrubbing and other devices to industrial polluters, in return for guaranteed lowering of emission levels.

Finally, let us consider, briefly, the possibility that effluent fees discriminate against small firms. The reasoning here is simple, and it hinges on the cost of abatement equipment. The smaller the firm relative to the average firm in an industry, the greater the probable financial burden of installing air pollution control installations. In one industry, it has been reported,[23] the cost of an air pollution control installation would exceed the value of the production facilities of many small firms in the industry.

CONCLUSION

We have attempted in this brief survey to evaluate the central problems economists have encountered in attempting to develop measures and tools to cope with the growing costs to society of air pollution. We have focused on the formidable difficulties posed by the pervasiveness of air pollution and described some of the efforts directed to its measurement and control. Here is a summary of our principal conclusions and suggestions for directions in which we might concentrate our efforts.

(1) Current estimates of total damage inflicted on this nation by air pollution are totally unreliable and most experts working on this problem are pessimistic in their prognosis for more acceptable estimates: this would not be an insurmountable difficulty for policy makers if there were a simple (linear) relation between the level of pollution and the costs of control. But, it is more likely that they are nonlinear. We suggest, therefore, that effective policy determination requires serious and substantially supported efforts to estimate the costs of air pollution and the benefits of abatement over a range of pollution levels.

(2) The very difficulty of this task, a difficulty stemming from the paucity of data and the primitive state of pollution measurement and control technology, suggests the need to experiment with alternative methods of studying control costs.[24]

(3) Air pollution cannot be studied and controlled in isolation; for it is one of a number of interrelated problems affecting the quality of the environment. As a consequence, significant economies would be possible if policies for the control of air pollution were to be treated as part of overall research and of planning for improvement of the quality of the environment and conservation of our scarce resources *including* clean air. Expenditures on roads, tunnels, air travel, conservation, mass

---

[23] Letter from Albert W. Spitz to J. Spitz.

[24] One possible approach would be patterned after a systems concept recently developed for a problem shed. This is a study in the Nashville, Tennessee area being conducted by Azriel Teller. According to Allen Kneese, "Teller was able to wed his cost figures . . . to an atmosphere diffusion model of the Nashville area." Kneese, *supra* note 5, at 534.

transportation, urban development, recreational facilities, and industrial development must be guided by research and policies which take into account their inter-dependencies.

(4) There is no clear consensus on what kinds of economic measures should be taken to control pollution. The range of choices lies between, at one extreme, sole reliance on the market mechanism with schemes of effluent fees and the other extreme of complete reliance on government fiat with or without various forms of subsidies. We have asserted that the indeterminativeness of the market, the possibility of discrimination, and serious questions about its interpretation of business behavior raise serious questions about the former. Therefore, the solution may lie in between the two extremes, with some combination of regulatory setting of standards (such as those of the Air Quality Act of 1967), and supplemental market incentives. But only further research and continuous experimentation can lead to optimal solutions; meanwhile, the mounting qualitative evidence of the cumulative consequences of air pollution suggest that we cannot wait for such "optimal" solutions. In the short run, "educated" guesses must serve us.

A GUIDE TO THE AIR QUALITY ACT OF 1967*

Robert Martin and Lloyd Symington†

I

Introduction

On November 21, 1967 the President signed into law the Air Quality Act of 1967,[1] the most important step to date in organizing government's response to the nation's growing air pollution problems. The new law builds on earlier legislation going back as far as 1955 and is in form an amendment of the Clean Air Act of 1963.[2] Nevertheless, it sets forth a better defined approach to air pollution control than had yet emerged in either federal, state, or local legislation and begins to indicate the shape of the coordinated federal-state-local regulatory effort that air pollution control requires.

For the first time the federal government has decreed that regulation shall be undertaken by the states and has prescribed both a broad timetable for its coming into being and a basis for measuring the adequacy of that regulation. By recognizing health requirements, economic and technological realities, and the necessity for a flexible approach, the Air Quality Act provides a framework for an active government-industry partnership directed toward achieving the goal of clean air.

This article attempts to delineate the act's scope and ultimate effects in controlling air pollution attributable to stationary sources of contaminants. The act's provisions on automotive vehicle emissions are outside of the scope we have elected to adopt.[3]

A. The Background of the Legislation

The Air Quality Act builds on the foundations established in the Clean Air Act of 1963. The Clean Air Act authorized a broad federal program of research, technical assistance, and other aids to state and local air pollution control programs. It included provision for various conferences intended to promote voluntary pollution abatement and enforcement procedures where voluntary abatement could not be obtained. These programs were administered by the Secretary of Health, Education, and Welfare (hereinafter "HEW" designates the Secretary or his Department), and HEW actively participated in air pollution control conferences and proceedings in a

---

* This article is adapted from a pamphlet bearing the same title which was prepared by the authors for and distributed by the National Coal Policy Conference, Inc.

† Members of the Washington, D.C., bar and of the firm of Leva, Hawes, Symington, Martin and Oppenheimer, Washington, D.C., general counsel to the National Coal Policy Conference, Inc.

[1] 81 Stat. 485. (Hereinafter the act is cited by section number without reference to *Statutes at Large*.)

[2] Pub. L. No. 88-206, 77 Stat. 392.

[3] Automotive vehicle emissions are dealt with in §§ 201-12 of the act. For a full discussion, *see* Kennedy & Weekes, *Control of Automobile Emissions—California Experience and the Federal Legislation*, in this symposium, p. 297.

number of areas. Those conferences aroused considerable public concern about air pollution.[4] On the other hand, as industry pointed out, it seldom was invited to participate in those conferences, thereby minimizing the opportunity for a cooperative government-industry effort to improve air quality.[5]

In 1967, the President and the Congress both reflected and stimulated the increasing public concern about air pollution. The President proposed sweeping new authority for HEW, including the establishment of national emission standards, whereby each industry would be subject to uniform nationwide controls regardless of plant location, atmospheric conditions, and so forth. Senator Edmund Muskie, chairman of the Air and Water Pollution Subcommittee of the Senate Public Works Committee, which had the principal responsibility on the Senate side for the Air Quality Act, spoke of air pollution as "a serious national problem" and served notice that "no one has the right to use the atmosphere as a garbage dump."[6] He also recognized, however, that the problem had to be approached in the broader context of "the economic-technological-environmental relationship."[7]

Unfortunately, as the extensive congressional hearings leading to the Air Quality Act of 1967 demonstrated, the growing concern about air pollution was not matched by a concomitant advance in knowledge or effort adequate to cope with the complex problems of environmental control.[8] This lack of knowledge and technology, the inadequacy of prior research efforts, and the confusion in regulatory effort which resulted, were typified by the sulfur oxides issue which was often discussed in the congressional hearings.

1. *The Sulfur Oxides Controversy*

The 1963 act contained a specific research mandate to HEW as to sulfur oxides. The act also authorized HEW to develop information criteria on "air pollution agents" indicating their likely adverse effects if present in the air in varying quantities. Even though HEW's sulfur research program was most limited and still in an incipient stage, HEW, on March 23, 1967, issued criteria relating to oxides of sulfur.[9] These criteria, and certain standards of control of sulfur oxides which HEW had proposed or promulgated during the preceding year,[10] were, as HEW conceded in the Senate hearings, beyond the reach of existing control technology.[11] Misinforma-

---

[4] *Hearings, Air Pollution—1967, Before the Subcomm. on Air and Water Pollution of the Senate Comm. on Public Works*, 90th Cong., 1st Sess. 1149-50 (1967) [hereinafter cited as *Senate Hearings*].

[5] *Id.* at 2035-36, 2014-15.

[6] 113 CONG. REC. S9853-54 (daily ed. July 18, 1967) (statement of Senator Muskie, chairman of the subcommittee which considered the act).

[7] S. REP. No. 403, 90th Cong., 1st Sess. 8-9 (1967) [hereinafter cited as S. REP.].

[8] *Id.* at 3-4.

[9] PUBLIC HEALTH SERVICE, AIR QUALITY CRITERIA FOR SULPHUR OXIDES (1967).

[10] PUBLIC HEALTH SERVICE, REGULATION OF SULPHUR OXIDE EMISSIONS FROM FEDERAL FACILITIES 6-11 (1967).

[11] *Senate Hearings* 780, 2250.

tion on the nature and limited purpose of the criteria concededly could (and did) generate pressure in communities, leading to hasty and improvident regulatory action.[12] Furthermore, the hearings raised major questions as to the accuracy of the criteria, with significant American and English authorities contradicting the HEW conclusions.[13]

While the congressional hearings were in progress, the President issued a directive ordering accelerated research on the control of sulfur oxides emissions and requested additional funds from the Congress for this purpose.[14] The Congress, in the Air Quality Act, ultimately directed HEW to reconsider the sulfur oxides criteria.[15] And the Senate Committee stated,

> The oxides of sulfur controversy is indicative of the need more precisely to define the relationship between pollution and health and welfare. Because the committee is concerned with both long- and short-term hazards as well as the need for valid scientific data to substantiate the correlation between pollution and health and welfare the Secretary is urged to move forward with diligence and perseverance in the area of scientific analysis as well as research into ways feasibly and effectively to control potentially dangerous emissions.[16]

2. Emergence of a New Mandate

The careful and thorough approach taken in the hearings helped to establish a new tone for the nation's approach to its air pollution problems. As HEW Secretary John W. Gardner stated, "We must now enter a new era in the nation-wide struggle against air pollution .... The scattered hit-or-miss, uncertain control efforts on the part of all levels of government which have characterized the past must give way to a much more rational and scientifically valid national effort."[17] There was unanimity that the authority granted by the 1963 act was inadequate for this purpose. It came perhaps as a surprise to some that virtually all industry supported new legislation that would lead to a more effective air pollution control effort. There was very broad support for a cooperative approach to bridge the gaps in knowledge and technology and to promote voluntary compliance in achieving higher air quality standards wherever it was necessary and economically and technologically feasible to do so. Regulations and reasonable enforcement procedures generally were accepted as necessary, with the states to bear the prime responsibility.[18]

The hearings and the committee reports recognized HEW's position that HEW

---

[12] *Id.* at 2253, 2027, 2038-42.

[13] *Id.* at 2659-81, 2103-28.

[14] Memorandum from the President to the Secretary of Health, Education, and Welfare, April 21, 1967.

[15] § 107(b)(1).

[16] S. Rep. 10.

[17] *Hearings on the Air Quality Act of 1967 Before the House Comm. on Interstate and Foreign Commerce*, 90th Cong., 1st Sess. 204 (1967) [hereinafter cited as *House Hearings*].

[18] *See, e.g., Senate Hearings* 2016, 2001, 213-39, 1783, 1803-04; *House Hearings* 393-444, 539-626.

must take the lead in research and information on pollution controls; but they also reflected a desire that the research be more aggressive and the information supported by more substantial evidence than in the past.[19] Moreover, the consensus of the Congress was opposed to HEW's request for national emission standards at this time. Instead, the revised act reflected the view that solution of air pollution problems required flexibility and different approaches as regions differed in atmospheric conditions, industrial concentration, and so on.

All agreed that industry should be given increased opportunity to participate in achieving improved air quality and that it had a real obligation to do so. Senator Muskie stated, "As each day passes there is a greater urgency for closer cooperation between Government and industry . . . ."[20] Senator Jennings Randolph, chairman of the full Senate Public Works Committee, who played a most active role in formulating the legislation, emphasized "the need for participation by all segments of our national economy if air pollution control and abatement are to be achieved."

Senator Randolph also commended the proposed legislation because of its "workability, its potential for advancing the quality of the nation's air without inordinately disturbing economic balances . . . ."[21] In urging "a truly comprehensive attack" on the nation's air pollution problems, Dr. John T. Middleton, director of HEW's National Center for Air Pollution Control, testified that "a very high priority must be given to finding ways of making continued full use of our fuel resources without simultaneously adding to air pollution problems that are already serious in many places."[22]

The context of the legislation thus was one not only of urgent need but also, as both Chairman Harley Staggers of the House Committee and Chairman Muskie had pointed out, of recognition that there was no immediate panacea to the nation's air pollution problems, in large part because of the gap in knowledge and technology.[23] The committee made clear that while research was "not intended as a substitute for regulation," nevertheless it was "imperative"; for "reasonable regulation should . . . be based on an accurate measurement of the health and welfare needs, technological feasibility of abatement of pollution and economic factors involved."[24] HEW concurred that accelerated research both by government and industry was required.[25] The Congress left no doubt that it intended closely to monitor that research effort.[26]

The legislation had complete bipartisan support and was enacted without dis-

---

[19] See, e.g., S. REP. 10-11; H.R. REP. No. 728, 90th Cong., 1st Sess. 14, 25 (1967) [hereinafter cited as H.R. REP.].

[20] 113 CONG REC. S9854 (daily ed. July 18, 1967).

[21] Id. at S9858.

[22] House Hearings 206.

[23] 113 CONG. REC. H14401 (daily ed. Nov. 2, 1967); id. at S9853 (daily ed. July 18, 1967).

[24] S. REP. 10-11, 17-19; H.R. REP. 25.

[25] Senate Hearings 786.

[26] 113 CONG. REC. H15165 (daily ed. Nov. 14, 1967).

sent in both the Senate and the House of Representatives. It reflected the congressional determination concurred in by the Administration, industry, and many state and local authorities that air pollution had to be dealt with on a more comprehensive, cooperative, and accelerated basis than theretofore, using the best available scientific and research tools and recognizing both the paramount demands of public health and the very real limitations imposed both by the lag in technology and by economic considerations. The Administration labelled the bill as "a very important and constructive forward step in the continuing development of effective legislation to deal with a serious national problem"; it also expressed the view that the Congress would be directly concerned with the air pollution problem for years to come.[27]

B. Summary of the Purposes Underlying the Air Quality Act

The Air Quality Act became law on November 21, 1967. It amended the Clean Air Act of 1963 in a number of significant respects. The main purposes of these amendments were these:

(1) to lead to state control of air pollution problems, reflecting the need for differences in controls in different regions on account of varying atmospheric, topographic, industrial, and other conditions. Such pollution control action would be (a) in air quality regions designated by HEW based on pertinent conditions, (b) responsive to air quality criteria and recommended control techniques developed by HEW for particular air pollution agents, and (c) in accordance with air quality standards and enforcement plans developed by the states. (The earlier HEW concept of national emission standards for particular industries was deleted, although the new law provided for HEW to make a two-year study of their possible application later.)

(2) to assure that the HEW criteria and recommended control techniques, which are necessary to trigger the state programs, will (a) be based on full consultation, consideration of the best available scientific information, and supported by substantial evidence, (b) provide sufficient information to permit flexibility to the states in establishing control plans within the limits of technological and economic feasibility, and (c) in the case of the previously issued sulfur oxides criteria, be reconsidered in view of the new requirements.

(3) to assure adequate outside consultation by HEW in carrying out all of its major responsibilities as to air quality criteria, control techniques, research, and so on—particularly through an Air Quality Advisory Board and a number of advisory committees.

(4) to authorize HEW to establish standards if a state fails to act or if state action is considered inadequate and to enforce those standards by court action where the pollution can be shown to affect another state.

---

[27] Id. at S9856 (daily ed. July 18, 1967).

(5) to authorize immediate court action to stop pollution in emergency situations endangering health, regardless of the economic or technological feasibility of pollution control.

(6) to give highest priority to expanded research, with specific reference to fuels.

C. Outline of Steps in Setting and Enforcing Air Quality Standards

Before beginning our detailed examination of the act, it is useful to set forth in outline form the basic scheme whereby HEW will promulgate and the states will enforce air quality standards. The authors' advice to industries affected by the various steps in the process is printed in italics. This generalized advice is, of course, no substitute for the advice of each firm's own counsel.

1. *Initial Actions by HEW*

Before the states are obligated to set standards, HEW must take several initial actions, as follows:

(1) Designate broad *atmospheric areas* or air basins based on meteorological and topographical factors. (Eight national atmospheric areas covering the forty-eight contiguous states were announced on January 16, 1968.[28])

(2) Designate *air quality control regions*, containing communities in one or more states, with a common air pollution problem (by May 21, 1969). HEW must consult with state and local authorities before making such designations.

(3) Develop and publish *air quality criteria* for particular air pollution agents, which would describe the effect on health and welfare of varying concentrations of each agent or combination of agents in the ambient air. These criteria must reflect the best available scientific data, including views of other agencies and the advisory committees which the law requires to be established.

(4) Develop and publish *recommended control techniques*—that is, the best available information on how to achieve air quality levels set forth in the criteria, including technology, effectiveness, costs, and economic feasibility of various alternatives. Again, consultation with other agencies and advisory committees is required.

(5) Undertake *expanded research programs*, the results to be utilized in developing and revising these criteria and control techniques.

Before HEW designates regions or issues criteria, it must obtain the requisite advice. It was intended that HEW obtain the best advice available. Industry members should be prepared to do all they can to help develop sound criteria and accurate control information. Individuals invited by HEW to be a consultant or to work with an advisory committee in either of these areas will not be acting as in-

---

[28] 33 Fed. Reg. 548 (1968).

dustry representatives as much as experts in their fields. Therefore, other members of industry not serving on such committees must also seek an opportunity to present their points of view and information. This may be done by contacting members of an advisory committee after they have been announced or in consultation with state and local officials who will confer with the federal government on the local problems.

Industry also has a vital interest in the boundaries of the air quality control regions. In appropriate cases it should seek to be heard by the appropriate state and local officials, as well as by HEW, as to whether a particular area should be included in the region. It is suggested that local and state officials be asked for information on the recommended boundaries of air quality regions and if industry is affected by such boundaries any comments or representation may be made at that time.

In these, as in all other phases of air pollution control, it is essential that industry participation be based upon full understanding of the health, technology, and economic considerations involved, and where possible, offer an affirmative, not a negative, approach. The whole thrust of the legislation is toward a cooperative, scientific, and economically sound approach to workable and effective abatement.

2. State Air Quality Standards

As soon as HEW has taken the steps outlined above, each state in the designated regions must move promptly to develop standards and controls with respect to each substance, or group or combination of substances, in the atmosphere which are the subject of HEW criteria. Each state must do the following:

(1) File a *letter of intent* to set appropriate standards and controls, within ninety days after receiving HEW criteria and control information regarding any designated substance emitted into the atmosphere.

(2) Adopt, within the next 180 days, *ambient air quality standards* for the substance in question applicable to each designated air quality control region or portion thereof within the state. Standards must be consistent with HEW's criteria and control data. The state must hold a public hearing, and must consider any recommendations received from state or interstate planning agencies before adopting such standards.

(3) Adopt, within another 180 days, a *plan* on how to achieve each of the standards within a reasonable time, including emission control requirements and means of enforcement by the state. The plan may include various alternative control methods and a timetable for achieving ultimate standards within the limits of technological and economic feasibility.

(4) File the standards and plan with HEW. They will become effective when HEW finds them consistent with the act.

In keeping with the intent of the Air Quality Act, state and local authorities should establish their own mechanisms for hearings and consultation. Voluntary compliance with sound standards should be the objective of all concerned.

Businessmen should prepare to participate in any such organization and should be alert to the need to present their view at all appropriate state, local, and interstate levels—particularly at the public hearings. The implementation plan is at least as important as the standards, because it sets the timetable for compliance based on technological and economic feasibility.

3. Federal Standards (if State Action is Deemed Inadequate by HEW)

If a state fails to set standards as outlined above, or if HEW deems a state's action inadequate, HEW may act to develop standards for the portion of an air quality region (or regions) within that state, as follows:

(1) HEW holds a *conference* including representatives of all interested agencies and industries.

(2) HEW issues *regulations* setting forth air quality standards for the particular region, consistent with the HEW criteria and control information.

(3) The state then has six months either to adopt state standards satisfactory to HEW or to request a hearing.

(4) If the state objects to HEW's proposed standards and requests a hearing, HEW sets up special *hearing board*, including members selected by states involved, to receive evidence from all concerned, including industry. The board then makes a binding final decision on the standards to be adopted.

(5) If a state fails to act within the six-month period, the standards in the HEW regulations become effective for such region or portion thereof.

Industry should participate actively in such proceedings, and if there is a sound and significant basis for objecting to HEW's proposed standards, should request the appropriate state governor to propose alternate standards and/or to seek a hearing and participate in that hearing.

4. Enforcement of Standards; Abatement Action

Each state will normally enforce its own standards in accordance with implementation and enforcement plans approved by HEW (which must include authority to act promptly in emergencies). If a state fails to take reasonable enforcement action in cases where apparent violations are causing air quality to fall below the new standards, HEW may act, as follows:

(1) *Nonemergencies where standards have been adopted*: HEW gives notice to local authorities and to alleged polluters. If the violation is not corrected within 180 days,

(a) in a case of interstate pollution, HEW may seek abatement in a federal court; the court reviews the standards and the alleged violation de novo (*i.e.*, the burden of proof is on HEW).

(b) where pollution is limited to a single state, HEW may take the matter to federal court only if requested by the state, or the state may request federal assistance in a state court action.

(2) *Nonemergencies where there are no standards in effect under the new act*: HEW may use the above-described pollution abatement procedure, on its own initiative in an interstate pollution situation and at the request of the governor in an intrastate pollution situation, with modifications as follows:

(a) HEW makes available a *report* on the problem.

(b) HEW calls a *conference* on thirty days' notice to hear the views of all interested parties.

(c) HEW recommends any necessary *abatement measures*.

(d) If no remedial action is taken within six months thereafter, a special *hearing board*, named by the Secretary but including members recommended by the states, will be convened and will recommend any abatement measures.

(e) If an alleged polluter fails to comply with the hearing board's recommendations within six months, HEW may take the matter to a federal court for a de novo hearing in the case of interstate pollution; where intrastate pollution is concerned, a federal court action is permitted only if requested by the state concerned. State action in a state court with federal assistance is also possible.

(3) *Emergency health situations*: HEW may seek immediate federal court action to stop pollution regardless of any problems of economic or technological feasibility of controls.

In a federal court action not involving an emergency, the court must consider economic and technological feasibility. A company or industry involved in a nonemergency court proceeding must consider whether it is in violation of the applicable emission standards, whether those standards or the applicable air quality standards or even the criteria should be challenged and whether compliance is economically and technologically feasible.

Pending the establishment of standards, the conference-abatement procedures most likely will be utilized. The modification made by the new legislation provides an opportunity for full industry participation in the conference, which should be utilized.

D. Where We Stand Today

In the discussion of the Air Quality Act of 1967 it will become apparent that while the act creates a broad plan for effective air pollution control, there is room for considerable flexibility under the act. As a result, the interpretations given to the legislation—not only by HEW and by state and local jurisdictions but also in possible court decisions and in reviews by congressional committees—will do much to shape the precise course of the nation's air pollution control effort. The act leaves the formulation of enforcement programs to state and local governments, and the scope of HEW's power to review and override the state legislation and implementing regulations adopted is not yet clear.[29] Even if HEW might be held to have broad powers to dictate the machinery to be employed at the local level, it might wisely choose to leave room for innovation and experimentation in control programs. For these reasons and because developing technology may greatly affect the nature of enforcement programs and administrative procedures, it is still too soon to know whether existing local laws, which for the most part appear to have been adapted from zoning laws,[30] represent the statutory pattern for future control programs. The initial impression, however, is that existing local laws do not manifest (on their face, at least) the flexibility needed to administer a program giving due weight to health requirements and economic and technological realities.

At the time of the writing of this article we are still at the incipient stage. Within HEW, responsibility for administration of the Air Quality Act has been placed in the National Air Pollution Control Administration, which is a part of the Consumer Protection and Environmental Health Service within the Public Health Service. This latter organization is headed by an administrator who reports to the Assistant Secretary for Health and Scientific Affairs.[31]

By the end of 1968 a number of the preliminary steps prerequisite to the regulatory scheme envisaged by the act will have been taken, and within the following two years the general control program will unfold. Thus for all those who have responsibilities for improving the nation's air, the time for a full understanding of those responsibilities has arrived. The Air Quality Act of 1967 contemplates effective opportunities for all interested persons to participate in the important processes which will lead to the establishment of specific regulations.

II

DEVELOPMENT OF AIR QUALITY STANDARDS AND CONTROL PLANS BY STATES

As indicated above, the act provides essentially that states are to develop their own air quality standards and control programs within broad federal guidelines. The several steps in this process are as follows: (a) HEW designation of atmospheric areas and specific "air quality control regions," (b) HEW development and publication of "air quality criteria" and "recommended control techniques" relating

---

[29] See the discussion of HEW's power over state implementation and enforcement plans, p. 260 infra.

[30] See PUBLIC HEALTH SERVICE, A DIGEST OF STATE AIR POLLUTION LAWS (1966 ed.). Most statutes and regulations provide flat emission standards but allow variances to be granted in narrow circumstances.

[31] 33 Fed. Reg. 9909, 9911 (1968).

to particular air pollution agents or combination of agents, both arrived at after consultation with and advice of appropriate advisory committees, (c) development by each state of appropriate standards and control plans for each portion of the state within an air quality region and concerning those air pollution agents for which HEW has published criteria and control recommendations, and (d) evaluation and approval (or disapproval) of state actions by HEW.

A. HEW Designation of Atmospheric Areas and Air Quality Control Regions

1. *Atmospheric Areas*

The first step is for HEW to delineate the broad atmospheric areas or air basins in the U.S.—mainly on the basis of those meteorological and topographical factors that influence the diffusion and transport of pollutants in the air. The act requires that this be accomplished by November 21, 1968, twelve months after passage of the act,[32] but the eight areas were designated by HEW on January 16, 1968, as follows: Great Lakes-Northeast; Mid-Atlantic Coastal; Appalachia; South Florida; Great Plains; Rocky Mountains; California Oregon Coastal; and Washington Coastal. HEW stated that each atmospheric area is "a segment of the country in which climate, meteorology, and topography—all of which influence the capacity of the air to dilute and disperse pollution—are essentially homogeneous."[33]

2. *Air Quality Control Regions*

By May 21, 1969, eighteen months after pssaage of act, HEW must designate existing "air quality control regions," after consultation with state and local authorities.[34]

The Senate committee stated that such regions should be established whenever HEW determined that "protection of health and welfare requires establishing air quality standards," presumably because the region has "significant air pollution problems."[35] The House committee stated that a region should include communities which are affected by a common air pollution problem requiring uniformity of control action.[36] There does not in fact appear to be any statutory requirement that the air pollution problems in the region be such as to require uniform controls, or even that a region have common problems as to one or more possible air contaminants. The existence of such a common problem requiring a concerted approach does, however, seem a logical factor to consider in establishing a region.

In designating the regions, the statute provides that HEW is to consider existing jurisdictional boundaries, urban-industrial concentrations, atmospheric areas, and any

[32] § 107(a)(1).
[33] 33 Fed. Reg. 548 (1968).
[34] § 107(a)(2).
[35] S. REP. 25, 4.
[36] H.R. REP. 14-15.

other factors which will affect the adequacy of regional controls. It is expected that HEW will also consider the boundaries of air basins or regions already designated by state governments. It is unlikely that air quality control regions would be coterminous with an atmospheric area, in view of the size of the areas which HEW has delineated. The region may be wholly within a state or include portions of several states.

In interstate situations, the affected states are encouraged under section 106 of the act to set up interstate planning agencies, wih federal financial aid, to help in recommending appropriate air quality standards for the region in question. In the absence of state action, HEW may establish an interstate planning commission.

While a critical factor in establishing a region may well be the fact that there is a common pollution problem, the act certainly does not assure uniform pollution control action when more than one state is included in the region, and does not appear to require it in a wholly intrastate region. Nevertheless, since uniform controls within a region may be the easiest (even if not the most desirable) controls to impose, it can be important to industry where the boundaries of a region are set.

On July 10, 1968, the Commissioner of the National Air Pollution Control Administration was delegated the authority by the Secretary of HEW to designate air quality control regions.[37] Some regions already have been proposed, including an interstate region which includes the District of Columbia and parts of Maryland and Virginia and an interstate region which includes the metropolitan New York area and adjacent counties in Connecticut and New Jersey.[38] These proposed designations include provision for hearings thirty days after the notice of designation, in which state and local authorities may participate. In addition, all interested parties have been invited to submit their views in writing. In fiscal year 1969 a number of other regions will be designated, with the same procedure being followed.

Thus industry should be sure that state and local officials have all pertinent information to pass on to HEW; and also that such officials understand clearly the importance of the state's making such information available to the federal government. This is a matter requiring very prompt attention in view of the timetable for establishing air quality control regions. A plant within such a region may be disadvantaged as compared with a plant outside of it. A region too broadly defined may result in controls being imposed in part of the region where in fact they are not necessary.

Moreover, it should be remembered that in an interstate region the governor of a state any part of which falls within such a region may intervene with regard to the standards and control plans of any other state within the region.

If a sound job is done in establishing the regions, much additional flexibility will be gained in improving air quality and establishing an effective control program

---

[37] 33 Fed. Reg. 9909 (1968).

[38] 33 Fed. Reg. 10882 (1968) (Washington, D.C.); 33 Fed. Reg. 12260 (1968) (New York City).

where it is really necessary, while avoiding the setting of rules which are unnecessarily restrictive and oppressive. For example, including in a region only those areas absolutely necessary may permit a wider choice in location of new power plants outside of the area where the pollution problem is in fact serious.

This would permit plant location to be a meaningful alternative to substitution of fuels, or other controls. It is clear that the Congress so intended. For the next few years this may prove to be most important to the fuels-burning industries, and others, in view of the control technology gap that may exist. This alternative at least provides a temporary solution while control technology is being developed.

In addition to the regions initially established (mandatory by May 21, 1969) and after similar consultation with state and local authorities, HEW may revise the designation of such regions and designate additional regions as necessary to protect the public health and welfare. This suggests that no matter where a company may decide to locate a new plant, appropriate pollution controls should be part of its planning. The fact that a particular area may have no serious pollution problem now does not mean that controls may not be needed sometime in the future.[39]

B. HEW's Air Quality Criteria and Recommended Control Techniques

As indicated, it is primarily up to the states to set adequate air quality standards in the designated regions. But, first, to assist the states in developing such standards, HEW will develop and publish "air quality criteria" on the adverse effects of specific air pollution agents or combinations of agents. It will also develop and recommend techniques for preventing or controlling the forms of air contamination so identified. In carrying out its functions in each of these areas, HEW must consult with other federal agencies and with advisory committees representing all interested groups, including industry.

In general, these criteria and recommended control techniques also are designed to be advance warning to industry and other contaminant sources to spur them to analyze their possible pollution problems and to plan adequate control programs.[40]

1. Air Quality Criteria

The new act continues the directive to HEW to develop such criteria, but with some important procedural modifications.[41] The principal change is the new requirement of consultation with advisory committees and others. This, however, is not intended to diminish HEW's responsibility, since the Secretary of HEW will make the "final determination on all questions involved in criteria development."[42]

These air quality criteria must accurately reflect the best available scientific knowl-

---

[39] See S. REP. 4.
[40] See S. REP. 27.
[41] § 107(b).
[42] See H.R. REP. 15.

edge on the adverse effects on health and welfare of particular contaminants present in the air in varying quantities. They must also reflect available knowledge of atmospheric and other environmental factors that may alter or otherwise influence these adverse effects. The House Commerce Committee indicated that these criteria will have to be "based upon the most careful studies and analysis," with "substantial evidentiary backup," so that they may be relied on by the states in developing effective and reasonable abatement programs.[43]

The above requirements apply also to the already-issued criteria on sulfur oxides, which, along with any other criteria presently under development, must be re-evaluated in accordance with the new requirements. The House and Senate committees had heard much testimony questioning the validity of the sulfur oxides criteria, and the House Commerce Committee stated, "There should be no hesitancy in revising such criteria as a result of these changes in the law."[44]

The new requirements, coupled with the de novo court consideration in any federal abatement action (see below), impose a substantial obligation on HEW to be certain that the criteria it promulgates are based upon established facts and are not just opinions based on limited information. The reason for this, of course, is that implementation of the criteria by the states can have very major health and economic consequences. This comports with testimony of representatives of HEW that as scientists they would only make findings where the evidence was "considerable" or "substantial" and that controls should be "related to measurable and demonstrable effects on public health and welfare."[45]

This is true even though air quality criteria are descriptive rather than prescriptive or regulatory. Their role is to define the health and welfare considerations that must be taken into account by the states in the development of standards and regulations. Thus, according to the House committee, economic and technological considerations (although essential to implementing the criteria) have no place in the development of criteria. "Air quality criteria should provide a clear statement of how well air pollution should be controlled in order to safeguard the public health and welfare, economic and technical factors notwithstanding. If control technology is not adequate, it must be improved."[46]

Thus the criteria provide the ultimate objective to be achieved. The Congress made it clear that economic and technological considerations relating to the controls needed may postpone the time of accomplishment. The criteria set the goals towards the achievement of which the state standards, and all research, must move.

In July 1968, the Subcommittee on Air and Water Pollution of the Senate Committee on Public Works commenced a series of hearings designed to develop

---

[43] See H.R. REP. 14.
[44] Id.
[45] Senate Hearings 2524, 2517.
[46] See H.R. REP. 16.

what factors should be considered by HEW in setting air quality criteria. A number of expert witnesses have been heard, and both government and industry have been invited to submit their views. The one certain thing established by the expert testimony is that even the best available evidence may be totally insufficient to form the basis for the kind of scientific conclusion on which one would expect broad regulations in this field to rest.

A subcommittee staff report on air quality criteria issued in July 1968[47] in advance of the hearings, while anticipating this problem, also pointed out that regulation should not await the development of adequate scientific data, but must proceed on the basis of the best evidence available. While that conclusion is the subject of considerable dispute, since there are those who believe that absent adequate scientific data the effort may move in totally erroneous directions, and while the timetable for issuance of the various criteria now is uncertain, undoubtedly some criteria will be issued by early 1969. Since the same staff report also made clear that in the standard-setting process (as distinguished from the establishment of criteria), "economic and technological considerations . . . are to be given full attention," the possible uncertainty as to the validity of the criteria to be issued may be ameliorated through the avoidance of standards and timetables which could result in significant economic disruption.

It is important to note the staff report conclusion that "throughout the standard setting process it should be recognized that precise limits for the protection of health and welfare are not possible."[48] This suggests the desirability of caveats in those circumstances where HEW's conclusions as to criteria may be subject to legitimate scientific question. For example, HEW might delineate, as part of the published criteria themselves, those areas in which the data promulgated is uncertain. This would assist the state agencies when they weigh the competing considerations with respect to particular regulations and timetables.

2. Recommended Control Techniques

Concurrently with its development of air quality criteria for particular air pollution substances, HEW must also develop and publish detailed information on the technology and costs of recommended control techniques.[49] These recommendations are to reflect the latest available technology and the economic feasibility of achieving various levels of air quality, including alternative control methods with cost-effectiveness analyses.

Consultation with other federal agencies and with appropriate advisory committees also would be a mandatory step in the development of this information. In

---

[47] STAFF OF THE SUBCOMM. ON AIR AND WATER POLLUTION OF THE SENATE COMM. ON PUBLIC WORKS, 90TH CONG., 2D SESS., AIR QUALITY CRITERIA (Comm. Print 1968).

[48] *Id.* at vi.

[49] § 107(c).

particular, the congressional committees indicated that HEW should consult with the Department of Commerce, including its Business and Defense Services Administration.[50]

These requirements derive from the fact noted above, that HEW's air quality criteria will not take into consideration the technological and economic feasibility of achieving the air quality defined in the criteria.[51]

As in the case of its criteria, the control techniques recommended by HEW are to be based upon the most careful studies and analysis, with substantial evidentiary backup. They should also permit maximum possible flexibility so that each area may pick the means most suitable to resolve its own pollution problems. Furthermore, as noted in the House Report,

> It is important that the Secretary call to the attention of the States in connection with his recommendation of control techniques, the various methods which may be used to achieve cleaner air, and provide information as to the economics of the more significant of these methods. Thus, for example, it may be possible to remove a pollutant from a fuel, or from stack gasses, or to so disperse the pollutant through the use of high stacks so that ground level concentrations are lessened by the stack emissions. The careful selection from among these various methods even within an area may greatly reduce the economic disruption involved and permit more rapid achievement of improved air quality.[52]

Along the same lines, the Senate committee referred to the desirability of alternatives such as tall stacks to alleviate a particular pollution problem pending the development of additional control technology.[53]

It should be noted, too, that the act does not prevent a private firm from utilizing an appropriate control technique even if it is not included in HEW's recommendations.[54]

The Senate committee felt that the federal role in the development of control technology should proceed along three lines: (1) support for research by industry, (2) joint support and direction of research, and (3) federal research activities. The method chosen would depend upon the size of the industry concerned and its capabilities to carry out or share in support of the needed investigations.[55]

Although the act is silent as to when HEW should publish the control technology information, the House committee felt that information on the control of sources of a given pollution agent should be made available as soon as possible. While this might occur after the publication of the related air quality criteria, simultaneous publication would be desirable.[56]

---

[50] See S. Rep. 28; H.R. Rep. 15, 35.
[51] See S. Rep. 27.
[52] H.R. Rep. 14.
[53] See S. Rep. 28.
[54] See H.R. Rep. 17.
[55] See S. Rep. 28.
[56] See H.R. Rep. 16.

Similarly, the Senate committee "strongly urges" HEW to develop this information as quickly as possible, giving due regard to the need for reflecting the best available scientific knowledge. Even though existing control technology may not be adequate, the committee felt that "control methods must be implemented as soon as economically feasible and technologically available." The committee recognized that these scientific and technical documents are "more than just the tools for a standard setting procedure."[57]

In brief, this provision gives HEW a major new responsibility, the purpose of which is to insure access to enough technical information to permit an informed and intelligent choice among various control techniques—the choice being left to those who are actually responsible for sources of air contamination. The extent of control needed to achieve the necessary degree of abatement will depend on various factors to be determined by the states for each region.[58]

C. State Standards and Control Plans

The heart of the new act is the required adoption of regional air quality standards. These provisions are similar to existing federal law on water pollution control, with heavy reliance upon action by the states and with due weight given to both health and feasibility considerations.

The Senate committee succinctly described its concept of regulation under the act as follows:

> Reasonable regulation should be based on an accurate measurement of the health and welfare needs, technological feasibility of abatement of pollution and economic factors involved. Where health considerations permit and there are technological obstacles or known and seriously adverse economic results which would grow out of precipitous abatement action, the timetable for developments through research should be synchronized so that the pollution problem can be solved in an orderly manner.
>
> On the other hand, where there are health hazards, it is expected that State and local authorities will take the necessary abatement action, and if they do not, the Secretary is specifically authorized to commence abatement action.[59]

As indicated, HEW must first take steps to designate particular regions and to issue air quality criteria and recommended control data for one or more air pollution agents. The publication of such criteria and data then triggers state action to develop appropriate air quality standards and controls in respect to each of the designated contaminants, applicable to each region or portion of a region within the state.[60]

Specifically, each state involved has ninety days after receiving the HEW criteria

---

[57] *See* S. REP. 27.
[58] *See* H.R. REP. 17.
[59] S. REP. 10-11.
[60] §§ 108(a), (c)(1).

and control information to file a letter of intent—that is, indicating its intent to set air quality standards for the contaminants in question consistent with the purposes of the act; 180 days thereafter to conduct public hearings and set the standards; and another 180 days after setting the standards to adopt a plan to implement and enforce them. This procedure must be followed for each air pollution agent as to which HEW publishes criteria and control data and for any modification in the state standards.

These state standards must be adequate to protect the public health and welfare and consistent with HEW's air quality criteria and recommended control techniques. The implemenation plan must assure achieving the standards of air quality within a reasonable time, as economic and technological feasibility permit. It must also provide means of enforcement—including authority to seek prompt court action in emergency situations similar to that given in the act to HEW.

1. *State Standards*

These ambient air quality standards of the state, when effective, will prescribe levels for contaminants in the ambient air that cannot legally be exceeded during specific times and within specific geographic areas. They have been described as imposing "actual requirements for performance by polluters or potential polluters."[61]

According to the congressional committees, the development of these standards from air quality criteria will be influenced not only by a concern for the protection of health and welfare but also by "economic, social and technological considerations." The House committee emphasized that "technological and economic feasibility are a prerequisite to sound regulation." The Senate committee also felt that "wherever possible standards should be established which enhance the quality of the environment."[62]

In developing the standards the states must hold public hearings during the first 180-day period. In addition, for interstate regions, they will normally receive recommendations developed by interstate air quality planning agencies designated by the affected state governors—or by HEW in urgent cases.[63]

There is no requirement that either the air quality standards or the control plans be uniform throughout a region. While a region may well have a common pollution problem, nevertheless the states are permitted and in fact encouraged to observe the maximum flexibility in the interests of a realistic and effective program. Moreover, even if uniformity throughout the region is appropriate for some particular contaminant, it may not be appropriate for others. Each situation must turn on its own facts.

Similarly, where a region involves portions of more than one state, and thus

---

[61] S. REP. 28.
[62] *Id.* at 29; *see* H.R. REP. 19.
[63] *See* §§ 106(a), (b)(1).

permits separately promulgated standards and control plans for each state, some variance is a possibility.[64] This may be because of different conditions in various parts of the region, or because the respective governors did not reach identical conclusions, or both. On the other hand, there will be a tendency towards uniformity within a region, deriving from HEW's right of approval, particularly concerning standards, and the right of a governor of an affected state to petition for revision of standards of another state. Thus, it is important for both government officials and industry to be aware that differences within a region may well be justified, and upheld, or that need for particular requirements in a given part of the region may be uncertain,—and that the act permits broad discretion on such matters.

In this connection, however, the House committee felt that no state should be permitted to set air quality standards which, even if fully implemented, would impair air quality in any portion of another state below that state's own standards.[65]

2. Control Plans

Within 180 days after adoption of any standards (and from time to time thereafter) the state must adopt an implementation, maintenance, and enforcement plan.[66] The main purpose of the plan is to assure that the standards will be met within a reasonable time. Economics and technology clearly are the limiting factors.[67]

According to both committees, the plan should include emission standards or controls applicable to the sources of the particular contaminants. Emission controls are "legally enforceable limitations on the amount of pollution that a single source or category of source may discharge in the atmosphere." Where a state lacks sufficient information on pollution sources, the implementation plan should include a timetable for obtaining it and for subsequent adoption and enforcement of emission control standards.[68]

Such emission control requirements may include such alternative courses of action as process changes, flue gas stack controls, stack height requirements, fuel use limitations, or plant location rules. In any event, they should include the "best available technology required to achieve the desired level of ambient air quality."[69]

Any emission control requirements should be based on a survey or inventory of the emissions within the region, including types and amounts of pollution agents and the effect of meteorological factors and other factors. These inventories should be updated from time to time to keep pace with changing conditions such as increased urbanization, industrialization, and population trends.[70]

---

[64] See H.R. REP. 18.
[65] Id.
[66] See § 108(c)(1).
[67] See S. REP. 3-4, 30; H.R. REP. 18-19.
[68] See S. REP. 29-30; H.R. REP. 18.
[69] See S. REP. 29.
[70] Id.

Emission control requirements applicable to particular sources of air contamination must also keep pace with technology and the economics of control. Those methods of control that are technologically and economically feasible today may not be sufficiently effective to achieve the desired ambient air quality standard. Therefore, where this is true, as technology advances, the states should prescribe new requirements on a continually more restrictive basis until a satisfactory standard is achieved. This means, too, that individuals close to a given source must be assured, where feasible, of an ambient air quality equivalent to that set for the entire region.[71]

A recent report by HEW concerning federal research and development relating to sulfur oxides control clearly illustrates both that new technology will play a major role in solving our air pollution problems and that there is a great technological lag between air pollution control objectives and our present capability to accomplish them. That report lists numerous different approaches to control of sulfur oxides emissions which will be under active research over the next five years. It specifically points out that "no single universal solution exists to the sulfur oxide control problem but . . . a broad spectrum of solutions applicable to the diverse combination of factors surrounding each case is necessary."[72] Hopefully the data on control techniques which HEW must publish along with the criteria will provide a sufficiently full picture concerning both availability and economic feasibility to encourage "a broad spectrum of solutions." The states thus would be able to provide realistic regulatory frameworks which both permit and result in voluntary compliance rather than lengthy disputes. This would reverse a prior trend where issuance of sweeping regulations which ignored both feasibility and flexibility has resulted in litigation challenging the validity of the regulations instead of compliance.[73]

3. Industry Participation at the State Level

Obviously, a state's determination of the standards and control plans applicable to the air quality region(s) within the state are of major importance to industry. Moreover, after the initial determinations, there will be continuing revisions.

Industry thus must inform itself and actively participate in the public hearings. Each plant, new or old, where there is a potential pollution problem, must be reviewed. This review should include the effects of the plant's emissions on air quality in the region, and the economic and technological feasibility of the various means for controlling those emissions. Clearly what is feasible for one plant may not

---

[71] See S. REP. 30.

[72] NATIONAL CENTER FOR AIR POLLUTION CONTROL, SULFUR OXIDES POLLUTION CONTROL: FEDERAL RESEARCH AND DEVELOPMENT PLANNING AND PROGRAMMING, 1968-1972 (1968).

[73] See, e.g., Consolidation Coal Co. v. Kandle, No. A-1070-67 (N.J. Super. Ct., App. Div., filed April 18, 1968). In this litigation a broad spectrum of coal, railroad, and industrial groups challenged the New Jersey regulations as being neither supported by the record nor technologically and economically feasible. The regulations, which were scheduled to go into effect in early May 1968, have been held in abeyance by court order pending disposition of the case on the merits. At the time of this writing the case, which was argued in June 1968, had not been decided.

be practicable for another. Industry has the prime responsibility for presenting this information.

The objective of the legislation is "to achieve cleaner air with the minimum possible economic cost or disruption . . . ,"[74] and industry's efforts should be directed toward that joint objective. Note that technological and economic feasibility are factors applicable both to the ambient air quality standards and to their implementation, including emission standards.

D. HEW Approval of State Action

All state air quality standards and control plans must be submitted to HEW for evaluation. Such standards and plan will become effective for each state involved if HEW finds (1) that the standards are consistent with HEW's related criteria and control techniques; (2) that the control plan is consistent with the purposes of the act, in assuring achievement of the standards within a reasonable time; and (3) that a means of enforcement by state action, including emergency authority, is provided.[75]

To warrant HEW approval, in the opinion of the House committee, the state standards "must call for air quality levels which, based on the Secretary's criteria, are at a minimum adequate for the protection of public health and which can be achieved through the application of feasible control techniques."[76]

Despite such HEW approval, any state, interstate, or local authority may set more stringent standards for stationary sources in order to achieve a higher level of ambient air quality than approved by HEW.[77] Since under some circumstances such action in industrial communities could impose a heavy economic burden on industry in that area, and conceivably could cause both relocation of existing plants and loss of possible new plants, industry must be alert to furnish the pertinent economic data to the state, interstate and local authorities.

III

PROCEDURE FOR FEDERAL STANDARDS IF STATE FAILS TO ACT
OR IF ITS ACTION IS INADEQUATE

HEW may develop its own air quality standards for particular pollution agents with respect to any air quality region, or portion thereof, within a state if (a) the state fails to file a letter of intent, or (b) it fails to set standards or file an implementation-enforcement plan, or (c) HEW determines that the state's standards are not consistent with the applicable air quality criteria and recommended control techniques, or (d) if a governor of another state affected by such state's standards (for

---

[74] *See* H.R. REP. 14.
[75] § 108(c)(1).
[76] *See* H.R. REP. 18.
[77] § 109.

example, where there is an air quality region encompassing portions of more than one state) petitions for a revision of such standards.[78] Afterwards, if the state so requests, the standards must be reviewed by a special hearing board. (It is expected, however, that HEW will seldom, if ever, have occasion to exercise this residual authority.[79])

A. Act Ambiguous on HEW Authority as to Implementation and Enforcement Plans

The act is not clear whether, in addition to such federal standards, HEW may also promulgate a federal implementation and enforcement plan. The act, in section 108(c)(1) dealing with state action, appears to use the word *standard* ambiguously. It requires a state to establish both "air quality standards" and an implementation "plan," and clearly distinguishes between the two. It then provides that if approved by HEW, such *"standards and plan* shall be the air quality *standards* applicable to such State." Section 108(c)(2), which is the authorization of HEW action, refers to promulgation of "standards" of air quality by HEW upon failure of a state to establish appropriate "air quality *standards*," with no reference to a "plan."

The section-by-section analysis of the act in each of the committee reports mentions only "standards"[80] in respect to section 108(c)(2). On the other hand, one portion of the House committee report, and a passage in the Senate report, indicate that it was intended that HEW be authorized to promulgate both standards and an implementation plan, where a state fails to do so.[81]

The matter is particularly troublesome because, as the House report makes clear, regardless of whether the state or HEW promulgates the "standards," it is the state which has initial responsibility for enforcement. Federal enforcement action appears limited to the abatement actions specifically provided in the act in the absence of state enforcement.[82] It is at least questionable whether an HEW-promulgated implementation plan could vest jurisdiction in state courts or agencies or in any way create a state implementation procedure. Thus, one might argue that the statutory scheme contemplates HEW standards only, with no HEW implementation plan, but with HEW abatement action in appropriate cases if the state fails to set up an adequate plan to implement the HEW-promulgated standards, or otherwise fails to enforce them.

Similarly, it is perhaps arguable that mere inadequacy of a state's proposed implementation and enforcement plan (as distinguished from its air quality standards) will not be enough to authorize HEW to set federal standards or a federal plan. Certainly regardless of the adequacy of the enforcement plan, if the state standards were adequate, HEW should not promulgate its own standards. And, as noted

---

[78] § 108(c)(2). *See* S. REP. 29; H.R. REP. 19.
[79] *See* H.R. REP. 12.
[80] *See* S. REP. 44; H.R. REP. 34.
[81] H.R. REP. 18; *cf.* S. REP. 29.
[82] H.R. REP. 13.

above, HEW may lack authority to issue an enforcement plan. Under this view, HEW's authority would be limited to the abatement remedies provided by section 108(c)(4), discussed below.[83]

Thus in the case of a "recalcitrant" state, effective federal authority (apart from setting standards alone) conceivably would be limited to situations where the contamination involved has an adverse effect on another state. HEW enforcement officials, however, may well feel that HEW has the right to promulgate an implementation and enforcement plan under the act where state control plans are deemed inadequate.

B. Conference and Proposed Federal Standards

Whenever it becomes appropriate for HEW to develop air quality standards for a given region or portion thereof, it must first call a conference, after reasonable notice. This conference is to include representatives of all interested agencies and industries.

While the act is silent on what the conference does and how it should operate, it presumably would receive evidence and make recommendations for consideration by HEW. The Senate committee report suggests that HEW should issue detailed regulations concerning the various hearings and conferences for which it is responsible under the act. These regulations would be expected to provide for full participation by all interested persons and, to the extent practicable, would conform to the Administrative Procedure Act.[84]

Following such a conference, HEW will prepare and issue regulations setting forth air quality standards for the area in question, consistent with its already-issued air quality criteria and recommended control techniques. The state has six months from the date of these regulations to adopt standards satisfactory to HEW, or to request a public hearing. If neither is done, HEW promulgates the air quality standards set forth in the regulations.[85]

C. Standards Set by Hearing Board if State So Requests

Any affected state which objects to these HEW standards may request a hearing during the first six-month period, and up to thirty days after their promulgation.[86] HEW must then set up a special hearing board consisting of representatives of the affected states, HEW, and other interested federal agencies—with HEW not to have a majority. (This standards hearing board composition is similar to the composition of the abatement hearing board under the earlier law described below.[87])

It is expected that the Department of Commerce and other appropriate agencies

[83] See p. 263 infra.
[84] See S. Rep. 30.
[85] § 108(c)(2).
[86] § 108(c)(3).
[87] See p. 266 infra.

will be represented on any such hearing board, to provide technical and economic advice and in order to achieve "the objective of air pollution abatement, with minimum economic disruption to the various industries involved."[88]

The hearing is to be held in or near the affected region, after at least thirty days' notice to parties who received notice of the earlier conference, as well as publication of such notice in the *Federal Register*. At the hearing, the board would receive testimony and other evidence from state and local air pollution control officials, and from industries and other parties affected. Thereafter, on the basis of the evidence presented, the board would recommend that the HEW standards either be approved or modified. These findings must be made in ninety days, although the Secretary may grant a longer time, if necessary, up to 180 days.

In event of approval of the HEW standards, they take effect immediately. Any modifications recommended by the hearing board are binding upon HEW, and would become effective upon publication of revised regulations by HEW.[89]

IV

IMPLEMENTATION, MAINTENANCE, AND ENFORCEMENT OF AIR QUALITY STANDARDS

A. State Implementation, Maintenance, and Enforcement

Upon completion of the procedures described above for setting air quality standards, the states would presumably begin action to implement, maintain, and enforce them. While the act does not so require, it is expected that such action would include, where appropriate, specific emission standards for the control of particular air contaminant sources, or provisions for setting such emission standards, and a schedule for enforcing them.[90]

As noted above,[91] the Senate committee considered meaningful emission controls, based on the pollution problems of the region involved, to be essential to implement the air quality standards and to permit legal enforcement action where necessary. The committee specifically noted that such emission controls were subject to technological and economic feasibility; they must, however, keep pace with advances in technology where needed to achieve the desired ambient air quality.[92]

As indicated above, the act is unclear as to whether HEW has any authority over the methods and procedures for implementation, maintenance and enforcement of either the state's own air quality standards or of any standards promulgated by HEW. While a state must submit to HEW its proposed plan to accomplish these objectives, and HEW has the right not to approve such plan, it is possible that there

---

[88] H.R. REP. 34-35.
[89] § 108(c)(3).
[90] *See* S. REP. 29; H.R. REP. 10.
[91] *See* p. 257 *supra*.
[92] S. REP. 30.

are no immediate consequences of such HEW failure to approve so long as the state's air quality standards themselves are adequate. This is because the legislation provides for HEW authority to act only if the "standards" are inadequate, and it is uncertain whether the term *standards* includes the control plan. In this part of the act, *standards* is used both ways.

In this same connection, as also noted above, there is no express provision for a federal implementation plan in conjunction with federal air quality standards. There is even no apparent requirement that a state promulgate such a plan (as it must to implement its own standards) after federal promulgation of air quality standards for a given region or portion thereof. Thus it appears legally possible that the act will be construed to impose no ultimate requirement on the states to adopt federally acceptable "plans" of implementation, maintenance and enforcement, with federal intervention limited to that described in the following section.

B. Federal Enforcement by Court Action if State Enforcement Inadequate

Federal enforcement action of air quality standards may occur only if HEW finds (i) that air quality in a given region falls below the prescribed air quality standards for that region, and (ii) that a state has not taken reasonable action itself to implement and enforce them.[93] (It should be noted, however, that, where no standards are in effect under the new act, HEW may still act to abate existing pollution under the abatement procedure provided in the earlier act, which is left substantially unchanged.[94])

If HEW finds it necessary to act, it must first give notice to the state and all other persons contributing to the alleged violation. If the violation has not been corrected within 180 days, then HEW may seek abatement action in the appropriate federal district court in the case of interstate pollution—that is, where the air quality region involved includes portions of more than one state, and where the pollution sought to be abated is considered to be endangering the health or welfare of persons in a state other than that in which the discharges originate.

If the alleged pollution is limited to a single state, such federal district court action may be taken only if the governor of that state so requests; or the governor may request federal assistance in bringing a state enforcement action.[95] These provisions for federal action are similar to those in existing law for taking abatement actions to court, as described below.[96]

In any such court proceeding the burden of proof on all issues establishing the violation is on the government. While any transcript and recommendations of a hearing board, or of HEW, must be received in evidence, the court is required to

---

[93] § 108(c)(4).
[94] *See* p. 264 *infra.*
[95] § 108(c)(4).
[96] *See* p. 266 *infra.*

make a complete de novo review of the air quality standards in question, as well as the alleged violation. The review of the standards could very well include consideration de novo of the HEW criteria and recommended control techniques. Since the court must receive evidence on all other pertinent issues, this clearly also includes whether the pollution in fact endangers the health or welfare of persons in another 'state.

If an interstate violation of the standards is found, the court must also consider the economic and technical feasibility of compliance with the applicable standards. On this issue it is uncertain who has the burden of proof.

The court ultimately will enter judgment "as the public interest and the equities of the case may require."

Obviously, court abatement proceedings are the last resort for all concerned. Thus the research provisions and advisory committee procedures, the encouragement of industry participation, and the recognition of the limits imposed by technological and economic feasibility, all make the major thrust of the act a cooperative endeavor to solve the pollution problems through technological advances and voluntary compliance. Presumably the states will follow a similar pattern as the quickest and least costly way to achieve clean air.

V

INTERIM AND EMERGENCY ABATEMENT PROCEDURES

A. Continuance of Prior Federal Procedures for Interim Purposes

It is not intended that the time required to establish air quality standards under the new act interfere with the protection of public health and welfare. Accordingly, the federal pollution abatement procedures provided in the earlier law are continued in effect, pending establishment of state standards and control plans, with some helpful modifications.[97]

The Senate committee has directed HEW to continue to act expeditiously to abate pollution under these procedures before the new act is fully effective. When appropriate in these situations, however, HEW is to take cognizance of any air quality criteria and control techniques, already issued, and give the state opportunity to establish standards for the air pollution agents in question.[98]

Briefly, these existing procedures provide for (a) an initial conference of affected state or local agencies called by HEW; (b) recommended abatement measures by HEW as a result of the conference; (c) recommended abatement measures by a special hearing board, following hearing, if no remedial action is taken within six months; (d) abatement action in a federal court if alleged polluter fails to comply with the hearing board's recommendations within six months.

---

[97] §§ 108(d)-(i).
[98] See S. REP. 30-31.

Emergency situations are covered by a brand new provision in the act, which is discussed below.

1. *Initial Conference*

In the case of air pollution alleged to endanger health or welfare in any interstate, state, or local situation, HEW must first call a conference of affected state or local agencies. Such a conference is initiated by request from the governor of a state, a state air pollution control agency, a municipality (with the governor's concurrence), or by HEW itself in appropriate cases. The conferees consist of the interstate, state, and local agencies concerned, but there is no industry representation unless invited by one of the agencies.[99]

In order to provide all parties affected by an abatement action a greater opportunity to participate, the new act has enlarged the notice period from three weeks to thirty days, and requires HEW to make available a federal report at the time of the notice. This report is to define the matters coming before the conference, including pertinent data and any recommended conclusions or findings by HEW.[100] Interested parties must be given an opportunty at the conference to present their views on this report, and a transcript of the proceedings must be kept.[101]

In this connection, the Senate committee suggested that HEW issue detailed procedural regulations covering these conferences and other hearings provided for in the act . The objective would be to invite maximum participation by all persons having a substantial interest in the matter under consideration, so as to give the conferees the broadest review of the pollution problems in a given area.[102]

After the conference, HEW prepares and furnishes to the agencies a summary of conference discussions on (i) the occurrence of air pollution subject to abatement under the act, (ii) the adequacy of abatement measures taken, and (iii) the nature of delays, if any, being encountered in abating the pollution.[103] Furthermore, if HEW believes at the end of the conference, or thereafter, that effective progress towards abatement is not taking place, it recommends necessary remedial action to the appropriate agencies.[104]

2. *Reports*

In connection with any such conference, HEW may require any person causing or contributing to pollution to file a report on the alleged pollutant emissions in question and any control devices being used. After the conference has been held, similar reports may be required as the conference might recommend. No processes

---

[99] §§ 108(d)(1), (2).
[100] *See* S. REP. 30.
[101] § 108(d)(2).
[102] *See* S. REP. 30.
[103] § 108(d)(3).
[104] § 108(e).

constituting trade secrets need be divulged, and all information reported is considered confidential.

Failure to file any such report subjects the person in default to a penalty of $100 per day, recoverable by the federal government in a civil action, brought in the federal court.[105]

3. *Special Hearing Board*

If appropriate remedial action is not taken within six months after HEW's recommendations, HEW calls a public hearing before a special hearing board appointed by the Secretary. This board consists of representatives selected by the affected states, HEW, other federal agencies, and any interstate agency—with HEW not to have a majority.

The hearing is held at one or more of the places where the alleged pollution originates, after at least three weeks' notice to the affected agencies and the alleged polluter. All interested parties are to be given a reasonable opportunity to present evidence. The hearing board then makes findings as to the alleged pollution and any progress towards abatement, and may recommend suitable abatement measures if necessary. These findings and recommended abatement action are sent by HEW to the alleged polluters and to the affected agencies.[106]

4. *Court Abatement Action*

If the alleged polluter fails to comply within six months (or longer period specified by HEW), HEW may ask the Attorney General to bring an abatement action in federal court in the case of interstate pollution. If the pollution is limited to a single state, such federal court action may be taken only if the state so requests; or the state may request federal assistance in bringing a state abatement action.

In any such federal court action, the evidence will include a transcript of the hearing board proceedings and a copy of its recommendations. As in the act's other court enforcement provisions, de novo consideration of all pertinent factual and legal questions is required with the burden of proof on the government. The court must consider the practicability of complying with any applicable standards, and the physical and economic feasibility of abating any pollution proved. The court then will enter judgment as the public interest and the equities of the case may require.[107]

B. Emergency Court Action

A new provision in the act authorizes HEW to seek immediate court action to stop emission of alleged pollutants where there is evidence of "imminent and substantial endangerment to the health of persons" and where state or local authori-

---

[105] § 108(j).
[106] §§ 108(f), (i).
[107] §§ 108(g), (h).

ties have not acted.[108]   Unlike other provisions in section 108, there is no feasibility limitation on the court; accordingly, an injunction could issue, where necessary, regardless of technological or economic feasibility.[109]

This provision is intended to provide a remedy for the emergency situations specified. It is not intended as a substitute control for chronic or generally recurring problems, which should be dealt with under the other provisions of the act. For example, the emergency procedure is available for use in cases of unusual atmospheric inversion or other extraordinary circumstances of imminent danger to public health. Both congressional committees gave as examples the incidents in Donora, Pennsylvania, in 1948, in New York City in 1953, and in London in 1952 and 1962.[110]   HEW could go to court in such a case to stop traffic or shut down offending industries until the crisis is over.

This special procedure is also available to enjoin an individual source of pollution where there is evidence of a direct effect upon public health.[111]

It is expected, however, that before invoking this emergency authority, HEW will want to be as fully informed as possible on the local conditions and how best to meet the emergency problem. The Secretary's statement on this point in the House committee hearings was as follows:

> Appropriate action in emergency situations would require detailed knowledge of the nature and location of pollution sources, immediate access to information on local meteorological conditions and air quality levels, and detailed plans tailored to the local need to shut down or curtail pollution sources.
>
> I will take steps, therefore, to further encourage the local and State control agencies, primarily responsible for the quality of the air in their jurisdictions, to develop appropriate air-monitoring systems and emergency procedures for curtailing sources of pollution.
>
> Only in this way could I be assured that a decision to seek emergency court action would be based on sound technical information gathered and developed in the locality concerned.

The House committee felt that these proposed procedures were reasonable.[112]

VI

RESEARCH AND RELATED ACTIVITIES

A. Increased Emphasis on Research

"Research is the key to effective pollution control."[113]   It is not "a substitute for regulation," but sound regulation is dependent upon it.[114]

---

[108] § 108(k).

[109] *See* H.R. REP. 19.

[110] *See* S. REP. 31; H.R. REP. 19. For a discussion of these incidents, *see* Cassell, *The Health Effects of Air Pollution and Their Implications for Control,* in this symposium, p. 197.

[111] *See* S. REP. 31.

[112] H.R. REP. 20.

[113] *Id.* at 25.

[114] S. REP. 10-11.

The new act keeps and strengthens the emphasis on general federal research programs in existing section 103. It also adds a new section 104, with enlarged authority, on "Research Relating to Fuels and Vehicles," in place of the specific references in the old law to research relating to sulfur removal from fuels and sulfur oxide emissions.

The act, therefore, still requires HEW to conduct research programs on the causes, effects, extent, prevention, and control of air pollution in general, and to assist air pollution control agencies and others to that end. In carrying out this responsibility, HEW is given broad authority, among other things, to collect and publish basic data on chemical, physical, and biological effects of varying air quality; to make grants to pollution control agencies, other organizations (not including private industry), and to individuals; to provide fellowships and other forms of training; and to develop effective and practical control methods and prototype control devices. And the act provides for the first time for technical advisory committees of recognized experts to help HEW in evaluating its research projects and proposals and to avoid duplication.[115]

In administering these research programs, HEW is directed to make maximum use of the expertise and resources of other federal agencies—such as the Departments of Commerce and Interior and the Tennessee Valley Authority's research into pollution control techniques.[116]

In its report, the Senate committee commented at some length on research areas which it felt needed special attention.[117] In addition to the special emphasis on fuel research, outlined below, the committee suggested certain areas where additional federal assistance to industry in developing improved control equipment could be effective—such as joint efforts with control equipment manufacturers to study common problems, and joint support and direction of research and development with trade associations concerning unsolved pollution problems.[118]

Other research needs on a more general scale would be to determine the effects of cities on air flow; to develop methods to reduce urban pollution concentrations; and to measure and document national and global trends in atmospheric pollutants.[119]

B. Fuel Research

As indicated above, the new act eliminates the specific references in the old law to research relating to sulfur and adds a new section 104 covering the more general area of fuel research—in effect, to determine which fuels are most to blame for air contamination and how to prevent or control such contamination.

---

[115] § 103.
[116] See S. REP. 118; H.R. REP. 25.
[117] S. REP. 17-22.
[118] Id. at 18-19.
[119] Id. at 21-22.

This section directs HEW, under expanded authority, to give special emphasis to accelerating research in three fuel areas—control of combustion by-products, removal of potential pollutants from fuels, and control of fuel evaporation emissions. The section also provides specific authority for such items as the development of new control methods having industrywide application, pilot plant testing, demonstration plants, studies on commercial use of by-products, and federal grants to public or nonprofit private agencies.

This new research authority of HEW is designed to include economics as well as technology—such as finding markets for by-products to make a particular control method economically feasible. And it encourages practical applications authorizing funds for the building of pilot plants, demonstration plants, and prototype equipment.[120]

The Senate committee noted particularly that the enlarged research efforts provided for in section 104 include specific authority to enter into demonstration contracts with industry. Such contracts are to "prove the technological and economic feasibility of the control of pollutants from the combustion of fossil fuel and shorten the time-lag between research, development, and full-scale practice."[121]

The committee commented on the need for further research on the effects of low concentrations of exposure of various contaminants for extended periods; and on the "immediate need" to develop methods to control the emission of sulfur compounds, oxides of nitrogen, carbon monoxide, and carbon dioxide. The committee also described in some detail the sulfur oxide problem and various processes being developed to meet this problem economically.[122]

The House committee, too, was keenly interested in the critical pollution problems relating to the combustion of fuels—and commented that HEW should "pursue a most aggressive policy of research" directed toward solving these problems.

> The economy of the Nation depends on an adequate supply of low-cost energy. Only through technological breakthroughs can such a supply be assured consistent with our requirements for cleaner air. Since effective regulation therefore will depend upon such technological breakthroughs, this research must be of the highest priority. Further, while the language of the legislation is discretionary in terms of how the Secretary shall proceed with regard to research activities, the imperative nature of this work should clearly be understood by all, including those who will administer the legislation.[123]

The new act authorizes appropriations totalling $125 million over two years for this fuel research program. For all other operations under the act, including nonfuel

---

[120] See H.R. REP. 25.

[121] See S. REP. 18.

[122] Id. at 19-21.

[123] H.R. REP. 25. For a full discussion of FPC policy toward the use of natural gas in electric power generation as a means of combating air pollution, see Rein, *Obtaining Boiler Fuel Gas to Reduce Air Pollution: The Policy of the Federal Power Commission*, in this symposium p. 399.

research, the act authorizes $303.3 million over three years (considerably more than the approximately $65 million per year currently authorized).

C. Studies and Reports

1. *National Emissions Standards Study*

In lieu of national emissions standards for stationary sources, which had been proposed by the Administration, section 211(a) of the act directs HEW to make a two-year study and report to Congress on the need for and feasibility of such standards and their effect. Several specific aspects to be included in such report are specified in that section:

2. *Comprehensive Economic Cost Studies*

Section 305 of the act directs HEW, in cooperation with state and local pollution control agencies, to make comprehensive economic cost studies—including studies of the cost of pollution programs to such agencies and the economic impact of air quality standards on industry and others. The results of such studies are to be submitted to Congress not later than January 10, 1969. HEW is also directed to study the personnel needs for effective air pollution control programs, and to report the results to Congress not later than July 1, 1969.

VII

SUPPORT FOR INTERSTATE AGENCIES AND OTHER PLANNING AND CONTROL PROGRAMS

The Congress recognized that the air quality standards to be established under the act will require careful planning to insure that they are tailored to the needs of the particular regions, the types of pollution there, and the technological and economic feasibility of proposed controls. In addition, the activities of different jurisdictions will have to be coordinated. The act therefore contains new provisions for the support of planning bodies to help the states in such regional control efforts.[124]

A. Interstate Air Quality Agencies and Commissions

There are obvious administrative and political difficulties inherent in the establishment of effective pollution control planning agencies on an interstate basis. Accordingly, section 106 of the act authorizes HEW to pay up to 100 per cent of the air quality planning program costs of any interstate agency designated by the affected states for up to two years. After this initial period, grants are authorized for up to three-fourths of such costs.[125]

The interstate agency is to concern itself with recommending standards of ambient

---

[124] §§ 105, 106. *See* H.R. REP. 26.
[125] H.R. REP. 25-26.

air quality, and plans for implementing and enforcing the emission controls required to achieve the recommended standards.[126]

In addition, HEW may establish an "air quality planning commission" whenever this is deemed "necessary to expedite the establishment of standards for an interstate air quality control region" designated under the act. Such commission, to be chaired by HEW, would be set up only after consultation with the states involved.[127] The Senate and House committees indicate that such a commission will be formed only in the absence of action by the affected states to set up their own interstate agency.[128]

According to the House committee, an air quality planning commission, when established by HEW in the absence of state action, will be essentially an arm of the federal government, in that it is "designed to assist the Secretary in establishing standards and plans for implementation."[129] Provision is made, however, for consultation with the affected states and representation of appropriate agencies within the region.

B. Grants for Other Planning and Control Programs

The earlier legislation provided for federal grants to state and local pollution control agencies to help them develop and maintain their air pollution control programs. This authority is expanded in section 105 of the new act to include grants for planning by these agencies to help the states in developing air quality standards and implementation plans under the act.

The revised section authorizes grants of up to two-thirds of the cost of planning, establishing, or improving such control programs, and up to one-half of the cost of maintaining them. For air quality planning or control purposes in regional areas including two or more municipalities (whether in the same or different states), the grants can be three-fourths and three-fifths of such costs, respectively. Grants for programs in any one state may not exceed ten per cent of the total federal funds allocated for that purpose.

Grant recipients must be capable of carrying out certain specified conditions. For example, a pollution control agency administering an interstate planning or control program must provide for adequate representation of state, interstate, and local interests.

Subsection (b) of section 105 specifies various conditions and criteria to be observed by HEW in making these grants, including population of the area in question, extent of pollution, and financial need. The House committee noted that the objective of the grant program is to provide impetus to the establishment and improvement of state and local control programs—not to provide a substitute for state and local funds. The committee also spelled out its intention that "financial

---

[126] *Id.* at 26.
[127] § 106(d).
[128] *See* H.R. REP. 26; S. REP. 24-25.
[129] *See* H.R. REP. 26.

need" meant ability to pay, and not merely budgetary limitations. Finally, the committee expressed its expectation that HEW would not give a grant to a local pollution control agency without clearance with the appropriate state agency.[130]

C. Interstate Pollution Control Compacts

The 1963 act encouraged states to enter into interstate compacts for control of air pollution, which would become binding upon congressional approval.[131] The new act added a provision that any state *not* part of a designated air quality control region should *not* participate in an air pollution compact relating to that region. The Congress currently is considering the relationship between the new act's regional system and pending interstate compacts.

VIII

AIR QUALITY ADVISORY BOARD; ADVISORY COMMITTEES

The Congress recognized the need for participation by all segments of our national economy in order to achieve effective air pollution control. For this reason, section 110 of the act proviues for a sixteen-member President's Air Quality Advisory Board to advise and consult with the Secretary on policy matters relating to HEW's activities under the act.

The Board is composed of the Secretary or his designee, as chairman, and fifteen members appointed by the President, none of whom may be federal employees. Appointed members are to be representative of state, interstate, and local government agencies, and of public or private interests with active interest or expertise in the field of pollution control.[132]

HEW is also directed to establish advisory committees from time to time in order to obtain assistance in the development of air quality criteria, recommended control techniques, standards, research and development, and to encourage continued efforts by industry to improve air quality and to develop economically feasible methods of control[133]

Committee members are to include, but not be limited to, knowledgeable persons from the standpoint of health, welfare, economics, or technology. The Senate and House committees felt that these advisory committees should contain sufficient representation (including state and local authorities, medical and scientific personnel, and industry experts in pollution abatement) to permit both effective and useful consultation between HEW and other interested parties.[134]

According to the House committee, representation both on the Board and the advisory committees should permit HEW fully to obtain the views of individuals

---

[130] *Id.* at 32-33; *see also* S. REP. 42-43.
[131] § 102(c).
[132] §§ 110(a)-(c).
[133] § 110(d); *see also* § 103(a)(4).
[134] *See* S. REP. 32; H.R. REP. 28.

familiar with the regulatory, medical, technical, and economic aspects of air pollution abatement; of communities which bear the brunt of air pollution problems; and of those industries which will bear the brunt of the necessary regulation. It is hoped that the representation will permit frank discussion between HEW and the various affected groups so as to achieve the most meaningful and reasonable solutions to the increasing air pollution problem.[135] It is also intended that HEW consult with the Air Quality Advisory Board and with the advisory committees on all major policy issues.[136]

The purpose of both the Air Quality Advisory Board and the advisory committees is two-fold. First, they are to provide a means whereby HEW may obtain the best possible advice and information available on pollution and pollution control from sources outside the government. Second, they are to provide a means of liaison with the various state and local authorities, medical and scientific groups, and industrial groups.[137]

The Air Quality Advisory Board has been appointed by the President and a number of committees and subcommittees dealing with such matters as criteria and available control technology have been appointed by the Commissioner of the National Air Pollution Control Administration. While the Board and the committees generally represent a broad spectrum of governmental, industry, and other expert and interested groups and individuals, there have been some instances where industry expertise, which could be most helpful for information and liaison purposes, is not reflected in the membership. However, HEW, through subcommittees and the use of consultants, apparently intends to fill out such gaps.

IX

REGISTRATION OF FUEL ADDITIVES

Section 210 of the act provides new authority requiring certain information to be furnished to HEW by manufacturers of fuels designated by HEW (not limited to motor vehicle fuels), and by the manufacturers of additives contained in such fuels.

The fuel manufacturers must furnish the name, range of concentration, and purpose in use of any additive contained in any designated fuel to be delivered in interstate commerce. The additive manufacturer must have each such additive registered by furnishing information as to its chemical composition, recommended range of concentration, recommended purpose in use, and, where available, its chemical structure. Any trade secrets are held by HEW in confidence. Any violation is punishable by a penalty of $1,000 per day, recoverable in a civil action brought by the United States in federal court.

---

[135] *See* H.R. REP. 28.
[136] *Id.*
[137] *Id.*

These new provisions are intended to provide an opportunity for full assessment of the effects of fuel additives, both old and new, on the environment and on public health. And their main purpose is to insure full access to the technical information needed to evaluate the possible hazards of these additives, many of which may become widely dispersed before recognition of their possible danger to human health.[138] Among such additives which are widely used, the Senate committee referred particularly to tetraethyl lead, barium, and nickel.[139]

Registration of additives in fuels other than motor vehicle fuels is expected to be required where evaluation of known or suspected health hazards is deemed necessary.[140]

The conference report stated that the secrecy and registration provisions cannot be construed to require research by an additive manufacturer relating to health or other effects of the additive as a prerequisite to registration.[141]

CONCLUSION

It is hoped that the Air Quality Act of 1967 will provide all concerned about air pollution, whether it be the federal government, state or local authorities, industry, or the public, with a better perspective on air pollution control. The public concern about air pollution and the present vacuum of information on the health, technology, and economic aspects of pollution control, have given rise to hasty, ill-conceived regulatory proposals at state and local levels, occasionally with support at some levels in HEW. The orderly, step-by-step procedure, scientific and comprehensive in approach, provided by the Air Quality Act, should cause a halt in such proposals or their implementation.

The act provides a number of excellent tools to government and industry for meeting the nation's air quality needs. If properly administered, and adequately funded, it should produce in a reasonable period of time a significant improvement in the nation's air quality with a minimum of economic disruption. This is because the approach taken has in fact been comprehensive, as HEW urged; because, in the absence of compelling health considerations, regulation must be geared to technological and economic feasibility, as industry urged; and because research has been given a major impetus, as everyone urged.

The appropriate use of the advisory committees and implementation of the act's provisions for broad participation in all conferences and hearings should promote a cooperative atmosphere. If both industry and government at all levels do their respective parts, this should result in voluntary compliance with scientifically sound and economically realistic regulations.

---

[138] See S. REP. 35; H.R. REP. 23.

[139] See S. REP. 35.

[140] See H.R. REP. 23.

[141] CONF. REP. No. 916, 90th Cong., 1st Sess. 26-27 (1967).

DEFICIENCIES IN THE AIR QUALITY ACT OF 1967

JOHN E. O'FALLON*

INTRODUCTION

In 1955, the Eighty-fourth Congress enacted Public Law 159.[1] This first federal legislation dealing with air pollution control stated "that the prevention and control of air pollution at its source is the primary responsibility of states and local governments." Public Law 159 authorized the Department of Health, Education, and Welfare (HEW) to provide technical support for state and local programs, and to conduct research. This 1955 federal law officially recognized the presence of a nationwide air pollution problem and provided for a study of the problem. It did not take positive steps to control air pollution.

Studies fostered by Public Law 159 revealed the imminent threat of air pollution. Meanwhile, the situation grew worse. Awareness of the inadequacy of then existing control efforts led to adoption of the Clean Air Act of 1963.[2]

The Clean Air Act launched an attack on air pollution. Federal activities were greatly expanded and federal grant funds were made available to state and local air pollution control agencies for the first time. The availability of grants for air pollution control did much to stimulate abatement activity. Not all state and local control programs initiated under the Clean Air Act of 1963 were sufficiently vigorous, however; and more sophisticated understanding of the complexities of air pollution and its control demonstrated the need for further legislation at the federal level. In November of 1967, Senate Bill 780, cited as the Air Quality Act of 1967, was signed into law.[3]

The Department of Health, Education, and Welfare has referred to the Air Quality Act of 1967 as a blueprint for systematic effort to deal with air pollution problems on a regional basis calling for coordinated action at all levels of government and among all segments of industry.

The act provides for:

* B.S. (Civil Engineering) 1937, University of Colorado; LL.B. 1947, Denver University. Director of the Building Department and Director of Air Pollution Control, City and County of Denver, Colorado. Registered Professional Engineer. Member of the Colorado bar and of the Federal Bar Association, American Society of Public Administrators, Building Officials Conference of America, Steering Committee of the National League of Cities and Natural Resources Committee, American Society of Testing and Materials; Director, Regional Air Pollution Control Agency.

[1] Ch. 360, 69 Stat. 322 (1955).
[2] 42 U.S.C. §§ 1857-1857l (1964).
[3] 81 Stat. 485.

Financial aid
{
Continuing grant support to state and local agencies.

Financial aid for interstate air quality planning activities.

Awarding of grants to states to assist them in developing programs for inspection of motor vehicle pollution control systems.
}

Expansion of the federal government's research and development activities.

Studies
{
Comprehensive economic studies of the cost of controlling air pollution.

An investigation of manpower and training needs in the air pollution field.

A study of the feasibility of controlling pollution from jet and conventional aircraft.
}

Continued efforts to control pollution at federal installations.

Control of motor vehicle emissions
{
Continuation of federal standard-setting to control motor vehicle pollution.

Registration of fuel additives.
}

Creation of a fifteen-member Presidential Air Quality Advisory Board.

Authority for federal action
{
Retention of authority for federal action to abate interstate air pollution problems, and, on request from states, intrastate problems.

Action by the Secretary of the Department of Health, Education, and Welfare to obtain court orders to curtail pollution during emergencies.
}

Establishment of advisory groups to assist the Department of Health, Education, and Welfare.

These provisions of the Air Quality Act of 1967 represent a practical, meaningful approach to many important aspects of the air pollution problem. However, the Act also provides for:

(1) A study of the need for and effect of national emission standards for stationary sources of air pollution.

(2) Definition of broad atmospheric areas of the nation and designation of specific air quality control regions by the Department of Health, Education, and Welfare.

(3) Development and publishing of air pollution criteria indicating the extent to which air pollution is harmful to health and damaging to property and detailed

information on the cost and effectiveness of techniques for preventing and controlling air pollution by the Department of Health, Education, and Welfare.

(4) Development of air quality standards and plans for implementation of the standards by the states, as soon as air quality criteria and data on control technology are made available for a pollutant or class of pollutants. They will have ninety days to submit a letter indicating that they intend to set standards, 180 days to set the standards, and 180 days to develop plans for implementing them.

(5) Development and application of air quality standards on a regional basis. Wherever an air quality control region includes parts of two or more states, each state will be expected to develop standards for its portion of the region.

(6) Adoption of air quality standards and plans for implementation of the standards in an air quality control region, if the Secretary of Health, Education, and Welfare finds that these standards and plans are consistent with the provisions of the Air Quality Act. If a state fails to establish standards, or if the Secretary finds that the standards are not consistent with the act, he can initiate action to insure that appropriate standards are set. States may request a hearing on any standards developed by the Secretary; the hearing board's decision will be binding.

(7) Primary responsibility for application of the air quality standards being assumed by the states. If a state's efforts prove inadequate, the Secretary is empowered to initiate abatement action.

Deficiencies inherent in these seven provisions will permit pollution to be poured into the air we breathe for some time to come. A stronger, more immediate attack could have been—and should have been—launched against industrial sources of air pollution.

The Air Quality Act of 1967 is deficient because it puts priority on the adoption of ambient air standards, and only provides for a study of the necessity for national emission standards for stationary sources of pollution. The Act should call for an immediate and direct frontal attack on the air pollution problem by demanding a reduction of industrial emissions at the source as soon as possible. National industrial emission standards should precede ambient air standards as a logical and necessary prerequisite to their attainment. The Act does not recognize the urgency of the problem stemming from stationary sources of pollution. It is possible for several time-consuming preliminary negotiations to take place before the Justice Department goes into federal court to seek to abate interstate air pollution. In many instances, HEW's inclination to act stands in place of deadlines. In other instances, HEW is prevented from taking action until an excessive amount of time has elapsed. The act attempts to force states to assume greater responsibility in air pollution abatement under threat of federal intervention. In addition, Congress has placed responsibility and the political power to develop and control regional programs in the hands of state governments. This responsibility has been delegated to the states in spite of the fact that, in the field of air pollution control, the state government has been, in most instances, the weak link in the federal-state-local government partnership.

The Air Quality Act of 1967 does not give proper priority to the establishment and enforcement of national industrial emission standards, nor does it properly recognize and support the activities of local air pollution control agencies which have been, to date, the best equipped and most effective in abating air pollution.

I

AMBIENT AIR STANDARDS VERSUS EMISSION STANDARDS

Public Law 159 enacted by the Congress in 1955 placed primary responsibility upon states and local governments for the prevention and control of air pollution *at its source*. This law recognized that air pollution must be controlled at the source—air pollution expelled into our atmosphere cannot be removed by a giant filter or other device. Enforcement of industrial emission standards limits air pollution at the source. Senate Bill 780, as proposed, provided for such emission standards. Unfortunately, however, Congress disregarded all plans for national industrial emission standards after lengthy public hearings in which representatives of industry loudly decried the adoption of emission standards. As a result, a much weaker approach was adopted, and ambient air standards in designated air sheds were substituted for the proposed emission standards.

Why does substitution of ambient air standards for national industrial emission standards seriously weaken the effectiveness of the Air Quality Act?

Ambient air standards serve one primary purpose—they define the extent or limit of an air pollution problem. They do not tell who the polluters are, or provide guidelines for reducing pollution levels. An ambient air standard says in effect that a given pollutant *should not* exceed a predetermined level in the atmosphere because of aesthetic, economic, or health effects. Emission standards, on the other hand, limit the permissible discharge from sources of pollution. Emission of known pollutants in excess of specified levels is a violation subject to enforcement action. The enforcement of emission controls constitutes a direct attack on the problem.

Dr. John T. Middleton, Director of the National Center for Air Pollution Control, in hearings before Senator Muskie's Subcommittee on Air and Water Pollution on Senate Bill 780, stated:[4]

---

[4] *Hearings on Air Pollution—1967 (Air Quality Act) Before the Subcomm. on Air and Water Pollution of the Senate Comm. on Public Works*, 90th Cong., 1st Sess., pt. 3, at 1155-56 (1967).

But no matter how stringent they may be, air quality standards are not, in themselves, a means of dealing with the sources of air pollution. There is no practical and equitable way of achieving an air quality standard in a given geographic area unless emission standards are established for the sources of pollution located in the area. An emission standard is, of course, a legally enforceable limitation on the amount of pollution that a single source or a category of sources can discharge into the atmosphere.

. . . .

There is, however, another purpose for which emission standards can and should be established, for the fact is that individual sources of air pollution may produce injury to human health and damage to property independently of their effects on overall community air quality. Pollutant emissions from an individual source inevitably contribute to ground-level concentrations of pollution—either in the immediate vicinity of the source or even at substantial distances. It is to prevent such direct and needless hazards to public health and welfare that Federal emission standards would be established under the proposed Air Quality Act of 1967.

. . . .

This approach represents a logical and reasonable way of achieving emission control at many of the most important sources of air pollution in all parts of the country—sources which everyone agrees must be controlled.

Dr. Ivan L. Bennett, Jr., Deputy Director, Office of Science and Technology, Executive Office of the President, emphasized the need for prompt adoption of emission standards during the subcommittee hearings:[5]

Effective techniques for the reduction of air pollution from industrial sources of several types are known. Indeed, the Department of Health, Education, and Welfare has published several technical manuals on this subject. These technologies, however, have been incompletely utilized and have not come into general use. This unsatisfactory but understandable state of affairs is attributable mainly to the lack of firm guidelines and uniform standards.

The establishment and enforcement of uniform standards will undoubtedly ameliorate this situation. . . .

. . . .

Many of the chemicals that pollute our air are known to be highly toxic, even lethal when inhaled in large amounts over a short period of time—sulfur oxides and carbon monoxide are familiar examples. However, what the long-term effect of exposure to low concentrations of these substances, 24 hours a day, 7 days a week, for years on end will be is not known.

Furthermore, it will not be known with the scientific exactness that we would hope eventually to achieve until we have had opportunities to make the long-term observations, under appropriate conditions, that will give the definitive answer. And by the time that answer is available, the critical decade that lies ahead will have passed long since.

The question, then, is this: How much do we have to know before we begin to act?

---

[5] *Id.*, pt. 2, at 791-93.

Without denying at all the urgent need for increased research to sharpen our knowledge and understanding of the physical effects of pollutants, I submit that we cannot wait until we have absolute and elegant proof before initiating action programs.

I am a biomedical scientist. It is time that we need to broaden the base of our understanding of the effects of air pollution. It is true that we are knowledge-limited in many areas, but these facts need not delay the initiation of action based on what we already know.

State and local air pollution control agencies should not be made responsible for enactment of industrial emission standards; basic emission standards should be nationwide. Industries in widely separated regions of the country are in direct competition with one another. To impose unequal restrictions on members of the same industry located in different regions would harm the more restricted firm and its community. This problem can only be avoided by well-defined national emission standards. A program which merely encourages state and local governments to adopt standards without setting any objective criteria which the standards must meet will be ineffective. Fear of economic injury to the community would of necessity keep state and local governments from setting suitably stringent emission standards.

John W. Gardner, then Secretary of the Department of Health, Education, and Welfare, testified before the Muskie Subcommittee on the need for national emission standards:[6]

> The Clean Air Act and its amendments have been extremely useful. The proposed Air Quality Act of 1967 will enable us to take the additional steps that are needed.
>
> First, emission control levels must be established for those industries which are major contributors to community air pollution problems in many parts of the country.
>
> Currently, the responsibility for setting such levels is assigned almost entirely to State and local governments. But experience has proven that most States and cities will not take the initiative in requiring control measures beyond those required in other places; nor will industries support local or State control action which may place them at a competitive disadvantage.
>
> By setting emission control levels that apply to all communities and all competitors in a given industry, we move toward pollution control in a manner that is fair to everyone, to all industries and to all communities.
>
> The proposed Air Quality Act of 1967 would authorize the establishment of emission control levels for those industries which are nationally significant sources of air pollution. Following publication of the levels, each State would have an opportunity to adopt equivalent or more stringent levels. Federal action to enforce the standards would be authorized only in those States which fail to adopt adequate standards of their own. Establishment of such nationwide emission control levels will undoubtedly provide an attractive economic incentive to the development of

---

[6] *Id.* at 762.

control technology, and will result in better, cheaper, and most important, widely applicable ways of reducing pollution from specific sources.

Concerning national emission standards, Dr. Middleton testified:[7]

One of the major provisions of the proposed new legislation concerns the development of emission standards for the control of major industrial sources of air pollution. The responsibility for developing such standards is currently assigned to State and local governments, but for many reasons it is a responsibility that many of them cannot realistically be expected to meet in full measure.

Perhaps the most important of the factors that tend to discourage standard setting at the State and local levels is that such action seems inevitable to bring one major function of State and local governments—the protection of public health and welfare—into direct conflict with another—that of insuring economic growth. No matter how often we remind ourselves that effective control of air pollution is not incompatible with economic progress, the history of air pollution control efforts in this country provides abundant evidence that State and local officials are unable to take decisive action to adopt and enforce effective standards for the control of sources unless the problems have become so obvious, so severe and obnoxious as a nuisance that they cannot be tolerated. In most of our communities, as I have already emphasized, the air pollution problem today is not that flagrant, but I, for one, cannot accept the idea that we must allow it to become so.

Even if we were to make what I consider to be the unrealistic assumption that State and local governments could be expected to adopt emission standards as soon as they had access to the necessary technical information, the results would still be unacceptable. Inevitably, some State and local agencies would adopt fairly stringent standards, while others would take no action at all. Industries in one community might be free to pollute the air even though applicable control technology existed, while their competitors in a neighboring community might be required to invest in the most effective control equipment available. There would be no justice in such a situation, either for the people who must breathe the polluted air in the first community or for the industry which must control its pollutants in the second community.

Federal emission standards, as proposed in the new legislation, offers an approach that is inherently equitable to both industry and the public. This will mean the setting of standards for all those industries which are responsible for significant air pollution problems, wherever they happen to be located. There will necessarily be separate standards for individual types of pollutants, but in each instance they would be applied industrywide.

Some pollutants have been shown to travel great distances. An emission which does not present a problem in its particular region, because there is not a great concentration of other polluting sources, may be carried to another region where, when mixed with other pollutants in the air, it will create a problem. General control regulations will necessarily vary in the different air regions; but basic national industrial emission standards should be the same to prevent the possibility of emissions from low concentration areas contributing to the problems in areas of high pollution concentration.

[7] Id., pt. 3, at 1153.

National emission standards would provide incentives to develop devices to control specific types of pollution. Also, the biggest polluters would be controlled first, thus giving results immediately notable, and making this application of ambient air standards more acceptable to the populace when better procedures to establish and enforce ambient air standards have been devised.

In response to questioning following his testimony, Secretary Gardner discussed the role of emission standard setting in advancing the "state-of-the-art" of control technology:[8]

> SENATOR RANDOLPH. . . . One of the problems, Mr. Secretary, with which the Congress of necessity will have to cope is the question of the degree of technological advance in this field. Could you state for the record of the subcommittee whether in your opinion there will be the so-called hand-in-hand procedure or whether the Federal standards would precede the technological advance?
>
> I think it is important that we know whether the so-called state of the art, to use an expression, will go hand-in-hand with the emission crtieria which properly should be set.
>
> SECRETARY GARDNER. Yes, sir. It is perfectly clear, and it has been stated in the President's message, that we must take into consideration economic and technological feasibility in setting the standards. It is equally clear to me that the state of the art has tended to meander along until some sort of regulation took it by the hand and gave it a good pull, so our effort will be to stimulate and go to the state of the art rather than wait for it.
>
> There has been a long period of waiting for it and it hasn't worked very well. It seems to me that the problem we face here is that industries, which will face problems as a result of air pollution control measures, will face more severe problems if they fail to control air pollution, because they will be walking head on not into the Federal Government, but into the interests of the American people, and the concern of the American people, the visible, rising concern of the American people.
>
> This has been quite a striking thing to all of us in the past couple of years. The concern of the public about air pollution, and the popularity of air pollution control measures, is something that industry must cope with. If we can stimulate more rapid development of the state of the art through setting the standards at a point which we really have to reach for them, so much the better.

At present, air pollution monitoring procedures are not sophisticated enough, no has monitoring been extensive enough to permit establishment of meaningful am bient air quality standards. A method of placing air monitoring devices to ensur the validity of comparisons made between various cities has not been devised Further, at the present time there are not sufficient personnel to man competentl the number of monitoring devices that would be necessary for effective nationa ambient air standards, even if an adequate national air monitoring system was i existence.

Pollution concentrations vary greatly with changes in weather conditions, an

---

[8] *Id.*, pt. 2, at 766-67.

it has not yet been determined what weather will be considered the mean on which air quality standards will be based and how air quality standards will be measured at times when weather conditions vary from this mean. For example, in Denver, for the month of December, six particulate sampling stations showed a percentage reduction of twenty-seven per cent of suspended particulates and thirty-six per cent of benzene soluble hydrocarbons for 1966 over 1965. Meteorological records show nineteen days with a surface inversion[9] in December 1965, and no inversions in December 1966. The average mixing depth of the air for December 1965 was 380 meters as contrasted with 1527 meters for December 1966. Denver Air Pollution Control's figures show an average reduction of emissions from stationary sources of about twenty per cent of both types of pollutants during the same time period. When the weather is favorable, ambient air records will indicate a greater reduction in emissions than has actually been achieved. When the weather is unfavorable, the reverse will be true.

Finally, there are problems in applying ambient air standards. How do you enforce an ambient air standard? If levels of a pollutant exceed the ambient air standard established for that pollutant, who is the violator? In the absence of emission standards, how can enforcement be carried out? If an individual pollutant was directly and indisputably traceable to one plant or one industry in an area, there would be little problem. But there are hundreds of contributors of each type of pollutant in most areas. Who will determine which one is to be cut down first? Will the states establish priorities, or will we wait for volunteers from among the industrial polluters? It is obvious that somewhere along the line the federal government will have to determine which industries come first and set emission controls as they have already done for the motor vehicle. But the obvious is going to be studied, and precious time will be lost because of it.

Section 211(a) of the Act requires the Secretary to submit to Congress a comprehensive report on the need for and effect of national emission standards for stationary sources no later than two years after the effective date of this section. Assuming that the Secretary does make a positive recommendation for the control of certain industries through the enforcement of national emission standards, it is almost a certainty that the same interests that lobbied so effectively to "buy time" to continue polluting the atmosphere, will again present a united front to emasculate the Secretary's recommendation, or at least to delay further the date when effective enforcement of such emission standards would require industry to take steps to clear the air. The failure to provide national industrial emission standards to be enforced within a reasonable time is a glaring weakness of the Air Quality Act of 1967.

The Air Quality Act of 1967 puts the cart before the horse and sets a time schedule for the establishment of ambient air standards that could delay the enact-

---

[9] A surface inversion is an unfavorable weather condition which permits a build-up of pollution.

ment of reasonable emission standards for a lengthy period of time; it fails to take into account the technological and personnel deficiencies that exist today that will further delay the development of air and weather monitoring systems requisite to the establishment of meaningful ambient air standards; and it fails to recognize that until such monitoring systems are a functioning reality, the ambient air cannot be proven to be unacceptable. In the meantime, flagrant violators can continue to spew pollution into the air.

The schedules for definition of atmospheric areas and air quality control areas by the Secretary of HEW, and those for adoption, implementation, and enforcement of air quality standards by the states permit too much time to elapse.

Section 107(a) of the Act allows the Secretary one year to establish atmospheric areas of the nation based on climate, meteorology, and topography. (The nation has already been divided into eight such regions by the Secretary.[9a]) The Secretary is further charged with the responsibility within eighteen months after passage of the act, of setting air quality control regions. These regions will be defined to a great extent by the boundaries of metropolitan areas. The regions will be designated on the basis of meteorological, topographical, social, and political factors which suggest that a group of communities should be treated as a unit for the purpose of setting and implementing air quality standards. Dr. Middleton indicated at the Briefing Conference on Air and Water Pollution held in Washington, D.C., March 14-15, 1968, that two to four of the more important control regions will be designated during Summer 1968, about thirty to thirty-five by July 1, 1969, and the remainder of two hundred—estimated to be the total—sometime after the eighteen month limit imposed by the Air Quality Act.

Under section 107(b)(1), the Secretary shall as soon as practicable develop and issue to the states such criteria of air quality as in his judgment may be requisite for the protection of the public health and welfare. Dr. Middleton indicated at the Briefing Conference that criteria and related control technique information for particulates and sulfur dioxide will probably be available during Summer 1968.

Only after atmospheric areas, air quality control regions, criteria, and related information on control techniques are published by HEW does the Act have a direct effect upon the states responsible for the air quality control regions that have been designated. Then, section 108(c) gives the governor of a state, after he receives the air quality criteria and the recommended control techniques from the Secretary, an additional ninety days to file a letter of intent to hold a public hearing to adopt, within an additional 180 days, ambient air standards as proposed. The state then has an additional 180 days to adopt a plan to implement, maintain, and enforce the air quality standards adopted. If the Secretary decides that the air quality criteria adopted by the state and the means proposed to achieve these ends within a reasonable time are consistent with the recommendations of the Secretary and

---

[9a] 33 Fed. Reg. 548 (1968).

that the state has ample enforcement authority to achieve these ends, then such standards and plan are consistent with the purpose of the Act and shall be the air quality standards and plan applicable to the state. The opportunity for delay in taking any positive abatement action adds up to thirty-nine months if the Secretary and the governors take full advantage of the time allotted to them under these sections.

Subsections 108(c)(2) and 108(c)(3) provide for intervention by the federal government to implement adoption and enforcement of air quality standards either upon request of the governor of a state, or if the governor fails to act within the time limits prescribed. Obviously, the less prepared a state is to meet the deadline, the greater the probability of the governor's relying on federal action with the consequence of even further delay in positive abatement action.

If the state or states involved fail to take adequate or reasonable action to implement the plan and standards, the Secretary shall serve notice on all interested parties and this failure must be corrected within 180 days or the Attorney General will bring an action against the erring state or states in an interstate region. If the problem is intrastate, the Attorney General, at the request of the governor, may assist in bringing suit in a state court or in the appropriate federal district court. Again, depending upon the enforcement capabilities of the state or municipal control agencies involved, the recalcitrance of the industries affected, the judgment of the Department of Health, Education, and Welfare as to whether reasonable efforts to control pollution are being exerted, and the condition of the court docket, the possibility for prolonged delay before positive abatement action is taken is all too apparent.

In entering a judgment, the court shall give due consideration to the practicality and to the technological and economic feasibility of complying with the standards promulgated. Thus, it is entirely possible for the court to rule that little or no abatement action over a period of as much as five years constitutes reasonable action toward compliance because the standards of air quality sought were impossible to attain due to technological or economic problems. The variables and intangibles involved in attempting to set economically, technologically, and equitably attainable ambient air standards for a single air shed are probably beyond the present capabilities of the units of government that will be involved in many air basins; and they will be for some time to come.

Where does one start to implement controls to meet nebulous and possibly unattainable standards? Whom do you tell to cut down first? And, how do you establish the fact that an industry is responsible for the excess pollution in the air over and above that prescribed in the standards when the actual condition of the air is an unknown factor?

National industrial emission standards imposing control first on the known major industrial pollutors would present no such problem. Immediate progress toward acceptable ambient air would be possible. Air monitoring networks could bet set up over a period of time, and competent personnel trained to operate the stations and evaluate the data obtained. Then, by the time a region reached or approached the desired air quality level, the science of accurate evaluation of the ambient air would probably be developed to the point where significant ambient air standards could be set. Only through the elimination of pollution at the source will clean air be achieved. Air pollution control should begin with emission controls in all areas, and the science of air evaluation can be developed while abatement action is being taken.

II

THE ROLES OF STATE AND LOCAL AIR POLLUTION AGENCIES—
CAPABILITIES, AUTHORITY, AND POLITICS

The National Municipal Policy for the National League of Cities for 1968 states:[10]

All sources of air pollution—governmental, industrial, and private—must be controlled. For effective control, national industrial emission standards must be established to avoid increased pressure on industry to leave urban areas and to avoid local fears of economic injury that may result when strong pollution control standards are established in one community, but not in another.

To supplement the national emission standards, regional air quality commissions should be established to deal with the particular air pollution problems in different air sheds—local communities and States should join together and develop regional programs in order to cope with the air pollution problems common to communities sharing the same air resources. These interjurisdictional programs must have meaningful regulations, backed by effective programs of enforcement. *Local and regional pollution control agencies should have primary responsibility for enforcement of regulations as they are most immediately affected by pollution.*

Where an effective local or regional agency exists, individual, unrestricted authority for air pollution control enforcement should be vested in this agency.

Air pollution is a metropolitan problem. Any city or metropolitan area with a population of 50,000 or more has an air pollution problem. It is local government that has taken the lead in air pollution control, and it is local government that is geared to the kind of activity required to abate air pollution. The local government is the political entity closest to the urban dweller, most cognizant of his problems, and subject to political retaliation if a problem is not solved satisfactorily. Also, the local governments, especially those of the larger cities, have existing departments staffed with technical, administrative, and enforcement personnel to plan and enforce an effective attack on air pollution.

Despite local government's record of achievement in air pollution control, nowhere in the Air Quality Act of 1967 is there any recognition of existing local

---

[10] *National Municipal Policy*, adopted at the 44th annual Congress of Cities, July 29-Aug. 2, 1967, Boston, Mass., ch. 8, §§ 8.203, 8.204, 8.206. (Emphasis added.)

or regional agencies. The series of steps that must be taken to meet the requirements of the Act are all to be taken by governors of states. This state-oriented approach represents a departure from past policy of the federal government, which formerly dealt directly with the local government in matters of local concern or for the solution of urban problems where the state is acknowledged to be less well-equipped than local agencies, or less inclined to act. Secretary Gardner testified that:[11]

> We have been quite disappointed in the vigor with which the States have approached this problem, and there are complications in their approaching it which make it understandable, but it now appears clear that waiting for them to act is not going to get the job done.

Two questions are automatically raised in light of the federal government's reliance on state action: How well prepared are the states to enact air quality standards? More importantly, how well prepared are the states to enforce air quality standards?

By 1967, forty-five states had some sort of air pollution legislation, but having legislation on record is no guarantee of enforcement. A state statute calling for enforcement in the abatement field is a waste of time if qualified personnel and adequate funding are lacking. Most of the states are starting from scratch to build up a staff. The staffing problem of the state agencies is further complicated by inadequate budgets. A recent survey conducted by *State Government Administration* revealed some sad statistics as far as funding and personnel at the state level are concerned. "One of the major problems noted in many survey responses is recruitment of adequate staffs to implement air pollution control programs."[12]

A "Current Status Report on State and Local Air Pollution Control Programs," as of May 1967, was presented to the Muskie Subcommittee by Dr. Middleton.[13] It revealed the following:

When the Clean Air Act was passed in December 1963, only seventeen states had an action program. As of May 1967, thirty-three states had air pollution control programs.

With thirty-four states receiving grant support under the Clean Air Act, the average state expenditure per capita was 4.8¢. With 107 local agencies receiving grant support under the Clean Air Act, the average local agency expenditure per capita was 27.9¢.

Of the thirty-four states, twenty-three were spending less than 5¢ per capita per year on air pollution control. The highest yearly per capita expenditure for air pollution control by a state was 15.3¢ (California).

Of the 107 local agencies, fifty-six spent between 5¢ and 25¢ per capita per year

[11] *Hearings, supra* note 4, pt. 2, at 764.
[12] *Air Pollution . . . A Critical Problem*, STATE GOV'T AD., Nov. 1967, at 7.
[13] *Hearings, supra* note 4, pt. 3, at 1160-1283.

on air pollution control; only six spent less than 5¢; twenty-seven spent between 25¢ and 50¢; twelve spent between 50¢ and 75¢; and five spent over 75¢ per capita. The highest yearly per capita expenditure for air pollution control by a local agency was $1.04.

The average per capita expenditure by a local agency was 5.8 times the average state expenditure.

An appendix to this article shows the budgets, personnel, and per capita expenditures of state and local agencies receiving federal grant funds under the Clean Air Act in 1967. Of the thirty-two states that budgeted funds for air pollution control, only eight had operating budgets larger than the budget of the largest local agency located within that state. California and New York State had the largest budgets of the states—$2,407,000 and $2,371,280 respectively. Despite their large budgets, however, the total for local expenditures in New York ($2,005,300) approached the budgeted state expenditures, and the total of local expenditures in California ($5,252,700) was more than twice the state budget.

The state of Colorado is a case in point. Colorado first passed an air pollution control statute in 1964, but the first statute giving the State Health Department any enforcement powers became effective in July of 1966. The City and County of Denver, under the enabling provisions of the 1964 state statute, passed an ordinance in September of 1964, that was then and is today more restrictive and easier to enforce than the state statute. Prior to passage of the state statute and staffing by the Colorado Health Department of an air pollution control agency, Denver had a staff of twenty experienced members, including five professional engineers with many years of design and construction experience in the power plant, metallurgical, chemical, foundry, and other industries that are responsible for air pollution emissions.

The approach to staffing is important. All the large effective local or regional air pollution control agencies, of which Los Angeles, Chicago, and the Bay Area are the best known, have administrative, engineering, enforcement, technical services, and public information sections staffed with professional engineers, chemists, mechanical inspectors, laboratory technicians, and public relations personnel. Some of the states, and obviously they are the ones with sufficient funds, have set up air pollution control agencies as distinct entities within their State Health Departments with organizations similar in make-up to those of the effective local control agencies. Build-up of a competent staff is relatively expensive, however, and in the absence of adequate funding, there is a tendency to compromise. It is apparent that if less qualified personnel are used to staff an agency, that agency is weaker than a properly staffed organization.

Putting the state in an equal or dominant position in the field of air pollution control ignores the fact that air pollution is a problem of urban origin that states historically have not had to cope with. Local governments, on the other hand, have dealt with the problems of urbanization for some time now, and have departments already in existence that are staffed to operate effectively in the enforcement field. Most of the abatement of air pollution has been accomplished at the local level. It will be difficult for states to bridge the gap of years of experience in this field in order to become full-fledged partners with local and regional agencies.

State agencies have a definite role to perform in combatting air pollution. They should be adequately financed and staffed to support weak local programs and to handle abatement procedures that lie outside of local jurisdictions, and they should be given authority to take over a local enforcement program where the local agency refuses or is unable to provide effective enforcement for political or other consider-ations. But, where an effective local or regional agency exists, that agency should be given individual, unrestricted authority for air pollution control enforcement. The Air Quality Act, by the explicit wording of section 105 and by the interpretation of the Department of Health, Education, and Welfare, as indicated in the provisions which govern the awarding of federal grants for air pollution control programs, gives the state the dominant position—and some control over local and regional agencies regardless of their relative accomplishments to date or ability to accomplish the purposes for which this bill was enacted.

This has opened the door for political problems.

Department of Health, Education, and Welfare regulations on "Grants for Air Pollution Control Programs"[14] contain several references that would imply that an agency would have a difficult time obtaining federal funds without the approval of the state.   For example, section 56.4(c) states:

> No grant shall be made until the Surgeon General has consulted with the appropriate official as designated by the Governor or Governors of the State or States affected pursuant to section 104(b) of the Act.

Under section 56.2, HEW requires a workable program containing seven compre-hensive requirements that must be met before an applicant is eligible to receive federal funds.   Subsection 56.21(d) states:

> The Surgeon General shall approve a Workable Program and any revision or amendment thereof if, in his judgment, such program is reasonably calculated to prevent and control air pollution within the jurisdiction of the applicant: *Provided*, That prior to approving any Workable Program, or any revision or amendment thereof, the Surgeon General shall consult with the appropriate official as designated by the Governor or Governors of the States affected pursuant to section 104(b) of the Act.

Which takes precedence—the opinion of the Department of HEW or of the governor's official representative—as to whether or not the local or regional agency

---

[14] 42 C.F.R., ch. 1, subch. D, pt. 56 (1968).

has submitted a workable abatement program? The opportunity for political manipulations open to the governor and the state is obvious. And what if the political appointee of the governor is unqualified to judge the effectiveness or the potential of the local or regional agency submitting the application? The usual recourse will be to ask the opinion of the head of the state air pollution control agency whose qualifications may also be less than optimal. Yet, this individual can have vested in him the power to make a judgment that can seriously jeopardize the chances of a well-qualified local agency to get a federal grant.

The ultimate objective of any air pollution control program is to establish an air resources management program, not just an abatement program. Freeways, mass transit, solid waste disposal, location of industrial and residential areas all have an effect on air pollution. An air resources management program provides maximum utilization of existing air resources, and this requires complete coordination within the basin of all local planning, zoning, engineering, public works, and air pollution control programs. The expertise that has existed in these fields for years is concentrated in local agencies and not in the states. Planning for improvement of the urban environment has almost never been a function, or until recent years even a concern, of state government. Metropolitan planning, with the multiplicity of jurisdictions with their own axes to grind, is difficult enough to accomplish when only local governments are involved. To insert the state into this melange, with the authority to pass on the final, workable plan, puts just one more obstacle in the path of metropolitan cooperation.

Local jurisdictions have been able to achieve some degree of metropolitan cooperation acting through inter-regional planning commissions or councils of governments. The qualifications of the personnel in various planning, zoning, building, engineering and public works departments in a metropolitan area is usually very impressive. If these talents can be coordinated by a council of governments and a master urban plan for an air basin worked out, taking into consideration the effects of air pollution on the environment, then the air pollution problem can be conquered. If an effective abatement program does not lead into an effective air resources management program in time to ward off and reverse the overwhelming effects of urban sprawl on the environment, it will never solve the pollution problem. For this reason alone, it is extremely important that a state agency or political appointee not be given the power to throw more sand into the already poorly-meshed machinery set up to solve metropolitan problems.

In the Denver metropolitan area, the Inter County Regional Planning Commission (ICRPC) is responsible for coordinated planning. The Regional Air Pollution Control Agency is the technical advisory committee for air pollution control for the ICRPC, the council of governments for Denver. Five counties—Adams, Arapahoe, Boulder, Denver, and Jefferson counties—plus twenty-one major municipalities within the counties other than Denver, signed the Articles of Association. With the exception of Boulder County, which did not affiliate until October 1966, all counties and most of the municipalities contained therein have been participating members of ICRPC since its inception in 1955. Although membership and cooperation of the political entities which represent ninety-eight per cent of the metropolitan population is voluntary, ICRPC has a lever to snap reluctant counties or cities into line. It must approve most applications for grant-in-aid funds before the Department of Health, Education, and Welfare or the Department of Housing and Urban Development will even consider them.

ICRPC is well-qualified to coordinate planning in the Denver Metro area. It has a competent, professional staff that is familiar with local urban problems and able to evaluate the benefits of proposed programs, not just to the local applicant, but to the metropolitan region as a whole. Each project is considered in its relationship to the entire area. The Commission has the staff abilities to coordinate and utilize the efforts of manpower in the various local planning, zoning, engineering, and public works departments and experts in the private sector who comprise the various technical committees on air pollution, solid waste disposal, conservation, transportation and freeway studies—disciplines which are essential to the operation of an air resources management program. Over the past ten years, an average of over 500 knowledgeable experts have continuously contributed their expertise on urban problems through the advisory committees. Some of this advice has been disregarded and some has been rendered obsolete by the rapidly changing urban complex before it could be utilized; but most of it has been put to productive use. In thirteen years of operation, ICRPC has logged an impressive record of accomplishments. The State of Colorado, which entered the planning field in 1966, is not in a position to supplant the services of ICRPC at this time.

HEW does not demand that applicants for clean air grants clear their application through recognized councils of governments such as ICRPC. Logic and common sense dictate that, where an effective council of governments exists in a region, applicants for air pollution control grants should be required first to submit those applications to the local government coordinating body, in order to determine whether or not the program objectives can be integrated into a comprehensive air management program for the air basin. Instead, the Air Quality Act gives an appointee of the governor the authority to recommend or deny approval of a grant. Thus, in theory at least, the governor has the political prerogative to disregard the advice of a competent planning body and rely on the political judgment of his appointee. Since there is no mandate in the Act requiring the governors to utilize the services of metropolitan councils of governments or regional planning boards established pursuant to interstate compacts, it is obvious that a judgment decision by a governor based on incomplete knowledge or political considerations can nullify the effectiveness of local or regional air pollution control authorities. This act is so slanted toward state control that it can be a powerful political tool, if a governor should choose to take advantage of it.

SUMMARY

The Air Quality Act of 1967 is not the strong decisive instrument needed to bring about an immediate, significant reduction in air pollution levels. While the increased research and development activity, funding to local and state agencies, emission controls for motor vehicles, and knowledge-expanding projects provided for in the Act are commendable, the lack of emphasis on immediate utilization of existing technology to bring industrial sources of pollution under control severely weakens the Act.

Air pollution is a very serious problem which threatens the health and welfare of every inhabitant of our earth. The effects of air pollution are known to be harmful and widespread. The exact extent of the problem is not known, nor is technology developed fully enough now to control all sources of air pollution emissions. But, wherever technology is adequate, that technology should be applied as quickly as possible in order to effect reductions in pollution levels. The Act sponsors the delay of action programs while definitive data on the extent of the problem is accumulated.

The Air Quality Act of 1967 is deficient because it does not make full use of the tools available. Present technology should be forced into application by imposing emission controls on industry. Relative qualifications and records of achievement of local and state air pollution control agencies should have dictated delegation of responsibility for action programs. It is wishful thinking to expect to force states to enter the enforcement field and act to do a job as quickly or as well as local agencies that have been doing it for years merely by empowering the states to do it. The delegation of too much political power to the states could act as a deterrent rather than a stimulus to the accomplishment of the intended objectives of the Act. The Air Quality Act of 1967 does not fully recognize the urgency of the air pollution problem.

* * *

APPENDIX

BUDGETS AND PERSONNEL OF STATE AND LOCAL AIR POLLUTION CONTROL AGENCIES RECEIVING FEDERAL GRANTS UNDER THE CLEAN AIR ACT AS OF MAY 1967[15]

State Agency	1967 Budget	Personnel (man-years)	Per capita Expenditure (dollars)	Local Agency	1967 Budget	Personnel (man-years)	Per capita Expenditure (dollars)
Alabama	$ 50,000	6.5	$0.015				
				Huntsville	$ 14,700	1.5	$0.204
				Jefferson Co.	115,000	10.5	0.180
				Mobile Co.	29,400	3.0	0.094
Alaska	-0-	-0-	-0-				
Arizona	-0-	-0-					
				Maricopa Co.	135,600	14.0	0.205
				Pima Co.	33,600	3.5	0.127
Arkansas	58,020	7.0	0.032	None as designated by state law			
California	2,407,000	98.0	0.153				
				Los Angeles Co.	3,758,200	305.0	0.622
				San Bernardino Co.	301,000	26.0	0.598
				Bay Area	1,126,000	76.0	0.348
				Monterey Co.	67,500	5.0	0.341
Colorado	117,689	9.5	0.067				
				Denver City & County	200,600	18.5	0.406
				Tri County	75,000	7.5	0.321
				Jefferson Co.	20,000	1.5	0.157
				Pueblo Co.	35,500	3.5	0.301
Connecticut	151,616	17.0	0.060				
				Bridgeport	34,100	4.0	0.102
				Middletown	21,700	1.0	0.658
				Fairfield	32,800	1.0	0.713
				Stratford	31,400	2.0	0.70
				New Haven	60,700	5.0	0.40
				Stamford	41,600	3.0	0.452
				Greenwich	25,500	1.5	0.47
				Norwalk	36,600	2.0	0.546
				Milford	31,300	1.0	0.763
Delaware	-0-	-0-		None			
Florida	175,000	15-20					
				Dade County	131,500	16.0	0.141
				Palm Beach Co.	54,800	5.5	0.24
				Mantee Co.	55,100	3.0	0.80
				Hillsborough Co.	52,000	3.5	0.13
Georgia	48,735	8.0	0.012				
				Fulton Co.	30,000	3.0	0.054
				Macon-Bibb Co.	20,600	2.5	0.146
				Chatham Co.	18,600	1.5	0.10
Hawaii	75,966	6.0	0.12	None			
Idaho	26,982	2.5	0.04	None			

[15] The data presented here is based upon the Current Status Report on State and Local Air Pollution Control Programs, May 1967, in *Hearings, supra* note 4, pt. 3, at 1160-1283.

APPENDIX—Continued

State Agency	1967 Budget	Personnel (man-years)	Per capita Expenditure (dollars)	Local Agency	1967 Budget	Personnel (man-years)	Per capita Expenditure (dollars)
Illinois	$156,466	15.0	$0.916				
				Chicago	$1,162,700	140.0	$0.187
				Cook Co.	156,700	15.0	0.031
Indiana	81,790	9.0	$0.018				
				E. Chicago	40,300	3.5	0.707
				Gary	106,200	6.5	0.60
				Evansville	25,200	2.0	0.179
				Indianapolis	73,600	9.0	0.155
				Michigan City	7,400	0.5	0.206
				Hammond	56,000	4.5	0.315
Iowa	-0-	-0-	-0-				
				Cedar Rapids	26,800	3.5	0.20
Kansas	-0-	-0-	-0-				
				Kansas City-Wyandotte Co.	98,900	7.0	0.535
Kentucky	316,666	26.5	0.104	None			
Louisiana	103,213	8.5	0.032	None as designated by State Law			
Maine	-0-	-0-	-0-	None			
Maryland	95,000	9.0	0.031	None			
Massachusetts	10,500	0.5	0.002				
				Worcester	35,000	4.0	0.108
				Boston Metro	134,300	20.0	0.067
				Springfield Metro	44,000	5.0	0.092
Michigan	147,200	12.0	0.019				
				Muskegon Co.	21,200	1.5	0.14
				Wayne Co.	193,400	16.0	0.194
				Detroit	434,600	40.0	0.260
Minnesota	-0-	-0-	-0-				
				St. Paul	88,800	8.0	0.283
				Minneapolis	67,100	6.5	0.139
Mississippi	-0-	-0-	-0-	None			
Missouri	108,108	7.0	0.025				
				St. Louis Co.	209,800	17.0	0.298
				St. Louis City	252,300	7.5	0.336
				Kansas City	118,000	9.0	0.155
				Green Co.-Springfield	46,900	3.0	0.494
Montana	47,016	2.5	0.07				
				Missoula	23,700	3.0	0.539
Nebraska	-0-	-0-	-0-	None			
Nevada	-0-	-0-	-0-				
				Reno-Sparks-Washoe	47,000	5.0	0.56

APPENDIX—Continued

State Agency	1967 Budget	Personnel (man-years)	Per capita Expenditure (dollars)	Local Agency	1967 Budget	Personnel (man-years)	Per capita Expenditure (dollars)
New Hampshire	$ 31,160	2.0	$.0510	None			
New Jersey	808,081	69.0	0.133				
				East Orange	$ 18,900	1.0	$0.245
New Mexico	13,162	2.5	0.014				
				Albuquerque	78,600	8.5	0.30
New York	2,371,280	50.0	0.14				
				Schnectady	6,300	0.5	0.041
				Albany Co.	5,000	0.5	0.018
				Mt. Vernon	8,200	0.5	0.108
				Yonkers	13,500	0.5	0.071
				Columbia Co.	6,000	1.0	0.128
				Niagara Co.	50,000	6.0	0.207
				N. Y. C.	1,509,900	120.0	0.194
				Westchester Co.	11,900	0.5	0.015
				Rensselaer Co.	7,500	1.0	0.053
				New Rochelle	17,800	1.0	0.065
				Erie Co.	108,300	8.0	0.102
				Broome Co.	15,400	1.0	0.073
				Dutchess Co.	8,100	1.5	0.046
				Nassau Co.	237,400	12.0	0.183
North Carolina	–0–	–0–	–0–				
				Guilford Co.	25,600	2.0	0.104
				Durham Co.	17,900	2.0	0.16
				Buncombe Co.	17,700	5.0	0.136
				Rowan Co.	16,900	1.0	0.206
				New Hanover Co.	16,700	1.5	0.235
				Gaston Co.	21,000	1.5	0.165
				Mecklenburg Co.	45,600	4.0	0.168
				Beaufort Co.	37,400	2.5	1.04
				Cleveland Co.	23,200	1.5	0.35
North Dakota	–0–	1.5	–0–	None			
Ohio	128,000	8.0	0.013				
				Lorain	29,100	3.0	0.428
				Akron-Barberton	130,500	11.0	0.254
				Toledo	67,500	6.0	0.212
				Cleveland	276,700	33.0	0.316
				Canton	53,000	4.5	0.47
				Steubenville	29.000	4.0	0.906
				Portsmouth	25,700	2.0	0.78
Oklahoma	10,290	1.0	0.004				
				Okla. City	13,600	2.0	0.031
				Tulsa City-Co.	37,000	3.0	0.107
Oregon	187,393	15.0	0.106				
				Portland	49,500	15.5	0.06
				Lane Co.	42,600	4.5	0.263
Pennsylvania	369,475	44.0	0.03				
				Macungie	800	.1	0.21
				Philadelphia	445,900	28.0	0.223
				Allegheny Co.	423,000	39.0	0.26

APPENDIX—Continued

State Agency	1967 Budget	Personnel (man-years)	Per capita Expenditure (dollars)	Local Agency	1967 Budget	Personnel (man-years)	Per capita Expenditure (dollars)
				York	$ 20,000	$ 2.0	$0.084
				Lehigh Valley	20,000	2.0	0.45
Rhode Island	$ 10,471	2.0	$0.012	None			
So. Carolina	70,606	5.0	0.03				
				Spartanburg	18,100	2.5	0.41
				Charleston Co.	34,000	3.0	0.157
So. Dakota	–0–	–0–	–0–	None			
Tennessee	12,660	3.0	0.004				
				Chattanooga	42,300	4.0	0.325
				Nashville & Davidson Co.	32,900	4.0	0.082
Texas	107,611	10.0	0.011				
				Dallas	67,700	7.0	0. .71
				Lubbock Co.	20,100	1.0	0.129
Utah	39,268	3.0	0.044				
				None			
Vermont	–0–	–0–	–0–	None			
Virginia	25,000	2.0	0.002				
				Roanoke Co.	16,100	0.5	0.264
				Hopewell	12,400	1.0	0.73
				Richmond	43,400	5.0	0.106
Washington	115,410	8.0	0.04				
				Seattle King Co.	188,800	17.0	0.202
				Clark Co.	22,200	1.5	0.239
West Virginia	253,990	27.0	0.137				
				Wheeling	19,900	1.5	0.373
Wisconsin	–0–	–0–	–0–				
				Milwaukee	226,600	20.0	0.219
Wyoming	8,450	–0–	0.026	None			

CONTROL OF AUTOMOBILE EMISSIONS— CALIFORNIA EXPERIENCE AND THE FEDERAL LEGISLATION

HAROLD W. KENNEDY* AND MARTIN E. WEEKES†

INTRODUCTION

The cities in the East compare to the cities in the West in much the same way that mature women would compare to adolescent maidens. The cities in the East have compacted, restrained, well-positioned pockets of density; the population and industry in cities of the West seem to have the propensity to sprawl asymmetrically to occupy the greatest area with the least anatomy.

Since the population is so diversely distributed in the western states, transportation between concentrations of population and industry is not generally served through the use of rapid transit or other community transportation facilities. Furthermore, the more desirable residential areas were and are significantly distant from areas of industry. Therefore it became necessary, particularly during the Second World War, for the inhabitants of such areas as Los Angeles County to provide their own means of transportation to and from centers of commerce. The mode of transportation utilized was the automobile.

During the Second World War industrial growth in California proceeded at an astronomical rate. The great growth of industry, coupled with the unparalleled intensity of the use of the automobile as a method of transportation, brought with it mushrooming problems of air pollution.

Due to environmental conditions peculiar to the Los Angeles basin, this air pollution manifested itself in discomfort to the eyes and respiratory tract of the inhabitants. The County of Los Angeles became blanketed with a brownish haze which was given the misnomer *smog*.[1]

For a number of years it seemed as if this phenomenon was peculiar to Los Angeles and was not really indicative of an air pollution problem which would become national, if not international, in scope. However, the experiences first felt by those in Los Angeles have occurred with ever increasing frequency in other urban areas throughout the United States.[2] Greater use of the automobile and in-

---

* B.S. 1923, J.D. 1925, University of California at Berkeley; M.S. (Pub. Admin.) 1954, University of Southern California. County Counsel Emeritus, Los Angeles County, California. Member of the California bar. Contributor of articles to periodicals in the public law field.

† B.S. 1954, Manhattan College; J.D. 1961, University of Southern California. Deputy County Counsel, Los Angeles County, California. Member of the California bar.

[1] "Smog" is a contraction of the words "smoke" and "fog." The air pollution problem in Los Angeles County is generally conceded to be the product of oxides of nitrogen, oxides of sulfur, and photochemical reactions with hydrocarbons.

[2] *See* Air Quality Act of 1967, § 101(a), 81 Stat. 485; PRESIDENT OF THE UNITED STATES, MESSAGE ON

creased intensification of industry have brought with them burgeoning problems in air pollution.

The County of Los Angeles has for some twenty years waged an effective battle against air pollution caused by stationary sources. It is generally agreed, however, that there is still a serious problem with air pollution in Los Angeles County; and it is also agreed that the automobile is primarily responsible for the continuing problem.[3]

In order to combat air pollution emanating from the automobile, California, in 1960, enacted the Motor Vehicle Pollution Control Act.[4] A study of the history leading to, and developments under, this act will materially benefit those attempting to inaugurate an effective control program directed at air pollution emanating from the use of the automobile.

I

ATTEMPTS AT ABATEMENT PRIOR TO THE 1967 LEGISLATION

Prior to 1960 there had been only one California statute specifically directed at air pollution emanating from motor vehicles. It provided: "No motor vehicle shall be operated in a manner resulting in the escape of *excessive* smoke . . . *or fuel residue.*"[5] The constitutionality of the section was challenged unsuccessfully on the basis that the word "excessive" was too indefinite and uncertain to satisfy the requirements of due process.[6]

A. Duties of State Director of Public Health Under Previous Legislation

In 1959 the California legislature provided:[7]

It shall be the duty of the State Director of Public Health to determine by February 1, 1960, the maximum allowable standards of emissions of exhaust con-

---

AIR POLLUTION, H.R. Doc. No. 47, 90th Cong., 1st Sess. (1967); H.R. REP. No. 728, 90th Cong., 1st Sess. (1967); S. REP. No. 403, 90th Cong., 1st Sess (1967); H.R. REP. No. 916, 90th Cong., 1st Sess. (Conference report 1967).

[3] *See* CALIF. STATE DEP'T OF PUBLIC HEALTH, CALIFORNIA STANDARDS FOR AMBIENT AIR QUALITY AND FOR MOTOR VEHICLE EMISSIONS (1966).

[4] Ch. 23, § 1, [1961] Cal. Stats. 346 (repealed 1967).

[5] CAL. VEHICLE CODE § 27153 (West 1960). (Emphasis added.)

[6] In rejecting the contention, the district court of appeals quoted with approval from the case of Smith v. Peterson, 131 Cal. App. 2d 241, 280 P.2d 522 (1955), which construed the "excessive noise" statute:

"[A] statute, to be valid, [is not required to] have that degree of exactness which inheres in a mathematical theorem. It is not necessary that a statute furnish detailed plans and specifications of the acts or conduct prohibited. The requirement of reasonable certainty does not preclude the use of ordinary terms to express ideas which find adequate interpretation in common usage and understanding."

People v. Madearos, 230 Cal. App. 2d 642, 644, 41 Cal. Rptr. 269, 271 (1964).

[7] Ch. 200, § 1, [1959] Cal. Stats. 2091 (repealed 1967). In 1960 the Legislature modified this language by replacing the period at the end of the first paragraph with a comma and adding thereto "interference with visibility and damage to vegetation." The final paragraph was extended by the addition of another sentence: "In revising the standards the department shall, after February 1, 1960, take into account all emissions from motor vehicles rather than exhaust emissions only." Ch. 36, § 1, [1960] Cal. Stats. 380 (repealed 1967).

taminants from motor vehicles which are compatible with the preservation of the public health including the prevention of irritation to the senses.

The standards shall be developed after the department has held public hearings and afforded an opportunity for all interested persons to appear and file statements or be heard. The department shall publish such notice of the hearings as it determines to be reasonably necessary.

The department after notice and hearing may revise the standards, and shall publish the revised standards, from time to time.

In 1965 the provision was added:[8]

Whenever the department revises the standards it shall submit a copy of such revised standards to the Legislature if the Legislature is in session, or to the Senate Fact Finding Committee on Transportation and Public Utilities and the Assembly Interim Committee on Transportation and Commerce if the Legislature is not in session, and such revised standards shall not become effective until the 31st day after such submission.

Under this legislation, the State Director of Public Health developed the standards which have since been enacted into title 17, section 30500 *et seq.* of the California Administrative Code. The question then arose whether the Air Pollution Control Officer could cite those vehicles which did not comply with the standards set forth by the Director of Public Health on the ground that a vehicle which did not so comply would be operated in such a manner that it resulted in "the escape of excessive smoke or fuel residue." Although this specific question has never been considered by California's appellate courts, it has been answered in the negative by the Attorney General.[9] Since 1963 the Vehicle Code has been amended many times, but at no time has the legislature seen fit to negate the conclusions of the Attorney General.[10]

---

[8] Ch. 2031, § 1, [1965] Cal. Stats. 4607 (repealed 1967).

[9] "The view has been expressed that any standards adopted by the State Department of Public Health under section 426.5 would be applicable in prosecutions for excessive smoke emissions under the earlier provisions of the Vehicle Code and Health & Safety Code set forth above. We are unable to find statutory support for this argument. Rather, it appears that the intent of the Legislature was to make the standards adopted under section 426.5 applicable solely as guides for the Motor Vehicle Pollution Control Board in its consideration of control devices. Indicative of such legislative intent is Health & Safety Code section 24378(c), declaring, among other findings of the Legislature, 'That, as the Department of Public Health has established standards for . . . emissions of contaminants for motor vehicles pursuant to Section(s) . . . 426.5, the State has a responsibility to establish uniform procedures for compliance with these standards.' The procedures referred to are the certification of control devices by the Motor Vehicle Pollution Control Board." Opinion No. 63-144, 42 OP. CAL. ATT'Y GEN. 47, 48 (1963).

[10] "While the opinions of the Attorney General are not controlling as to the meaning of the statute the fact that his opinions have not been challenged and that he is the officer charged by law with advising the officers charged with the enforcement of the law as to the meaning of it, entitle his opinions to great weight." Smith v. Municipal Court, 167 Cal. App. 2d 534, 539, 334 P.2d 931, 935 (1959).

"Moreover, since the statute upon which plaintiffs rely was reenacted and transferred to the Government Code in 1949, as well as amended in 1951, it may be presumed that the Legislature was cognizant of the construction which had been placed thereon by the attorney general in his 1945 and 1956 opinions cited hereinabove. This is a factor which may be considered in applying the statute." Southwest Exploration Co. v. County of Orange, 44 Cal. 2d 549, 554, 283 P.2d 257, 259 (1955).

B. Duties of Motor Vehicle Pollution Control Board Under Previous Legislation

After the Director of Public Health acted under the 1959 legislation to promulgate standards, these standards were forwarded to the Motor Vehicle Pollution Control Board. The Board was charged with the responsibility for establishing a test procedure for any devices designed to abate air pollution emanating from a particular source in the vehicle. When the Board determined that a device existed which would control the emissions emanating from a particular source in the vehicle to within the specifications established pursuant to the law,[11] then the device would be certified. Installation of the device would not become mandatory until such time as two such devices were in fact certified.[12]

The intention of the Legislature in requiring certification of two or more devices was set forth in these terms by the Attorney General:[13]

> It has been suggested that the purpose of the "two or more" device require-ment is to insure competition between two or more companies in the manufacture of the device, thus preventing an excessive price due to monopolistic conditions. Consequently, it is argued that the licensing of a second manufacturer to produce the same device competitively should satisfy the intent of the Legislature in en-acting section 24388. This argument is rejected for the following reasons:
> 1. *Such an interpretation would not adequately conform to legislative intent.* Certainly one of the purposes of the "two or more" device requirement is to prevent an excessive price to the ultimate consumer. But such a purpose would be only partially met by competition without product diversity. If the same device produced by two different manufacturers is deemed to meet the requirements of the section, the identity of manufacturing standards and requirements, as well as the similarity of other cost factors may well result in the two devices having sub-stantially the same cost.
> In addition, as has been indicated previously by this office, it would appear that the purpose of the "two device" requirement is not to prevent monopolization but to encourage research. Memorandum to D. A. Jensen, Executive Officer, Motor Vehicle Pollution Control Board, March 9, 1961. At the time this legislation was being considered, some forty-four devices were in various stages of development.

It was argued that the general public could be adequately protected without the requirement that there be two certified devices before installation became compulsory. The opponents of this requirement urged that if the use of the Salk vaccine had been deterred until such time as a competing vaccine were developed, many more children would have known the crippling effects of polio.

Ultimately the statute was amended to provide that if the Motor Vehicle Pollu-tion Control Board found a device, the cost of which did not exceed $65.00, the

---

[11] Ch. 200, § 1, [1959] Cal. Stats. 2091, *as amended,* ch. 36, § 1, [1960] Cal. Stats. 380, ch. 2031, § 1 [1965] Cal. Stats. 4607 (repealed 1967).
[12] Ch. 23, § 1, [1960] Cal. Stats. 348 (repealed 1967); Opinion No. 64-304, 45 OP. CAL. ATT'Y GEN. 79 (1965). The schedule at which the device would be installed was set forth in sections 24391 to 24398 of the Health and Safety Code. Ch. 23, § 1, [1960] Cal. Stats. 349 (repealed 1967).
[13] Opinion No. 64-304, 45 OP. CAL. ATT'Y GEN. 79, 80 (1965).

maintenance of which would not exceed $15.00 per year, and the life of which would not be less than 50,000 miles, then the Board could certify the device. Further, if the company holding the patent for such a device would license other companies to manufacturer the same, the installation would become mandatory according to the time schedule originally provided in the statute.[14]

C. Permissibility of Delegation

It may be argued that the legislative scheme outlined above improperly delegates legislative authority to the Director of Public Health and the Motor Vehicle Pollution Control Board. Since the same attack might be launched against the state and federal programs as they now exist, this seems the proper place to discuss whether the current pollution control problems violate prohibitions against the delegation of legislative authority. California has long recognized the permissibility of delegating administrative functions to boards and commissions.[15] The legislature is not required to make detailed determinations of the facts which bring legislative policy into operation.[16]

In upholding administrative regulations the court has said:[17]

---

[14] Ch. 82, § 1, [1966] Cal. Stats. (repealed 1967). This provision has been replaced by CAL. HEALTH & SAFETY CODE § 39090 (West Supp. 1967).

[15] In both Stanislaus County Dairymen's Protective Ass'n v. County of Stanislaus, 8 Cal. 2d 378, 390, 65 P.2d 1305, 1310 (1937), and Leftridge v. City of Sacramento, 59 Cal. App. 2d 516, 523, 139 P.2d 112, 116 (1943), the courts quote with approval 1 T. COOLEY, CONSTITUTIONAL LIMITATIONS 231-32 (8th ed. W. Carrington 1927) as follows:

"Boards and commissions now play an important part in the administration of our laws. The great social and industrial evolution of the past century, and the many demands made upon our legislatures by the increasing complexity of human activities, have made essential the creation of these administrative bodies and the delegation to them of certain powers. Though legislative power cannot be delegated to boards and commissions, the legislature may delegate to them administrative functions in carrying out the purpose of a statute and various governmental powers for the more efficient administration of the laws."

[16] In Franchise Tax Bd. v. Superior Court, 36 Cal. 2d 538, 548, 225 P.2d 905, 911 (1950), the court quotes, as follows, from Yakus v. United States, 321 U.S. 414, 424-25 (1944), that it is not necessary that the Legislature

"find for itself every fact upon which it desires to base legislative action or that it make for itself detailed determinations which it has declared to be prerequisite to the application of the legislative policy to particular facts and circumstances. . . . The essentials of the legislative function are the determination of the legislative policy and its formulation and promulgation as a defined and binding rule of conduct. . . . These essentials are preserved when . . . [the legislative body] . . . has specified the basic conditions of fact upon whose existence or occurrence, ascertained from relevant data by a designated administrative agency, it directs that its statutory command shall be effective."

The court also notes that it is irrelevant that the legislature might, itself, have enacted the regulations. Id. at 425.

[17] California Employment Comm'n v. Butte County Rice Growers Ass'n, 25 Cal. 2d 624, 632, 154 P.2d 892, 895 (1944). Upholding an administrative regulation, in Nelson v. Dean, 27 Cal. 2d 873, 881, 168 P.2d 12, 21 (1946), the court quotes as follows from First Indus. Loan Co. v. Daugherty, 26 Cal. 2d 545, 549, 159 P.2d 921, 923 (1945):

"To narrowly proscribe the rule-making power of the [board] . . . would be to overlook one of the fundamental purposes of the policy of delegation of powers and to deprive the Legislature and the people of the state of one of the major benefits thereof. The essentials of the legislative function are the determination and formulation of the legislative policy. Generally speaking, attain-

Where the Legislature has by its enactments declared policies and fixed primary standards . . . there can be no question but that it may validly confer on administrative officers power to "fill up the details" by prescribing rules and regulations to promote the spirit and purpose of the legislation and its complete operation.

The reasons for the adoption of the Air Pollution Control Act[18] are crystal clear; they are the elimination, or at least the reduction, of all air contaminants, visible or otherwise. This standard seems fully adequate under California law.[19]

Various cases have approved standards at least as flexible as those set forth in the Motor Vehicle Pollution Control Act:

— "Water furnished in sufficient quantity at one or more places on each floor" for use of tenants.[20]
— Electrical equipment "dangerous to life or property."[21]
— Illuminating oils "safe, pure and [which] afford a satisfactory light."[22]
— Rules and Regulations as will "preserve the forests [within the federal reserve] . . . from destruction."[23]
— "[W]hen in the public interest it deems it necessary in order to protect the consumer against unreasonably high prices."[24]
— As the agency deems it to be "in the public interest" to so act.[25]

---

ment of the ends, including how and by what means they are to be achieved, may constitutionally be left in the hands of others. The Legislature may, after declaring a policy and fixing a primary standard, confer upon executive or administrative officers the 'power to fill up the details' by prescribing administrative rules and regulations to promote the purposes of the legislation and to carry it into effect, and provision by the Legislature that such rules and regulations shall have the force, effect, and sanction of law does not violate the constitutional inhibition against delegating the legislative function.
The court refers to a "primary standard." However, "[t]he standards laid down by the Legislature for administrative action need not be minutely defined, and it is sufficient if they can be found by implication from the general purposes of a statute and from the reasons which must have led to its adoption." Metropolitan Water Dist. v. Marquardt, 59 Cal. 2d 159, 176, 379 P.2d 28, 36, 28 Cal. Rptr. 724, 732 (1963).
[18] CAL. HEALTH AND SAFETY CODE §§ 24198-24382 (West Supp. 1967).
[19] In Holloway v. Purcell, 35 Cal. 2d 220, 217 P.2d 665, cert. denied, 340 U.S. 883 (1950), the standard attacked was the authority of the highway commission to designate and construct freeways on "such terms and conditions as in its opinion will best subserve the public interest." The court held that this delegation of legislative power was valid.
In California State Auto. Ass'n Inter-Ins. Bureau v. Downey, 96 Cal. App. 2d 876, 902, 216 P.2d 882, 899 (1950), the court recited some of the yardsticks which have been approved by the U.S. Supreme Court as follows:
— "Just and reasonable" rates for sales of natural gas.
— "Public interest, convenience, or necessity" in establishing rules and regulations under the Federal Communications Act.
— Prices yielding a "fair return" or the "fair value" of property.
— "Unfair methods of competition" distinct from offenses defined under the common law.
— "Just and reasonable" rates for services of commission men.
— "Fair and reasonable" rent for premises, with final determination in the courts.
[20] Health Dep't v. Rector, 145 N.Y. 32, 39 N.E. 833 (1895).
[21] Gaylord v. City of Pasadena, 175 Cal. 433, 166 P. 348 (1917) (municipal ordinance).
[22] Red "C" Oil Mfg. Co. v. Board of Agriculture, 222 U.S. 380 (1912).
[23] United States v. Grimaud, 220 U.S. 506 (1911).
[24] Sunshine Anthracite Coal Co. v. Adkins, 310 U.S. 381 (1940).
[25] National Broadcasting Co. v. United States, 319 U.S. 190 (1943).

In *People v. Aaron Ferer & Sons*,[26] three defendants demurred to the complaint, contending that the Air Pollution Control Act failed to provide sufficient legislative standards. Involved was Rule 57, Air Pollution Control District of Los Angeles County, which prohibits the burning of combustible refuse in any open fire in Los Angeles County.[27] The demurrer was overruled, and the decision affirmed by the appellate department.[28]

In *People v. Advance Furniture Manufacturing Co.*,[29] Judge Vernon W. Hunt, in an excellent memorandum opinion, held that the Air Pollution Control Act provides "a standard which is adequate to guide the administrative determination." The fact that these cases are unreported does not detract from their authority.[30]

In 1965, the oil interests in the County of Los Angeles challenged the constitutionality of the rules and regulations of the Air Pollution Control District of the county.[31] In its memorandum decision, the court rejected the challenge.[32] The

[26] Criminal No. 55525, Municipal Court of Los Angeles Judicial District (Los Angeles County, Cal., 1957).

[27] CAL. HEALTH & SAFETY CODE §§ 24198 to 24322 (West 1967, Supp. 1967) provides the statutory scheme giving the district power to enact such a rule.

[28] Criminal App. No. 3580, App. Dep't, Super. Ct. (Los Angeles, Cal., 1957).

[29] Criminal No. 48582, Municipal Court of Los Angeles Judicial District (Los Angeles County, Cal., 1956).

[30] MacDonald v. MacDonald, 155 Cal. 665, 672, 102 P. 927, 930 (1909); *In re* Estate of Little, 23 Cal. App. 2d 40, 43 (1937).

In Swisher v. Brown, 157 Colo. 378, 388-89, 402 P.2d 621, 627 (1965), the court said:

"It is not necessary that the legislature supply specific formula for the guidance of the administrative agency in a field where flexibility and adaption of the legislative policy to infinitely variable conditions constitutes the essence of the program. The modern tendency is to permit liberal grants of discretion to administrative agencies in order to facilitate the administration of laws dealing with involved economic and governmental conditions. In other words, the necessities of modern legislation dealing with complex economic and social problems have led to judicial approval of broad standards for administrative action, especially in regulatory enactments under the police power. With respect to such types of legislation, detailed standards in precise and unvarying form would be unrealistic and more arbitrary than a general indefinite standard."

[31] G.W.A., Inc. v. Air Pollution Control Dist., Los Angeles, Cal., Super Ct. No. SC 836864 (Memorandum Opinion, Jan. 26, 1966).

[32] The court stated:

"The Legislature cannot delegate its power to make a law, but for the proper enforcement of its laws it may make a law to delegate a power to determine some fact or state of things upon which the law makes or intends to make its own action depend. *In re McLain*, 190 Cal. 376, 379, 381 [212 P.2d 620, 621-22 (1963)]. In the case of *Marshall Field & Company v. Clark*, 143 U.S. 649, 694 [(1892)], the court in referring to whether a legislature could delegate such power stated:

"'To deny this would be to stop the wheels of government. There are many things upon which wise and useful legislation must depend which cannot be known to the lawmaking power, and, must, therefore, be a subject of inquiry and determination outside of the halls of legislation.'

"In the case of *United States v. Grimaud*, 220 U.S. 506, 521 [1911)], it is stated:

"'But the authority to make administrative rules is not the delegation of legislative power, nor are such rules raised from an administrative to a legislative character because the violation thereof is punished as a public offense.'

"The Supreme Court of California as early as 1917 in considering the delegation of administrative power by the legislative body of a city to a city official in the case of *Gaylord v. City of Pasadena*, 175 Cal. 433, 436 [166 P. 348, 349 (1917)] stated:

"'Even a casual observer of governmental growth and development must have observed the

plaintiffs appealed, but then abandoned the appeal in January 1968. It would appear, therefore, that neither the Motor Vehicle Pollution Control Act nor its successor statute[33] violate the prohibition against the delegation of legislative authority.

D. Areas in Which Installation of the Device Would Not Be Required Even After Certification

The history of air pollution legislation in California indicates a recognition that effects of air pollution will differ considerably, depending on such factors as topography, meteorology, and population density. Therefore, in those areas in which air pollution would not (at least initially) present a serious problem, the boards of supervisors of the various counties in California could determine that it was unnecessary for the preservation of air quality in the county to implement the air pollution control measures set forth either by the legislature or the Board of Motor Vehicle Pollution Control.[34]

E. Recapitulation of Statutory Scheme Prior to the Enactment of 1967 Legislation

Prior to enactment of 1967 legislation, the California statutory system embodied these assumptions:

1. Air pollution problems differ in intensity (and indeed in some areas are almost non-existent).

2. It is necessary to delegate the responsibility for deriving maximum levels of air pollution emanating from automobiles to some administrative agency possessing an expertise in medical and/or scientific research.

3. It would be necessary to delegate to an administrative agency possessing an expertise in engineering and/or scientific research the responsibility for testing (or having tested) and certifying proposed motor vehicle pollution control devices.

4. The public should be protected against the possibility of an undue economic burden which might emanate from monopolies in the field of motor vehicle pollution control devices.

5. The board of supervisors of each county should be given the power to determine whether the provisions of the motor vehicle pollution control legislation were

---

ever-increasing multiplicity and complexity of administrative affairs—natural, state, and municipal —and even the occasional reader of the law must have perceived that from necessity, if for not better grounded reason, it has become increasingly imperative that many quasi-legislative and quasi-judicial functions, which in smaller communities and under more primitive conditions, were performed directly by the legislative or judicial branches of the government, are intrusted to departments, boards, commissions, and agents. No sound objection can any longer be successfully advanced to this growing method of transacting public business.' "
Id.

[33] CAL. HEALTH & SAFETY CODE §§ 39080 to 39098 (West Supp. 1967), discussed 305-06 *infra.*
[34] CAL. HEALTH & SAFETY CODE § 39090(k) (West Supp. 1967). The efficacy of a state statute within a given area may be made to depend upon the action of some political subdivision of the state. *E.g.,* Housing Authority v. Dockweiler, 14 Cal. 2d 423, 446, 94 P.2d 794, 799-800 (1939); Hunter v. Adams, 180 Cal. App. 2d 511, 4 Cal. Rptr. 776 (1960).

necessary to preserve the air quality standards recommended by the director of public health.

6. In those areas of the state of California in which local agencies determine that control was necessary for the preservation of air quality, uniform standards should exist.

7. Failure to install a certified device is a misdemeanor; and any alteration of the device which reduces its efficiency is also a misdemeanor.[35]

II

THE STATUTORY SCHEME UNDER THE 1967 LEGISLATION

In 1967 the California Legislature adopted the Mulford-Carrell Air Resources Act.[36] Many of the earlier legal provisions, heretofore discussed, have been incorporated in the 1967 legislation. The major differences are as follows:

1. The director of public health recommends certain standards of air quality to the Air Resources Board.

2. The Air Resources Board is empowered to: (a) divide the state into basins; (b) adopt standards of air quality which may vary from basin to basin; (c) adopt standards for the emissions of motor vehicles; (d) adopt rules and regulations as required to effectuate the purposes of the act;[37] and (e) test and approve motor vehicle pollution control devices.[38]

3. In order to be exempted from the requirement that a certified device be installed on the motor vehicle there must not only be a finding by the board of supervisors in the county in which the motor vehicle is registered that the installation of such device is not necessary within that county for the preservation of air quality within that county, but apparently a similar finding with reference to the adjacent counties must be made by the respective boards of supervisors.[39]

Section 39087 of the California Health & Safety Code provides:

> Whenever the board issues certificates of approval for two or more devices for the control of emissions of pollutants from a particular source of emissions from motor vehicles for which standards have been set by the board, it shall so notify the Department of Motor Vehicles.

This section appears to have no place in the 1967 legislation, but is rather a vestigial appendage, the usefulness of which ceased to exist when the legislature decided that

---

[35] CAL. VEHICLE CODE § 27156 (West Supp. 1967). It would appear that in order to enforce this section testing devices or a system of test facilities would have to be provided. See CAL. VEHICLE CODE §§ 4000-4000.1 (West Supp. 1967).

[36] CAL. HEALTH & SAFETY CODE §§ 39000 to 39570 (West Supp. 1967).

[37] CAL. HEALTH CODE §§ 39051(a)-(d) (West Supp. 1967).

[38] CAL. HEALTH & SAFETY CODE §§ 39080 to 39098 (West Supp. 1967). It should be noted that § 39083(d)(2) refers to § 426.5 of the Health and Safety Code. Since § 426.5 has been repealed, it would appear that the legislature intended to refer to the standards promulgated by the Air Resources Board.

[39] See CAL. HEALTH & SAFETY CODE § 39090(k) (West Supp. 1967).

the general public could be adequately protected without requiring two certified devices prior to compulsory installation. The section would probably be interpreted to require the Air Resources Board to notify the Department of Motor Vehicles whenever a device was certified and the manufacturer agreed to license others to manufacture it.[40]

III

THE STATE LEGISLATURE HAS PREEMPTED THE FIELD TO THE EXCLUSION OF ACTIONS BY LOCAL GOVERNMENTAL BODIES

A. Legal Foundation of Regulating Air Contamination

The power to regulate smoke, smog, and atmospheric pollution is generally found within the police power of the governmental agency. In some instances, there is a specific power, granted under charter or statute, to adopt reasonable regulations to protect the public health, safety, and welfare.

The term "police power" is very broad and does not lend itself to any practical definition. It is a dynamic term subject to change and evolution as a commonwealth develops politically, economically, and socially.[41] It is a power of sovereignty inherent in a state and possessed by each of them. The police power of a municipality is never inherent but is a "delegated power" received by delegation from a higher source by constitutional, statutory, or charter provision.[42] The mode of delegation of the power ordinarily is not important, if it is in fact delegated.[43]

The police power delegated to cities and counties is not all-embracing, however, in that the state may take such power unto itself by direct enactment or by occupying the field.[44]

It is the general rule that there cannot be a conflict between local ordinances and the state law, unless the state law itself allows the difference.[45] Under this rule an ordinance ordinarily cannot permit that which the statute forbids, or prohibit that

---

[40] *See* CAL. HEALTH & SAFETY CODE § 39085 (West Supp. 1967).

[41] Miller v. Board of Pub. Works, 195 Cal. 477, 484-85, 234 P. 381, 383-84 (1925).

[42] *See, e.g.,* Leighton v. City of Minneapolis, 16 F. Supp. 101 (D. Minn. 1936); Denninger v. Recorder's Court, 145 Cal. 629, 79 P. 360 (1904); Commonwealth v. Plaisted, 148 Mass. 375, 19 N.E. 224 (1889).

[43] *See, e.g.,* People v. City of Chicago, 413 Ill. 83, 108 N.E.2d 16 (1952); City of Wichita Falls v. Continental Oil Co., 117 Tex. 256, 1 S.W.2d 596 (1928).

[44] *In re* Iverson, 199 Cal. 582, 250 P. 681 (1926).

In Roussey v. City of Burlingame, 100 Cal. App. 2d 321, 324, 223 P.2d 517, 519 (1950), the court, in considering the municipal police power granted by general constitutional provisions, stated:

"It is a power that may not be unreasonably invoked and applied. It is not illimitable. The marking and measuring of the extent of its exercise and application is determined by a consideration of the question whether or not the invocation of the power, in any given case and as applied to existing conditions, is reasonably necessary to promote the public health, safety, morals or general welfare of the community."

[45] *See, e.g., In re* Hoffman, 155 Cal. 114, 99 P. 517 (1909); State v. Dannenberg, 150 N.C. 799, 63 S.E. 946 (1909).

which a statute in effect directs to be permitted. Ordinances may ordinarily add additional restrictions to those established by state law.[46] In some states, ordinances which prohibit the same acts as the state statutes are invalid. The most common theory for so holding is that to allow both to stand would result in double jeopardy.[47]

B. A Consideration of the State Statutes in the Area

The Supreme Court of California has set forth these guidelines as to whether the state has preempted a particular segment of the police power:[48]

> Analysis of the many prior decisions on this subject indicates that although the language differs from case to case, the rationale of all have one thing in common, that is, that the chartered counties and cities have full power to legislate in regard to municipal affairs unless: (1) the subject matter has been so fully and completely covered by general law as to clearly indicate that it has become exclusively a matter of state concern; (2) the subject matter has been partially covered by general law couched in such terms as to indicate clearly that a paramount state concern will not tolerate further or additional local action; or (3) the subject matter has been partially covered by general law, and the subject is of such a nature that the adverse effect of a local ordinance *on the transient citizens* of the state outweighs the possible benefit to the municipality.

Applying any of these three tests, it is apparent that the state has, in fact, occupied the field:

(1) The subject matter has been fully and completely covered by general law, since the act contains a comprehensive scheme for the control of pollutants emanating from motor vehicle exhaust.[49]

(2) Legislation has been couched in such terms as to clearly indicate that a paramount state concern will not tolerate further or additional local action.[50]

(3) There has been legislation on a state level and local ordinances would only serve to confuse the transient citizen. The population of California is an extremely mobile one. (There are one and one-half cars per family in Los Angeles County.) Further, the population often crosses city and county lines in traveling to jobs and to recreation areas, for example. If those utilizing the automobile as a prime method

---

[46] *E.g.*, Borok v. City of Birmingham, 191 Ala. 75, 67 So. 389 (1914); Sternall v. Strand, 76 Cal. App. 2d 432, 172 P.2d 921 (1946).

[47] *E.g.*, State v. Welch, 36 Conn. 215 (1869).

[48] *In re* Hubbard, 62 Cal. 2d 119, 128, 396 P.2d 809, 814-15, 41 Cal. Rptr. 393, 398-99 (1964). (Emphasis added.)

[49] CAL. HEALTH & SAFETY CODE §§ 39080 to 39098 (West Supp. 1967).

[50] "Local and regional authorities have the primary responsibility for the control of air pollution *except for the emissions from motor vehicles. These authorities may control emissions from nonvehicular sources. . . .*" CAL. HEALTH & SAFETY CODE § 39012 (West Supp. 1967). (Emphasis added.)

"The Legislature finds and declares:

. . . .

"(c) That the state has a responsibility to establish *uniform* procedures for compliance with standards which control or eliminate such pollutants [*i.e.*, pollutants emanating from motor vehicles]."

CAL. HEALTH & SAFETY CODE § 39080(c) (West Supp. 1967). (Emphasis added.)

of transportation were to be subjected to a myriad of city and county regulations governing air pollution emanating from the automobile, hopeless confusion would result. Therefore, the state has clearly preempted any local regulation in the field of motor vehicle pollution.

Moreover, if local air pollution control districts ever had the power to issue regulations to control motor vehicle pollution,[51] that power has been impliedly revoked by subsequent legislation.

IV

INDIRECT MOTOR VEHICLE POLLUTION CONTROL THROUGH CONTRACT

As indicated above, California has preempted the field of motor vehicle pollution control to the exclusion of enactments by local governmental agencies. However, these same agencies might, through contract, exercise some indirect control. The County of Los Angeles did so by providing in orders of the county board of supervisors that no motor vehicle would be purchased by the county unless the emissions emanating from the vehicle met certain standards set forth in the board order.[52] Senate Bill 77 of the 1968 California Legislative Session provides for similar standards with respect to state-owned vehicles.

We believe that despite the preemption by the state with respect to activities by local governmental agencies in this particular area, the county could, by contract, impose these requirements. Similarly, the state could impose more stringent standards through the utilization of contract conditions.[53]

---

[51] See CAL. HEALTH & SAFETY CODE §§ 24198 to 24341 (West Supp. 1967).

[52] Board Order No. 155, Board of Supervisors for Los Angeles County, Nov. 19, 1963. See also the following orders of the Board of Supervisors: Board Order No. 17, Dec. 5, 1963; Board Order No. 181, Dec. 12, 1967; Board Order No. 181, Jan. 12, 1968.

[53] This would be possible even if the federal government has preempted the field. Federal preemption is discussed at pp. 312-14 infra.

In the case of Interstate Consol. St. Ry. v. Massachusetts, 207 U.S. 79 (1907), a corporation had been incorporated by a statute providing that the corporation must comply with all existing statutes. In holding that the corporation could not attack the constitutionality of the statute requiring public carriers (of which the corporation was one) to carry school children at a reduced fare, Justice Holmes said:

"If the charter, instead of writing out the requirements of Rev. L. 112, § 72, referred specifically to another document expressing them, and purported to incorporate it, of course the charter would have the same effect as if it itself contained the words. If the document was identified, it would not matter what its own nature or effect might be, as the force given to it by reference and incorporation would be derived wholly from the charter. The document, therefore, might as well be an unconstitutional as a constitutional law. . . . But the contents of a document may be incorporated or adopted as well by generic as by specific reference, if only the purport of the adopting statute is clear."

Id. at 84-85.

In Strange v. City of Cleveland, 94 Ohio St. 377, 381-82, 114 N.E. 261, 263 (1916), the court held as follows:

"The contract itself contained the following provision: 'The contractor agrees that he will comply with the provisions of the labor laws of the City of Cleveland and the State of Ohio, particularly as outlined in Section 196 of the City Charter.'

. . . .

". . . [I]n this case by the terms of the contract itself the parties thereto specifically bound

V

FEDERAL LEGISLATION

A. Legislative History Prior to 1967

In 1954 we urged the Congress to adopt legislation in the field of motor vehicle pollution control and argued that the federal government should compel automobile manufacturers to install exhaust control devices as part of the necessary equipment on new automobiles.[54]

Since the great bulk of the automobiles produced in this country are destined for interstate commerce or travel at one time or another, it is obvious that Congress has the authority to enact such legislation pursuant to its power to "regulate Commerce . . . among the several States."[55]

The argument against such a federal requirement is that a rancher in a remote area of Wyoming or Montana would have little if any need for an expensive exhaust control device. As a rejoinder, however, it was urged that the vehicle belonging to the rancher may later be owned by a factory worker in Los Angeles—such is the mobility of our society and of a motor vehicle.

In 1965 Congress amended the Clean Air Act.[56] This was the first federal legislation that, when implemented, would require the installation of air pollution control devices which would meet the standards set forth by the Department of Health, Education, and Welfare.

The 1965 Clean Air Act amendments did not contain any specific language with respect to the intention of Congress to preempt the field of motor vehicle pollution control. Moreover, the legislative history of the 1965 act would lead one to believe that it was the intention of the legislature to preempt the field of motor vehicle pollution control with respect to *new* motor vehicles.[57]

---

themselves to observe the regulations covered by the ordinance complained of. Plaintiff in error does not present a situation which avoids the enforcement of the ordinance."

[54] *Hearings on the Housing Act of 1954, Air Pollution Prevention Amendment, Before the Senate Comm. on Banking and Currency,* 83d Cong., 2d Sess., pt. 2, at 1205 (1954) (statement of Harold W. Kennedy). *See also Hearings on Water and Air Pollution Control Before the Subcomm. on Flood Control—Rivers and Harbors of the Senate Comm. on Public Works,* 84th Cong., 1st Sess. 257 (1955) (statement of Harold W. Kennedy).

[55] U.S. CONST. art. I, § 8, cl. 3.

[56] § 101, 79 Stat. 992 (1965).

[57] *See* H.R. REP. No. 728, 90th Cong., 1st Sess. 20-21 (1967):

"Public Law 89-272, enacted October 20, 1965, authorized the Secretary of Health, Education, and Welfare to establish national standards applicable to emissions from *new* motor vehicles and *new* motor vehicle engines. That legislation contains no explicit statement concerning the preemption of State laws on this subject, and no statements concerning this problem were made on either the House or the Senate floor when the bill was debated.

"The report of this committee on the bill (H. Rept. 899, 89th Cong.) contains the following statement: 'The committee is convinced that motor vehicle exhaust control standards on a national scale are necessary and would be of benefit to the entire country. . . . While the committee is cognizant of the basic rights and responsibilities of the States for control of air pollution, it is apparent that the establishment of Federal standards applicable to motor vehicle emissions is preferable to regulation by individual States.'

B. The Air Quality Act of 1967

The Air Quality Act of 1967[58] is almost a complete recodification of the Clean Air Act except that the 1967 act specifically sets forth the intention of the Congress to preempt the field of motor vehicle pollution control. Section 208 provides:[59]

SEC. 208. (a) No State or any political subdivision thereof shall adopt or attempt to enforce any standard relating to the control of emissions from new motor vehicles or new motor vehicle engines subject to this title. No State shall require certification, inspection, or any other approval relating to the control of emission from any new motor vehicle or new motor vehicle engine as condition precedent to the initial retail sale, titling (if any), or registration of such motor vehicle, motor vehicle engine, or equipment.

(b) The Secretary shall, after notice and opportunity for public hearing, waive application of this section to any State which has adopted standards (other than crankcase emission standards) for the control of emissions from new motor vehicles or new motor vehicle engines prior to March 30, 1966, unless he finds that such State does not require standards more stringent than applicable Federal standards to meet compelling and extraordinary conditions or that such State standards and accompanying enforcement procedures are not consistent with section 202(a) of this title.

(c) Nothing in this title shall preclude or deny to any State or political subdivision thereof the right otherwise to control, regulate, or restrict the use, operation, or movement of registered or licensed motor vehicles.

Section 202 provides in part:[60]

SEC. 202. (a) The Secretary shall by regulation, giving appropriate consideration to technological feasibility and economic costs, prescribe as soon as practicable standards, applicable to the emission of any kind of substance from any class or classes of new motor vehicles or new motor vehicle engines, which in his judgment cause or contribute to, or are likely to cause or contribute to, air pollution which

---

"The report of the Senate committee on the bill (S. Rept. 192, 89th Cong.) contains the following two statements: 'In view of the fact that the automobile is one of the principal sources of air pollution and manufacturers have the capability of incorporating air pollution reduction facilities in their vehicles, there is no apparent reason why the entire Nation should not benefit from such advances. Also, it would be more desirable to have national standards rather than for each State to have a variation in standards and requirements which could result in chaos insofar as manufacturers, dealers, and users are concerned[.]' (p. 6). 'The committee has found that the automotive industry has the capability for limiting the emissions of hydrocarbons and carbon monoxide from both the crankcase and exhaust systems of gasoline powered motor vehicles and found a willingness to accept legislation which would establish national standards, and it is the hope of the committee that individual States will accept national standards rather than additionally impose restrictions which might cause undue and unnecessary expense to the user.' (P. 8.)

"Since the enactment of Public Law 89-272, the Secretary of Health, Education, and Welfare has established national standards applicable to emissions from *new* motor vehicles for the 1968 and subsequent model years. [45 C.F.R. §§ 85.1-.87 (1967).] The Congress is therefore presented directly with the question of the extent to which the Federal standards should supersede State and local laws on emissions from motor vehicles."

(Emphasis added.)

[58] 81 Stat. 485.
[59] 81 Stat. 485.
[60] 81 Stat. 499 (1967).

endangers the health or welfare of any persons, and such standards shall apply to such vehicles or engines whether they are designed as complete systems or incorporate other devices to prevent or control such pollution.

Section 208, as originally proposed, stated in essence that the federal government preempts the area of motor vehicle pollution control unless California could show some immediate and peculiar problem which could not be adequately assuaged by the implementation of national standards. Thus, the burden was upon California to demonstrate that state standards were, in fact, necessary if the health and welfare of its inhabitants were to be preserved.

After a long and bitter battle, the section was reworded as indicated above to place the burden upon those who allege that the national standards are, in fact, adequate for California. Section 208 does not specifically refer to California; however, House Report 728 provides:[61]

> In other words, as passed by the Senate, section 208(b) provides for a waiver of preemption in the case of California, so that California could be permitted to establish (1) more stringent standards applicable to emissions control than federal standards, (2) standards applicable to emissions not covered by federal standards, and (3) enforcement procedures and standards with respect to emissions differing from Federal enforcement procedures and standard[s].

On July 11, 1968, after public hearings in San Francisco and Los Angeles, the Secretary found (1) that California requires standards more stringent than the applicable federal standards, and (2) that California has such standards. Therefore, in accordance with section 208(b), the Secretary waived the application of section 208(a) to certain provisions of the California Administrative Code.[61a]

It should be noted, however, that if, after a hearing, the Secretary determines that it is unnecessary for the preservation of the health and welfare of the citizens of California to allow said state to adopt additional or more stringent regulations, then California will be precluded from doing so. Furthermore, if, after hearing, the Secretary determines that the implementation of the California standards is not technologically or economically feasible, then California would also be precluded from implementing state standards.

On January 30, 1967, President Johnson requested the adoption of an Air Quality Act which would include provisions for state inspection of air pollution control devices. He proposed that such an inspection system be on a matching grant basis.[62] Section 209 of the Air Quality Act of 1967 provides:[63]

---

[61] H.R. REP. No. 728, 90th Cong., 1st Sess. 21 (1967).

[61a] 33 Fed. Reg. 10160 (1968). Applicability of § 208(a) was waived for 13 CAL. AD. CODE §§ 1925, 1935 (exhaust standards for 1969 model gasoline powered motor vehicles); § 1950 (fuel evaporative standards for model 1970 gasoline powered motor vehicles); and §§ 2100, 2102, 2105, 2108, 2109, 2500, 2502, 2504, 2507, 2508 (certification of control devices and test procedures). The waiver is applicable only for those model years specified.

[62] PRESIDENT OF THE UNITED STATES, MESSAGE ON AIR POLLUTION, H.R. Doc. No. 47, 90th Cong., 1st Sess. 4 (1967).

[63] 81 Stat. 502.

The Secretary is authorized to make grants to appropriate State air pollution control agencies in an amount up to two-thirds of the cost of developing meaningful uniform motor vehicle emission device inspection and emission testing programs except that (1) no grant shall be made for any part of any State vehicle inspection program which does not directly relate to the cost of the air pollution control aspects of such a program; and (2) no such grant shall be made unless the Secretary of Transportation has certified to the Secretary that such program is consistent with any highway safety program developed pursuant to section 402 of title 23 of the United States Code.

C. Power of Preemption by the Federal Government of the Regulation of Pollution Emanating from Automobiles

In our earlier discussion we indicated that the federal government intended to preempt the field of air pollution emanating from *new* automobiles, beginning with the model year 1968. The United States Constitution provides that Congress shall have the power to "regulate Commerce with foreign Nations, and among the several States."[64] Congress has found that with respect to the control of air pollution emanating from new automobiles beginning with the model year 1968 such control must of necessity be uniform and national in character. When the subject is national in its character, or of such a nature as to allow only a uniform system of regulation, any state law in the field will fall.[65]

It would, therefore, appear that no state, with the possible exception of Cali-

---

[64] U.S. CONST. art. I, § 8, cl. 3. Chief Justice Marshall, in Gibbons v. Ogden, 22 U.S. (9 Wheat.) 1, 189-90 (1824), stated: "Commerce, undoubtedly, is traffic, but it is something more: it is intercourse. It describes the commercial intercourse between nations, and parts of nations, in all its branches, and is regulated by prescribing rules for carrying on that intercourse." In that case, the state of New York had granted to Robert Fulton the exclusive right to operate steam boats in the waters of the state. In examining the "collision" between state and federal law, Marshall concluded: "In one case and the other, the acts of New York must yield to the law of Congress; and the decision sustaining the privilege they confer, against the right given by a law of the Union, must be erroneous." *Id.* at 210.

In the case of Liesy v. Hardin, 135 U.S. 100, 108 (1890), Mr. Chief Justice Fuller stated:

"The power vested in Congress 'to regulate commerce with foreign nations, and among the several States, and with the Indian tribes,' is the power to prescribe the rule by which that commerce is to be governed, and is a power complete in itself, acknowledging no limitations other than those prescribed in the Constitution. It is co-extensive with the subject on which it acts and *cannot be stopped at the external boundary of a State, but must enter its interior and must be capable of authorizing the disposition of those articles which it introduces, so that they may become mingled with the common mass of property within the territory entered.* . . .

". . . The power to regulate commerce among the States is a unit, but if particular subjects within its operation do not require the application of a general or uniform system, the States may legislate in regard to them with a view to local needs and circumstances, *until* Congress otherwise directs . . . ."

(Emphasis added.)

In Pennsylvania v. Wheeling & Belmont Bridge Co., 54 U.S. (13 How.) 518 (1851), the state of Virginia had authorized the construction of a bridge on the Ohio River. Congress had acted to regulate navigation upon the river. In holding that the bridge was an unlawful obstruction to navigation, the Court stated: "No State law can hinder or obstruct the free use of a license granted under an act of Congress." *Id.* at 566.

[65] Southern Pac. Co. v. Arizona, 325 U.S. 761 (1945); Welton v. Missouri, 91 U.S. 275 (1875); Cooley v. Board of Wardens, 53 U.S. (12 How.) 299 (1851).

fornia, could prohibit the sale of motor vehicles beginning with the model year 1968 even though said vehicles might not comply with air pollution standards which had been established by that state. It would also appear that a state air pollution control certificate could not be required as a condition for the use of said vehicles, except possibly in California, because this would be an attempt to do by indirection that which the state could not do directly. To hold otherwise would be to allow the state to thwart the rational and uniform plan for air pollution control promulgated by the federal government. Nothing in the Air Quality Act indicates an intention by the federal government to regulate vehicles manufactured prior to model year 1968. There is no constitutional rule that Congress must occupy the whole field.[66]

In fields in which the state and federal governments have purported to deal with the same subjects for the same purposes, the Supreme Court has relied on a number of tests to determine whether or not state regulation has been superseded by federal control. In *Pennsylvania v. Nelson*,[67] the Court delineated the following tests:

1. Is the scheme of federal regulation so pervasive as to make reasonable the inference that Congress left no room for states to supplement it?

2. Does the federal statute touch a field in which the federal interest is so dominant that the federal system must be assumed to preclude enforcement of state laws on the same subject?

3. Would enforcement of the state statute present a serious danger of conflict with administration of the federal program?

We believe that the answers to all three questions with reference to the control of pollution emanating from *used* motor vehicles must be answered in the negative. In the case of *Florida Lime & Avocado Growers, Inc. v. Paul*,[68] the Supreme Court refused to strike down a California statute which, in effect, excluded from the state of California certain Florida avocados which met federal standards for maturity. The Court said: "Congressional regulation of one end of the stream of commerce does not, *ipso facto*, oust all state regulation at the other end."[69]

Therefore, we conclude that the "field" of prescribing the air pollution control devices which must be installed on motor vehicles manufactured prior to the model year 1968 has been left by the federal government to the states; the states may prescribe

---

[66] *See* Kelly v. Washington, 302 U.S. 1 (1937). State laws have been upheld in the following cases, despite extensive congressional action in the field: Huron Portland Cement Co. v. City of Detroit, 362 U.S. 440 (1960) (air pollution from ships); Kelly v. Washington, 302 U.S. 1 (1937) (safety inspection of tugs); Mintz v. Baldwin, 289 U.S. 346 (1933) (diseased cattle); Atchison T. & S.F. Ry. v. Railroad Comm'n, 283 U.S. 380 (1931) (union passenger stations); Savage v. Jones, 225 U.S. 501 (1912) (branding of foods).

[67] 350 U.S. 497, 502, 504-05 (1956).

[68] 373 U.S. 132 (1962).

[69] *Id.* at 145. It would appear that if the regulation takes place after production has been completed for the purpose of imposing higher state standards, the regulation will be upheld. *Cf.* Cloverleaf Butter Co. v. Patterson, 315 U.S. 148 (1942); McDermott v. Wisconsin, 228 U.S. 115 (1913).

such rules and regulations as are reasonably necessary to protect or promote the health and safety of their inhabitants.

CONCLUSION

Many automobiles currently operating on the highways of the several states within the United States were manufactured prior to model year 1968. These automobiles will continue to function for a great many years. The state of California has adopted a system of legislation which is presently designed primarily to devise methods by which air pollution from these automobiles may be controlled. The California Legislature has not been unmindful of the costs to the operator of the motor vehicle of such a pollution control program.

At the present time, the California standards for emissions for automobiles manufactured, beginning with the model year 1968, are no more stringent than the federal government's standards.[70] It would appear that in deriving the standards, the Department of Health, Education, and Welfare took the standards for various pollutants recommended by the individual states, and combined them to establish a national standard.

California has proposed new standards which will be applicable to all motor vehicles registered in the state. These standards are more stringent than those which have, as of this date, been promulgated by the Department of Health, Education, and Welfare. As already noted, the preemption of these standards by federal law has recently been waived for 1969 and 1970 model-year vehicles.[71] It may well be that the ever-increasing population growth and urbanization will one day dictate even greater and more stringent regulations, both on the state and national level, but at least we have begun to deal with the dynamic health problems associated with air pollution emanating from motor vehicles.

[70] *Compare* the standards set forth in CAL. AD. CODE tit. 17, §§ 30500-30520 (1961 as augmented in 1966), *with* the federal regulations contained in 45 C.F.R. §§ 85.1-.87 (1967).

[71] 33 Fed. Reg. 10160 (1968). *See* note 61a *supra.*

STATE CONTROL OF INTERSTATE AIR POLLUTION

Lewis C. Green*

It is a truism that air contaminants do not respect political boundaries. It follows that in airsheds which include parts of more than one state, and especially in our large interstate metropolitan centers, air contaminants emitted in one state frequently cross the state boundary, and contribute to a condition of air pollution in the receiving state. Indeed, the contaminants may cross back and forth many times, perhaps undergoing chemical changes in the meantime.

How can the receiving state protect itself, or its citizens, from such contaminants emitted in a neighboring state? So far, no state has succeeeded in doing so. Some possibilities are considered below.

For convenience, it may be useful to consider this question in three different contexts: (1) the power of the receiving state, under traditional constitutional theory; (2) opportunities afforded to receiving states under federal legislation; and (3) the possibility of control achieved through an interstate compact.

I

The Constitutional Extent of the Power of the Receiving State

There are various procedures by which an intrastate polluter may be curbed. The state or local government might enforce a statute or ordinance controlling air pollution. A private party might bring an action for nuisance, trespass, negligence, or other common law remedies.[1] Such efforts will encounter various difficulties, in theory and in proof, beyond the scope of this paper.

The pursuit of the same remedies to curb the emission of air contaminants emitted in another state will encounter additional obstacles. First, one must obtain jurisdiction over the defendant. In the case of a large corporation with a place of business within the receiving state, this will pose no problem. In other cases, this may be a serious obstacle. In the case of a localized nuisance emission, immediately adjacent to a state boundary, it might be possible to present scientific proof that the contaminant complained of, in a reasonably identifiable form, crosses the state boundary and itself causes some harm or discomfort to the plaintiff. With proof that simple, it is highly arguable that the United States Constitution would not preclude the court of the receiving state from asserting jurisdiction over the defendant,

---

* A.B. 1945, LL.B. 1950, Harvard University. Member of firm of Green, Hennings, Henry & Arnold, St. Louis, Mo. Chairman, Missouri Air Conservation Commission.
[1] *See* Juergensmeyer, *Control of Air Pollution Through the Assertion of Private Rights*, 1967 Duke L.J. 1126.

and some of the modern long-arm statutes would appear to provide a mechanism for doing so.[2]

But the proof will rarely be that simple. By and large, it will be impossible to prove that a specific contaminant, emitted from a specific plant, identifiable in form, itself crossed the state boundary. The intermingling and interaction of the contaminants with one another in the ambient air, and the changing chemical composition of many of them, would usually preclude such a specific finding. The plaintiff could rarely prove more than that the contaminant complained of entered into the ambient air over the entire interstate region, and contributed to a condition of air pollution throughout that region.

Even if the individual contaminant could be specifically traced across the state line, it would still be exceedingly difficult, and usually impossible, to prove that the specific contaminant itself caused harm to the plaintiff; the most that could usually be proved would probably be that the air pollution in the receiving state, to which the contaminant contributed, caused harm in the receiving state. It may be predicted that this thin nexus between the defendant's emission and the plaintiff's injury will some day be sufficient to sustain the assumption of jurisdiction by the courts of the receiving state, but it is questionable whether most courts are ready to go this far.

Assuming that jurisdiction can be obtained over the defendant, at least in a suit for an injunction, one may still encounter the objection that the court of the receiving state will not order the defendant to do, or refrain from doing, something in another state, beyond the supervisory power of the court. Discussion of that issue is beyond the scope of this article.[3]

A possible variant of the traditional lawsuit is a suit by the receiving state, as parens patriae, against the polluter or against the state where the polluter is located, on the theory that the emitting state has wrongfully permitted its citizens to harm the plaintiff state and its citizens.

A suit by the state as parens patriae, in the courts of the receiving state, or the federal courts located within the receiving state, would not appear to stand on a much better footing than a suit by a private citizen, in overcoming the traditional jurisdictional and equity obstacles noted above. However, if it is necessary to show a causal relationship between the offending emission and some harm to the plaintiff, either as a matter of jurisdiction over the defendant, or as a matter of the plaintiff's standing, the state as parens patriae might be on sounder footing than the private citizen, in complaining that the offending emission from a neighboring state contributes to a generalized condition of pollution in the receiving state, which condition is generally offensive and harmful to the citizens of the receiving state.

---

[2] *Cf., e.g.*, Gray v. American Radiator & Standard Sanitary Corp., 22 Ill.2d 432, 176 N.E.2d 761 (1961); RESTATEMENT OF CONFLICT OF LAWS § 377 (1934; Supp. 1967); A. EHRENZWEIG, CONFLICT OF LAWS 116 (1962); H. GOODRICH, CONFLICT OF LAWS 126 (4th ed. E. Scoles 1964).

[3] *See, e.g.*, H. GOODRICH, *supra* note 2, § 78.

An alternative would be a suit by the receiving state as parens patriae, either against the offending polluter in the state or federal courts of the emitting state, or against the emitting state in the original jurisdiction of the United States Supreme Court.[4] The possibility of such litigation is exceedingly remote, and has become even more remote as a result of the creation of administrative remedies better designed to deal with these technical problems, in the Clean Air Act of 1963.

Under favorable circumstances, it would be possible for a state or municipal government to bring other pressures, outside the judicial or administrative systems, to bear upon an offending polluter. For example, government contracts could be denied; the charter of a domestic corporation could be forfeited, and the authority of a foreign corporation to do business in the receiving state could be revoked;[5] or access to the courts of the receiving state could be denied. Such sporadic pressures could hardly develop a comprehensive program to control emissions from numerous sources in an interstate metropolitan area.

II

FEDERAL LEGISLATION

A. The Clean Air Act of 1963

The first major congressional legislation dealing with air pollution was the Clean Air Act of 1963.[6] In that act, Congress discreetly, and perhaps wisely, adopted the position that "the prevention and control of air pollution at its source is the primary responsibility of States and local governments," and announced its purpose "to encourage and assist the development and operation of regional air pollution control programs."[7] Nevertheless, Congress recognized that there might be some instances where one state might be dissatisfied with a lack of control in a neighboring state, and in section 105 of the act provided an administrative remedy for the complaining state.[8]

The administrative proceeding may be commenced by a formal request from the governor of the complaining state, or a state air pollution control agency, to be lodged with the Secretary of Health, Education, and Welfare. A complaint lodged by a municipality may be sufficient to persuade the Secretary to begin an abatement proceeding, but will not invoke a mandatory administrative process unless it has the concurrence of the governor and the state air pollution control agency in which the municipality is situated.

From that point on, the proceeding is out of the control of the complaining state,

---

[4] Cf. Missouri v. Illinois, 180 U.S. 208 (1901); 200 U.S. 496 (1906).

[5] Cf. N.Y. GEN. CORP. LAW §§ 230-32 (McKinney 1943).

[6] 42 U.S.C. §§ 1857--1857*l* (1964), as amended, 81 Stat. 485 (1967).

[7] 42 U.S.C. §§ 1857(a)(3), (b)(4) (1964).

[8] 42 U.S.C. § 1857d (1964). In May 1968, the eighth such administrative proceeding was announced. 6 AIR/WATER POLLUTION REPORT 169 (May 20, 1968).

although that state participates in the proceeding to a greater extent, in some respects, than in an adversary judicial proceeding. The Secretary calls a conference of the complaining agency or agencies, the air pollution control agency, if any, of each state, or for each area, concerned, and any interstate air pollution control agency affected. Under the 1963 Act, any alleged polluters interested in the proceedings were not eligible to attend the conference as of right, but could be invited by the government authorities eligible to attend.

The conference is presided over by an appointee of the Secretary, who need not have legal or judicial experience. All parties who appear are permitted to present any witnesses or evidence they desire. Experience indicates that rules of evidence are foreign to the proceeding. Witnesses are not sworn, and may not be cross-examined, but the presiding officer permits what he regards as "clarifying questions."

Following the conference, the Secretary prepares what the statute calls "a summary of conference discussions," and may issue recommendations to the appropriate control agencies as to necessary remedial action. In practice, he has issued such recommendations following the opening session of a conference, without waiting for the conclusion of the entire conference, which may be continued over a matter of years. In practice, also, he has directed his recommendations to polluting industries themselves, as well as to control agencies. In executive session, the parties to the proceeding have an opportunity to suggest to the presiding officer what the Secretary's summary and recommendations should be, before they are issued.

In making any such recommendations, the Secretary must allow at least six months for the taking of recommended remedial action. If, at the conclusion of the period allowed, the Secretary is dissatisfied with progress being made, he calls a "public hearing" before a hearing board of five or more persons appointed by the Secretary. Each state affected may choose one of the five members; each federal department which the Secretary determines to have a substantial interest in the matter may choose one member; one member must be representative of any appropriate interstate air pollution agency; and a majority must be persons other than officers or employees of HEW.

The proceedings of the hearing board are apparently expected to be more formal than the conference.[9] Its findings must be based upon "evidence presented at such hearing." If the hearing board finds that pollution is occurring and "effective progress toward abatement thereof is not being made," it recommends to the Secretary "reasonable and suitable" measures to abate the pollution.

The Secretary apparently has no power to alter the "recommendations" of the hearing board, but he can allow a reasonable time for compliance (not less than six months). If action reasonably calculated to secure abatement of the pollution within the time specified by him is not taken, the Secretary may request the Attorney Gen-

---

[9] Procedures proposed by the Secretary, and followed in the only hearing held so far, are published at 32 Fed. Reg. 5514 (1967).

eral to bring a suit on behalf of the United States to abate the pollution. The transcript of the proceedings before the hearing board, and the board's recommendations, must be received in evidence in such a suit, and the court may receive such further evidence as it deems proper. The court has jurisdiction to "enter such judgment, and orders enforcing such judgment, as the public interest and the equities of the case may require."[9a]

In this way the complaining state may ultimately invoke the judicial process to abate pollution in a neighboring state. However, the course of the proceedings is entirely beyond the control of the complaining state, lying within the discretion of the Secretary at every stage. Moreover, the various time periods written into the statute establish a theoretical minimum of one year and six months from the date of the complaint to the initiation of the judicial process; a more realistic estimated minimum time lag would be two years.

The foregoing administrative procedure remains available under the Air Quality Act of 1967.[10] The only changes in the procedures are found in section 108(d)(2) and 108(f)(1). The only change which may be of substantial significance is the requirement that, at both the conference and the proceedings before the hearing board, "interested parties" must be given an opportunity to present evidence. The significance of this language is not clear. It may be designed to insure the right of an alleged polluter to be heard, even though he is not invited to appear by his state or local government. On the other hand, the use of the word "parties" rather than "persons" would appear to restrict the benefits of this guarantee to those persons invited by the governmental agencies.[11]

B. The Air Quality Act of 1967

The second principal piece of federal legislation on the subject of air pollution was the Air Quality Act of 1967, cited above. In 1967 the Congress clearly maintained its position that the control of air pollution "is the primary responsibility of States and local governments," and maintained its purpose to encourage the development of "regional air pollution control programs." At the same time, Congress, as noted above, retained the federal abatement powers outlined above. In addition, sections 106 and 107 of the act, together with section 108(c), provide an entirely new procedure for dealing with interstate air pollution problems, if they occur in what the act calls "air quality control regions." The Secretary of HEW is empowered to

---

[9a] The first suit to be filed pursuant to this section was United States v. Bishop Processing Co., No. 19274 (D. Md., filed March 7, 1968). On July 16, 1968, the District Court upheld the validity of the statute and the administrative process, ruling that the findings and recommendations of the hearing board should be received in evidence not as evidence of disputed facts, but only as recommendations respecting the public interest and the equities of the case. 37 U.S.L.W. 2062.

[10] 81 Stat. 485, *amending* 42 U.S.C. §§ 1857-1857l (1964).

[11] *See* S. REP. No. 403, 90th Cong., 1st Sess. 30 (1967); H.R. REP. No. 728, 90th Cong., 1st Sess. 27 (1967); Bermingham, *The Federal Government and Air and Water Pollution*, 23 BUSINESS LAW. 467, 483-84 (1968).

prescribe "air quality criteria," "air quality standards," and "recommended control techniques" for such regions. The role of the complaining state in this procedure is even more shadowy than in the abatement proceedings under the Clean Air Act of 1963—so shadowy that the new proceedings do not merit analysis in a paper on state control of air pollution emanating from another state. Suffice it to say that the procedures for bringing into court a recalcitrant polluter, located in a state which does not energetically implement the Secretary's recommendations, not only are outside the control of the neighboring state, but also are even more time-consuming than the abatement procedures under the 1963 Act, probably requiring at least three or four years, and more likely five or ten years, from the enactment of the Act through judicial action. Moreover, the law as finally passed is an outstanding example of wretched draftsmanship, leaving in a state of utter confusion the fundamental question of whether, and when, effective emission standards applicable to individual industrial plants may be promulgated by the Secretary.

III

INTERSTATE COMPACTS

If the state, rather than the federal government, is going to achieve any significant degree of control over air pollution emanating from a neighboring state, it would appear that such control will have to be developed through the device of the interstate compact. Both the 1963 and 1967 federal laws, in section 102(a), directed the Secretary of HEW to encourage the making of agreements and compacts between states for the prevention and control of air pollution. However, section 102(c) provides that no such agreement or compact may become effective unless it has been approved by Congress. The 1967 Act further provides, as to compacts entered into between states after enactment of the 1967 Act, that such a compact should not provide for participation by a state which is not included (in whole or in part) in the "air quality control region" which the compact deals with.

At this writing, no interstate air pollution control compact has won the approval of Congress. It remains to be seen whether the interstate compact will prove to be an effective device by which a state may achieve adequate control of air pollution emanating from a neighboring state.

A. Historical Development of the Interstate Compact

Consideration of the utility of the interstate compact in solving interstate air pollution problems may be enlightened by a thumbnail sketch of our experience with the compact device in other contexts. Interstate compacts have their roots deep in our colonial history. Most of the colonial charters were necessarily vague in their geographcial terms, dealing as they did with strange territory which had been poorly surveyed. As the populations of the bordering colonies came into conflict, territorial disputes between the colonies became commonplace. A common method of resolving such disputes was negotiation of an agreement by the two colonies, subject to approval by the Crown.

At the time of the adoption of the Constitution, there were existing controversies involving eleven states respecting their boundaries. The framers of the Constitution were familiar with the history of such disputes, and the procedures for settling them. This was the background in which the framers wrote:[12] "No State shall, without the Consent of Congress . . . enter into any Agreement or Compact with another State, or with a foreign Power . . . ." A search for contemporaneous articulation of the purpose of this clause is not rewarding. It appears that there is no reference to this clause in the records of the Constitutional Convention, or in the Federalist papers.[13]

From 1789 until the 1920s, the interstate compact was used exceedingly little. Until that time, every interstate compact (with one exception) concerned boundary matters. In the 1920s, however, the first compacts were adopted to create administrative machinery for continuous joint administration of a regional problem. The landmark was the New York Port Authority Compact of 1921,[14] creating the Port Authority which still exists today, with full responsibility for the planning and administration of the transportation problems of the Port of New York, divided by the New York-New Jersey state line. Other compacts in the 1920s provided machinery for allocation of waters, and operation of bridges, tunnels, and the like.

A new interest in the interstate compact clause was kindled in the 1930s, arising principally from two sources. First, in 1925 Felix Frankfurter and James Landis published their classic treatise on the interstate compact clause, calling for

> The imaginative adaptation of the compact idea . . . in the solution of problems presented by the growing interdependence, social and economic, of groups of States forming distinct regions . . . . The overwhelming difficulties confronting modern society must not be at the mercy of the false antithesis embodied in the shibboleths "States-Rights" and "National Supremacy." We must not deny ourselves new or unfamiliar modes in realizing national ideals. Our regions are realities. Political thinking must respond to these realities.[15]

A second factor giving impetus to the increased use of the compact clause was the emergence of a marked trend toward centralization of governmental authority

---

[12] U.S. CONST. art. I, § 10.

[13] The classic authority on the history of the interstate compact clause prior to 1925 is Frankfurter & Landis, *The Compact Clause of the Constitution—A Study in Interstate Adjustments*, 34 YALE L.J. 685, 691-708 (1925). *See also* Grad, *Federal-State Compact: A New Experiment in Cooperative Federalism*, 63 COLUM. L. REV. 825, 834 (1963).

[14] Act of Aug. 23, 1921, 42 Stat. 174; N.J. Laws 1921, ch. 151, p. 412; N.Y. Laws 1921, ch. 203, p. 841.

[15] Frankfurter & Landis, *supra* note 13, at 729.

and responsibility in Washington. It was in the 1930s that the Supreme Court finally changed its course, and upheld the power of the federal government to regulate many matters of social and economic concern which had previously been thought to be the exclusive domain of the state governments. As the need for governmental action in these areas became increasingly clear, and the fear of centralization of power in Washington increased simultaneously, a number of persons followed Mr. Frankfurter's advice, and looked to the compact clause, in the hope of forestalling federal intervention.

In subsequent years, the compact device has been used with increasing frequency, and directed toward a number of administrative, or proprietary, concerns. Compacts now in effect are directed toward such diverse subjects as supervision of parolees and probationers, recommending common procedures for oil and gas conservation, and for conservation of fisheries, administration of public transportation and flood control, development of common regional institutions such as the Southern Regional Education Compact, mutual aid in fighting forest fires, and a host of other subjects.

Of particular interest is the use of the compact to provide joint governmental operations in an interstate metropolitan area. It is said that thirty of the 216 metropolitan areas in the United States, containing about twenty-two per cent of the population, straddle state lines.[16] Nevertheless, from the date of the New York Port Authority Compact in 1921, it was not until 1949 that a similar joint agency was established in any other interstate metropolitan area; that is the Bi-State Development Agency in the St. Louis area.[17] Regrettably, the most significant goals of Bi-State have never been realized. That compact's contribution to the development of this governmental device was its designation of Bi-State as the general planning agency for the entire area. For one reason or another, Bi-State has never assumed that responsibility.

While the use of the compact device has been slowly increasing in such administrative or proprietary areas, there have been very few experiments with this device in the field of regulation. Several compacts have created commissions with authority to abate water pollution, in the New York-New Jersey-Connecticut area, and in the Ohio and Delaware River basins. In 1953 New York and New Jersey created the Waterfront Commission to regulate undesirable labor-management practices, racketeering, and violence along the New York waterfront, outlawing the "shape up" hiring system and other practices. In 1959 Maryland and Virginia created a

---

[16] Dixon, *Constitutional Bases for Regionalism; Centralization; Interstate Compacts; Federal Regional Taxation,* 33 GEO. WASH. L. REV. 47, 56 (1964); J. WINTERS, INTERSTATE METROPOLITAN AREAS 2-4 (Legislative Research Center, University of Michigan Law School, 1962). *Cf.* Leach, *Interstate Authorities in the United States,* 26 LAW & CONTEMP. PROB. 666, 680 (1961); Edelman, *Legal Problems of Interjurisdictional Air Pollution Control,* 13 J. AIR POLLUTION CONTROL ASS'N 310 (1963).

[17] Mo. REV. STAT. § 70.370 (1959).

compact commission with broad powers to regulate the disputed fisheries of the Potomac River.[18]

More recently, the first efforts have been made to direct the compact device to the field of air pollution. Several years ago the Interstate Sanitation Commission was given jurisdiction to deal with air pollution in the New York-New Jersey area, but its powers were limited to study and recommendations, and it was given no direct abatement powers.[19] Its success can be measured by the fact that a federal abatement action is now underway in New York, and the two states have agreed that a new compact is needed, with broad geographical jurisdiction and abatement powers.

B. Evaluation

As devices to settle boundary disputes, the compacts have clearly been useful. However, as devices to establish permanent administrative machinery, their value is less clear. They have been widely criticized as characteristically indecisive and ineffective, as inflexible, and as lacking effective political control or responsibility.[20] It has been said that the states are unwilling or incapable of discharging adequately their responsibilities in the formulation of major policies. Professor Dixon sadly describes "the sorry past record of interstate compact agencies in regard to their responsiveness and responsibility."[21] More bluntly, Professor McKinley describes the interstate compact commissions as "cumbersome, jerry-built structures lacking in region-wide political responsibility, parasitic on national finance, and negative or unduly dilatory in decision-making."[22]

As to regulatory functions, one can point to virtually no achievement, and very little effort. A few water pollution compacts, a waterfront racketeering compact, and a fisheries compact represent the most significant efforts in this direction.[23] Few citizens are satisfied with the cleanliness of the Ohio or Delaware Rivers, or New York Harbor. The present writer was recently informed that there were two pending federal abatement actions to clean up tributaries of the Ohio River, which the Ohio River Commission had failed to clean up.[24]

---

[18] Discussion of these compacts may be found in many sources, including F. ZIMMERMAN & M. WENDELL, THE LAW AND USE OF INTERSTATE COMPACTS 46-49 (Council of State Governments, 1966).

[19] N.Y. PUB. HEALTH LAW § 1299*l*, repealed in 1967 by passage of Mid-Atlantic States Air Pollution Control Compact (see note 35 *infra*); N.J. STAT. ANN. §§ 31:19A-1–32:19A-9 (repealed in 1967).

[20] *E.g.*, Engelbert, *Federalism and Water Resources Development*, 22 LAW & CONTEMP. PROB. 325 (1957); Forer, *Water Supply: Suggested Federal Regulation*, 75 HARV. L. REV. 332, 342-43 (1961).

[21] Dixon, *supra* note 15, at 77.

[22] McKinley, *The Management of Water Resources Under the American Federal System*, in FEDERALISM: MATURE AND EMERGENT 328, 347 (McMahon ed. 1962).

[23] In 1961, Leach observed that there were only six true interstate authorities in the United States, and "except for the two port authorities, none of them amount to much." Leach, *supra* note 15, at 666.

[24] *Cf.* Cohen, *Interstate Compacts—An Evaluaion*, 17 J. AIR POLLUTION CONTROL ASS'N 676, 677 (1967), reprinted in *Hearings on Air Pollution Compacts (Air Pollution—1968) Before the Subcomm. on Air and Water Pollution of the Senate Comm. on Public Works*, 90th Cong., 2d Sess., pt. 1, at 193, 195 (1968).

C. Alleged Deficiencies of Existing Compacts

Why have these compacts failed to achieve more? Partly, it is sometimes suggested, because the states which enter these compacts really do not want to achieve more, their principal objective being simply to establish a barrier between their regional problems and federal control.[25] And partly because (either inadvertently or by design) they are not calculated to foster effective action.

Many of the compacts by their very terms have shackled the compact commissions, with the result of discouraging, if not preventing, effective action. It is sometimes provided that no action can be taken by the compact commission without the approval of a majority of the members from every one of the participating states, or at least from the state to be affected by the action to be taken.[26] Often it is provided that a quorum requires the presence of a majority of the members from each state. In the case of a two-state compact, with each state voting as a unit, the probability of an impasse is ever present. Even in a multi-state compact, it is no surprise that, as Mr. Grad has pointed out, "the natural drift is in the direction of action by unanimity, since no member wishes to antagonize any other for the future when his state's pet project may be up for a vote."[27] Moreover, the compact commission is generally dependent upon the good will of the legislature of each of the states for its annual or biennial appropriations. Inevitably, with this kind of compact any possible action is geared to the lowest common denominator, the minimal action on which everybody is willing to agree.[28] As Senator Muskie recently observed at the St. Louis hearings of his subcommittee on air and water pollution, he knows of no instance in which an interstate compact commission has taken enforcement action in the state of a dissenting governor.[29] In short, effective action is sacrificed on the altar of unanimity. The caravan plods along at the pace of the slowest camel.

A second major reason frequently advanced for the "sorry record" of the compact clause is the lack of political responsiveness.[30] By and large, the members of the compact commission are appointed. They do not run for election, and cannot easily be held accountable by the voters. The absence of accountability to the voters is highlighted by the common practice of giving equal voting strength to each state, regardless of the relative numbers of persons affected by the compact.

---

[25] E.g., W. LEUCHTENBERG, FLOOD CONTROL POLITICS 250 (1953).

[26] For example, note Senator Douglas' objections to the proposed Illinois-Indiana compact. 112 CONG. REC. 14, 160-61 (daily ed. June 30, 1966). See LEUCHTENBERG, supra note 25, at 251; Hearings, supra note 24. Cf. Hart, Creative Federalism: Recent Trends in Regional Water Resources Planning and Development, 39 COLO. L. REV. 29, 44 (1966).

[27] Grad, supra note 13, at 853. See Draper, Regional Planning, in PLANNING FOR AMERICA 516 (G. Galloway ed. 1941).

[28] See V. THURSBY, INTERSTATE COOPERATION, A STUDY OF THE INTERSTATE COMPACT 136 (1953).

[29] Hearings on S. 780 (Air Pollution—1967) Before the Subcomm. on Air and Water Pollution of the Senate Comm. on Public Works, 90th Cong., 1st Sess., pt. 2, at 995 (1967).

[30] E.g., Dixon, supra note 15, at 72-75.

D. Suitability of the Interstate Compact for the Control of Air Pollution

What about air pollution control as the subject of an interstate compact? Air pollution control requires continuous day-to-day enforcement of detailed regulations, imposed upon thousands of sources in a large metropolitan area. No matter how tightly the regulations may be drawn, it seems inevitable that a great deal of discretion must be vested in the enforcement officials. A control program can be made or broken by the energy and enthusiasm, or the lethargy and reluctance, of the enforcement officials. The everyday decisions of when, and where, and how often, to take tests and samples, under what circumstances to grant variances, and what control devices or systems to encourage or approve, are the heart of an enforcement program.

Moreover, the subject is a very technical one. The average citizen will ordinarily be unable to form any judgment on the desirability of a given regulation, or a given variance or abatement order. He can only form a judgment on the over-all quality of the air, and cannot easily pinpoint lax enforcement of stringent regulations. As Dr. Forer has said of the relatively simple problems of water allocation compacts, "The far-reaching nature of the decisions, and the complexity of the facts, the hypotheses, and the evidence upon which such decisions must inevitably be based, preclude the local town-meeting type of decision-making to which lipservice is so often paid."[31]

Affecting as it does all industries throughout the area, an air pollution control program brings into play the economic rivalries between the jurisdictions, on a much broader scale than the rivalries confronted in the fisheries compacts. Uniformity of regulations, and uniformity of enforcement, are essential throughout the area, not only to insure coordinated planning, and not only as a matter of fairness to the taxpayer who pays for air pollution control in his own county or town, but also as a matter of equity, to prevent industrial pirating. And all of these factors are brought to bear upon one another, so that the natural suspicions and mistrust characteristic of a single metropolis divided by a state line are enhanced, and are focused upon the possibility of lax enforcement and industrial pirating.

In short, it would appear that air pollution control is an extremely difficult subject to handle by way of an interstate compact, probably much more difficult than the subject of labor racketeering, or of fisheries. It is in many ways analogous to the problem of water pollution, but a good deal more difficult even than that problem, because of the multiplicity of sources and the difficulty of tracing contaminants back to their sources, and the broader range of economic competition.

Thus it seems fair to conclude not only that the development of the interstate compact clause for regulatory purposes presents a "sorry record," but also that air pollution control is an extraordinarily difficult and sensitive problem to present to two contiguous states for solution. Many of the people most impatient for effective

---

[31] Forer, *supra* note 19, at 341.

air pollution control conclude that the record of the interstate compact is so dismal that it deserves no further consideration. They would have the federal government proceed forthwith to do the job of cleaning up the air, at least in these regional interstate areas. To some extent this conclusion is reflected in that part of the Air Quality Act of 1967 which authorizes the Secretary of HEW to designate air quality control regions, and prescribe standards for them.

Nevertheless, other persons believe that a further effort should be made to develop a really effective compact. As Professor Dixon says,

> We are teetering on the brink of a totally centralized federal system, under which many sub-national problems such as metropolitan mass transit, stream pollution and water supply, and air pollution, may pass by default to the federal government.[32]

Experience raises doubts that Washington can effectively regulate all these problems throughout the many metropolitan areas of the country. If the country is to thrive and prosper, our federal system, it is urged, must be used to develop local initiative, local leadership, and local responsibility.

The "sorry record" of the compact clause, while discouraging, does not necessarily preclude such an effort. At the 1966 National Air Pollution Conference in Washington, Vice President Humphrey and Senator Muskie both called for the development of "fresh thinking" to develop effective interstate air pollution control compacts.[33] As Mr. Grad has said:

> An emphasis on "states' rights" and a narrow emphasis on "local home rule" misses the mark entirely. An approach to problems of regional dimensions can only be in terms of larger units—and this leaves only two major alternatives: federal action, or interstate action with federal participation when necessary. . . . Whether such a system of federal-state compacts will succeed in the effective resolution of broad, region-wide problems, while bridging the gap in effective state participation in the formulation of policy, will depend on the states' maturity to assume this new role. The states will fail in this effort if they regard compacts like the Delaware River Basin Compact as an affirmation of a narrow concept of state sovereignty. They may succeed if, along with the assertion of legitimate interests of their own, they regard their role as historic, independently functioning parts of a regional polity and of a national union.[34]

E. Minimal Criteria for an Effective Interstate Air Pollution Control Compact

In March of 1968 Senator Muskie's subcommittee on air and water pollution held hearings on the proposed Illinois-Indiana, Mid-Atlantic, and Ohio-West Virginia air pollution control compacts.[35] At those hearings Dean W. Coston, Deputy Under-

---

[32] Dixon, *supra* note 16, at 87.

[33] PROCEEDINGS: THE THIRD NATIONAL CONFERENCE ON AIR POLLUTION 7, 598 (Public Health Service Pub. No. 1649, 1967).

[34] Grad, *supra* note 13, at 851, 854-55.

[35] *Hearings on Air Pollution Compacts (Air Pollution—1968) Before the Subcomm. on Air and*

secretary of the Department of Health, Education and Welfare, on March 26, listed six criteria recommended by the Department for determining whether a proposed compact would provide an effective basis for action to deal with air pollution, and would be consistent with the Air Quality Act of 1967.[36] His proposed criteria were as follows:

1. Only states included in whole or in part in a given air quality control region should participate in a compact dealing with that region, as provided by section 102(c) of the Act, but all of those states should be parties to the compact.

2. Federal representation on interstate compact commissions is desirable, but federal voting membership is not.

3. Each participating state should have one vote on a compact commission, regardless of the number of members of the commission provided by each state.

4. A compact commission should have broad powers of air monitoring, regulation, and enforcement.

5. The compact should provide a meaningful definition of air pollution; a compact which permits action only upon a showing that an identifiable contaminant has crossed a state line and actually inflicted identifiable injury upon some person is inadequate.

6. An interstate compact should enhance the ability of member states to carry out their functions under the Clean Air Act.

Except for the matter of voting participation by the federal government, all of these points appear to be well taken. The sixth point is rather obscure, and the matter of voting by states or by individual members appears to be legitimately debatable, but the other points are beyond question.

Perhaps the most fundamental of these points is the inclusion in the compact of direct authority in the compact commission to set standards and to enforce them. It would appear that there is no other way to achieve the essential uniformity of regulation and enforcement.[37] Such authority was contained in the Mid-Atlantic compact, and was also provided in the Kansas-Missouri compact passed by the

---

Water Pollution of the Senate Comm. on Public Works, 90th Cong., 2d Sess., pt. 1 (1968). The three proposed compacts are reprinted in the hearings volume: S.2350 (Ohio-West Virginia); S.J. Res.95 (Mid-Atlantic States); S.470 (Illinois-Indiana).

[36] *Id.* at 461.

[37] An interesting experiment is the proposal of various authorities in the so-called "Quad City" area (Rock Island County, Illinois and Scott County, Iowa) to adopt the "Quad City Area Regional Air Pollution Control Charter." The draft would create a single interstate air pollution control authority, with primary regulatory and enforcement powers. Wilson P. Burns, Chairman of the Joint Air Pollution Control Committee of the Quad Cities' Chambers of Commerce, states that the intention is to have both counties, and the cities within the two counties, approve the charter. (Mr. Burns is also Director, Foundries, at Deere & Company, Moline, Illinois.)

The writer's understanding is that local authorities do not intend to seek the approval of Congress. One presumes that they have communicated with the attorneys general of the two states, and have concluded that congressional approval is not necessary, notwithstanding the requirement of federal law that agreements or compacts between states for the prevention and control of air pollution must be approved by Congress before becoming effective.

Missouri General Assembly in 1967, but rejected by the Kansas General Assembly.[38]

To the extent that Mr. Coston was expressing opposition to a federal vote even in a case where the party states have created an impasse by a tie vote, it would appear that he has given insufficient attention to the lessons of history. In the case of a multi-state compact, it may be that the federal vote is unnecessary; perhaps the compact commission will progress, or settle to the lowest common denominator, at about the same speed, whether with or without a federal participating vote.[39] But a bi-state compact, without a federal tie-breaking vote, would be, as Governor Hearnes of Missouri has cogently stated, "worthless."[40] The ominous possibility of a tie vote would always be present. An impasse means inaction, and nothing more.

There may be some bi-state metropolitan areas where the interests of the two states are so similar that the possibility of disagreement, and a tie vote, is slim. But one need not tax one's imagination to conjure up an image of a bi-state metropolitan area which has historically developed so that the major heavy industrial complex is in one state, and the greater share of the residential area is in the other state. In such a case, it is surely not improbable that the one state government would be more inclined than the other to resolve close questions in favor of delay in control, or relatively lax standards—in short, in favor of the industrial polluters—while the second state government would be more inclined to reflect the interests of its citizens, the breathers.

Nor is it unlikely that the tensions inherent in such a situation would be exacerbated by suspicions and charges of industrial piracy.

In such a metropolitan area, the probability of disagreement is all too apparent. It is, also, constantly present. Such disagreements would be expected to occur, not only in the fundamental tasks of establishing air quality goals and emission standards, but also in the day-to-day administrative and enforcement activities, such as granting or denying delays, accepting or rejecting excuses for excessive pollution, use of effective enforcement procedures and tools, and even in providing the energy and enthusiasm to be put into enforcement.

Perhaps the members of the commission would not permit such disagreements to come to the surface. History indicates that such a commission would tend, instead, to settle to the "lowest common denominator." But the absence of any effective tie-breaking method would emasculate any air pollution control program. It is difficult to conceive of a more clearly appropriate and needed function which the federal government could perform in this area than to furnish a third member of the commission, with a tie-breaking vote.

Moreover, absence of voting power in the federal representative on a compact

---

[38] Kansas-Missouri Air Quality Compact, Mo. ANN. STAT. § 203.600 (Supp. 1967).

[39] For discussion of the federal role in interstate compacts, see Grad, supra note 13, and authorities there cited; Celler, Congress, Compacts and Interstate Authorities, 26 LAW & CONTEMP. PROB. 682 (1961).

[40] St. Louis Post-Dispatch, March 21, 1967, at 1, col. 8.

:ommission would ignore the federal interest. The interest of the federal govern-ment in the quality of the air which moves back and forth across state lines, injuring *reathers in a state which lacks the power of redress, is inherent in our federal system. The Air Quality Act of 1967 appears to reinforce that interest.

Several other significant lessons might be learned from the history of the inter-state compact.

First, it seems highly unlikely that an air pollution control compact will success-fully clear the air unless the purpose of those who sponsor the compact, and of those persons who will ultimately serve on the compact commission, is simply to clear the air. If the real motive is to delay or forestall the advent of federal intervention, there will be no effective action.[41]

Second, it would be wise to spell out in unmistakable detail the geographical juris-diction of any compact agency, to avoid litigation over jurisdictional issues. For example, Senate Bill 408, passed by the Missouri General Assembly in 1967, spe-cifically named the counties subject to the compact.

Third, to avoid financial strangulation, the compact commission should be given power to obtain necessary funds. This will not be easy to arrange, for the traditional method of financing such commissions is to depend upon appropriations from the state legislatures concerned, at least one of which may be less than sympathetic with the enforcement activities of the compact commission. There would appear to be no federal constitutional objection, however, to a provision authorizing the compact commission to allocate the cost of enforcement among the counties concerned, and levy assessments upon them.

Fourth, there is much to be said for the proposition that, as Senator Muskie has stated, the traditional compact "does not give adequate weight to local or metro-politan area participation in planning or implementing decisions."[42] Again, there would appear to be no federal constitutional objection to a compact which authorized the compact commission to create, under its aegis, a regional authority to enforce air pollution control regulations throughout the region, on both sides of the state boundary, such authority to consist in part of local elected officials.[43]

Fifth, it would seem desirable to build into the compact the maximum flexibility. The grant of regulatory and enforcement powers must be categorical and un-

---

[41] The industrial ancestry of some of the presently proposed compacts might raise an eyebrow. *See, .g., Hearings on Air Pollution Compacts (Air Pollution—1968) Before the Subcomm. on Air and Water Pollution of the Senate Comm. on Public Works*, 90th Cong., 2d Sess., pt. 1, at 30, 31, 431, 435, 441, 442 (1968). *See also* Lieber, *Controlling Metropolitan Pollution Through Regional Airsheds*, 18 J. AIR POLLUTION CONTROL ASS'N 86 (1968), reprinted in *Hearings, id.* at 141.

[42] PROCEEDINGS, *supra* note 33, at 598.

[43] *Compare* the composition of the Delaware Valley Urban Area Compact Commission, N.J. STAT. ANN. § 32:27-1 (West Supp. 1968). Note the composition of the intrastate San Francisco Bay Area Air Pollution Control District, which includes elected officials from each county affected. CAL. HEALTH & SAFETY CODE §§ 24345, 24351 (West 1967). *See* Jones, *The Organization of a Metropolitan Region*, 105 J. PA. L. REV. 538, 544 (1957); ADVISORY COMMISSION ON INTERGOVERNMENTAL RELATIONS, GOVERN-MENTAL STRUCTURE, ORGANIZATION AND PLANNING IN METROPOLITAN AREAS 29 (1961).

mistakable; the minimum geographical jurisdiction should be specifically set forth. But, beyond the minimal requirements, flexibility is clearly desirable. If an effective form of federal-state cooperation is to be developed, as an alternative to centralized federal government, it seems likely that an adequate degree of sophistication will be achieved only as a result of trial and error. The first efforts, of which the Delaware River Basin Compact might be considered the prototype, will necessarily be faltering. A compact constrained by rigid limitations will very likely be doomed to failure.

At this writing, it remains to be seen whether Congress will approve any of the compacts before it, and on what terms such approval may be given. A study of history, however, offers little basis for optimism that any of the three proposed compacts will be notably successful in achieving clean air.

CONCLUSION

It may be that our state governments (or some of them) are too debilitated, too much dominated by the influence of special interest groups, to make a meaningful contribution to the solution of interstate air pollution problems. If any such contribution is to be made, it would appear that the only avenue offering any hope is through the interstate compact mechanism. It further appears that any such contribution must be made in partnership with the federal government, not in opposition to the federal government. The next few years will determine whether the state governments have matured sufficiently to follow this course, in the spirit that has come to be known as the spirit of "cooperative federalism," or whether the federal government will reluctantly be compelled to establish and enforce detailed emission standards for the interstate air quality regions.

LEGAL BOUNDARIES OF AIR POLLUTION CONTROL—STATE AND LOCAL LEGISLATIVE PURPOSE AND TECHNIQUES

LAWRENCE W. POLLACK*

The Air Quality Act of 1967[1] has once again directed the nation's attention to the dangers of ever-increasing levels of air pollution. The new legislation, while increasing the role of the federal government, did not change the basic congressional findings of the 1963 Clean Air Act "that the prevention and control of air pollution at its source is the primary responsibility of States and local governments."[2]

One of the designated purposes for the passage of the 1963 act was:

> to provide technical and financial assistance to State and local governments in connection with the development and execution of their air pollution prevention and control programs.[3]

States and local governments have been attempting to "prevent and control" air pollution for many years. As might be anticipated, the major industrial cities were the first to enact legislation on the subject.[4] The recognizable increase in the problem and the increase in scientific knowledge about the problem have gradually led to the adoption of prevention and control legislation employing various and multiple techniques of regulation and enforcement. Among these techniques are limitations on the density and opacity of visible smoke, limitations on specific emissions, regulatory permits and requirements for installation and operation of equipment, limitations upon the kind and nature of fuels permitted, skill requirements and training for equipment operators, and the flat prohibition of certain industrial activities. These various techniques are directly related to the local function of "prevention and control of air pollution at its source."[5]

Enforcement of state and local statutes over the years has provided sufficient legal

---

* B.S.E. 1953, University of Pennsylvania; LL.B. 1956, New York University; LL.M. 1957, University of Michigan. Practicing attorney and Adjunct Assistant Professor of Law, New York University. Counsel, New York City Council Special Committee to Investigate Air Pollution, 1965; Special Counsel, New York City Council, 1966. Member of the New York bar.

[1] 81 Stat. 485 (1967).

[2] 42 U.S.C. § 1857(a)(3) (1964).

[3] 42 U.S.C. § 1857(b)(3) (1964).

[4] General smoke ordinances were adopted by Chicago in April 1881; Cincinnati in November 1881; St. Louis in 1893; City of Brooklyn in 1895; and New York City in 1898. Statutory limitations on the use of various coals date back at least to the years 1273 and 1306 in England. See Kennedy & Porter, *Air Pollution: Its Control and Abatement*, 8 VAND. L. REV. 854 (1955).

[5] 42 U.S.C. § 1857(a)(3) (1964).

experience to permit definition of some of the legal boundaries confronting new
legislative attempts to deal with a problem that has proved stubborn indeed.

The Air Quality Act of 1967 is a reflection of a relatively new legislative approach.
This approach, an outgrowth of modern "systems analysis" and computer technology, has been developed and advocated by the U.S. Public Health Service as
a program of "Air Resource Management."[6] Since the Public Health Service is
the most influential governmental organization in the field, its recommended legislation has had considerable influence upon new state and local legislation. The
"Air Resource Management" concept was explained in a recent Public Health Service
publication as follows:

> The air is a matter of public business, calling for good management practices.
> The public must have knowledge of air quality, effects of air pollutants, and the
> types and qualities of pollutants put into the air. Armed with this knowledge,
> the public depends on its governmental organizations to establish air quality goals
> and standards, and to develop the program goals, air-use plans, and action programs
> needed to reach the desired air quality. *Simply stated, the public embarks on an
> air resource management program to assure sound community growth in which the
> air resources of the air pollution basin are put to optimum use.*[7]

A legislative purpose of "good management so that air resources are put to optimum
use" contrasts sharply with the more traditional "public health and welfare" legislative purposes.[8]

The purpose of this article is to review the legal experiences encountered in the
development of the various state and local legislative techniques, so that future legislative efforts can be judged and guided accordingly. Because recent New York City
legislation employs most of the available legislative techniques, it is used throughout
this article as an example of "source control" legislation.[9] The ordinance provisions
recommended by the Public Health Service are hereinafter used as a model of "Air
Resource Management" legislation.[10]

---

[6] *Hearings on S. 780 Before the Subcomm. on Air and Water Pollution of the Senate Comm. on
Public Works*, 90th Cong., 1st Sess., pt. 2, at 958-77 (1967) [hereinafter cited as *Hearings on S. 780*];
Larson, *Determining Reduced-Emission Goals Needed to Achieve Air Quality Goals—A Hypothetical
Case*, 17 J. AIR POLL. CONTROL ASS'N 823-29 (1967).

[7] A PROPOSAL FOR AN AIR RESOURCE MANAGEMENT PROGRAM, VOL. VIII, PHASE II PROJECT REPORT,
ST. LOUIS METROPOLITAN AREA INTERSTATE AIR POLLUTION STUDY 3 (National Center for Air Pollution Control, May 1967) [hereinafter cited as PUBLIC HEALTH SERVICE MANAGEMENT PROGRAM]. (Emphasis added.)

[8] N.Y. CITY ADMIN. CODE §892-1.0 (1963). *See also* 42 U.S.C. § 1857(a)(2) (1964).

[9] New York City Local Law No. 14 of 1966, N.Y. CITY ADMIN. CODE §§ 892-1.0 *et seq.* (Supp.
1967). Local Law No. 14 of 1966 and the two New York City Council Special Committee Reports which
were the basis for the law are reprinted in full in *Hearings on S. 780*, pt. 3, at 1482-1622 (1967). The
New York City law is administered by the N.Y.C. Dep't of Air Pollution Control, an administrative
agency headed by a Commissioner appointed by the Mayor. The Department promulgates regulations,
hereinafter cited as "A.P.C. § ———."

[10] PUBLIC HEALTH SERVICE MANAGEMENT PROGRAM 89-132.

I

THE POLICE POWER AND CONSTITUTIONAL LIMITATIONS

A. Background—The Law of Nuisance

Most of the early law involving air pollution was a part of the common law tort of "nuisance" and the confusion associated with that word has been carried forward regularly to modern air pollution control. Dean William Prosser has commented that "[t]here is perhaps no more impenetrable jungle in the entire law than that which surrounds the word 'nuisance.' "[11]

While this paper cannot hope to clear a scholarly path through the "jungle," a summary of common law concepts of the law of nuisance is necessary to an analysis of air pollution control legislation.

The law of nuisance has been divided into "private nuisance" and "public nuisance" since ancient times.[12] Private nuisance is simply a traditional tort which lies for interference with a person's enjoyment of his property. The action is dependent upon proof of damage and a finding that the defendant's activity is "unreasonable." Since most private nuisance cases involving air pollution requested an injunction, the standard flexible powers of an equity court combined with the required determination of "reasonableness" to develop a judicial policy of balancing the harm to the plaintiff against any usefulness of the defendant's conduct. As explained in *Cogswell v. New York, New Haven & Hartford R.R.*:[13]

> The compromises exacted by the necessities of the social state, and the fact that some inconvenience to others must by necessity often attend the ordinary use of property, without permitting which there could in many cases be no valuable use at all, have compelled the recognition, in all systems of jurisprudence, of the principle that each member of society must submit to annoyances consequent upon the ordinary and common use of property, provided such use is reasonable both as respects the owner of the property, and those immediately affected by the use, in view of time, place and other circumstances.

When the difficulties of proving damages from air pollution are balanced against the usual economic importance of the accused factory, the plaintiff's obstacles are obvious. The wide judicial discretion exercised in private nuisance cases has allowed pollution from fifty coke ovens to be classified as only a "petty annoyance" to a neighboring home owner and a conclusion that air pollution is "indispensable to progress."[14]

---

[11] W. PROSSER, LAW OF TORTS 592 (3d ed. 1964).

[12] 3 BLACKSTONE, COMMENTARIES 215 (16th ed. 1825). The law of nuisance and other remedies available to private citizens is exhaustively discussed in Juergensmeyer, *Control of Air Pollution Through the Assertion of Private Rights*, 1967 DUKE L.J. 1126.

[13] 103 N.Y. 10, 13-14 (1886). The court held that even the careful maintenance of a railroad engine-house next to the plaintiff's house was beyond the line of reason, especially in view of an undisputed finding of fact that plaintiff's son had been made ill by smoke and dust.

[14] Bove v. Donner-Hanna Coke Corp., 142 Misc. 329, 254 N.Y.S. 403 (1931), *aff'd mem.*, 236 App.

The law of "public nuisance," however, involves damage to the *community* in the exercise of its common rights. Any such activity was a common law crime. The conducting of an offensive smelling business, for example, was among the early accepted species of public nuisance.[15] Smoke, as distinguished from many other activities injurious to public health, was not considered to be a "nuisance *per se*,"[16] and proof that a large number of persons actually suffered some impairment to their enjoyment of life was required for prosecution for the creation of a public nuisance.

The restrictions of the law of public nuisance caused by the damage proving requirements gave rise to two developments: courts began to find damage to the public by taking "judicial notice" that impure air was harmful, and legislatures declared dense smoke a public nuisance as a matter of law. Often, "judicial notice" of damage was used as a basis for upholding the legislation.[17] Unless the nuisance statute is carefully drafted, however, actual proof of harm might still be required. The state of New Jersey did not surmount this hurdle until 1950.[18]

Modern health requirements and modern air pollution control are concerned with invisible and odorless gases such as carbon monoxide and sulfur dioxide, with minute particles invisible to the naked eye, and with the complex chemical reactions that create photochemical smog. For the most part, increasing pollution levels result from the combined atmospheric contribution of thousands of installations and automobiles. No single identifiable source may be large enough or visible enough to be held responsible for specific damage. As a result, the laws of public and private nuisance have little application in the routine enforcement of modern air pollution legislation.

In *Leone v. Paris*,[19] the court enforced designated water pollution control standards although the defendant's pollution contribution alone did not prevent the water from being usable and the stream involved had not been classified as "polluted." The court held:

> If there is a substantial threat to the community it need not be hoveringly current. . . . The indirect, impersonal specter of menace created here, without substance to most *at this instant in time*, is nevertheless real and escalating, to be stunningly present in due time.[20]

Div. 37, 258 N.Y.S. 229 (1932). Some twenty years later, the City of Buffalo was still having air pollution difficulties with the same factory and, like the neighbor, having little success. *See* People v. Savage, 1 Misc. 2d 337, 148 N.Y.S.2d 191, *aff'd mem.*, 309 N.Y. 941, 32 N.E.2d 313 (1955).

[15] 4 BLACKSTONE, COMMENTARIES 168 (16th ed. 1825).

[16] *See* Dep't of Health v. Philip & William Ebling Brewery Co., 38 Misc. 537, 78 N.Y.S. 13 (1902).

[17] City of Rochester v. Macauley-Fien Milling Co., 199 N.Y. 207 (1910); State v. Tower, 185 Mo. 79, 84 S.W. 10 (1904); Bowers v. City of Indianapolis, 169 Ind. 105, 81 N.E. 1097 (1907). *Cf.* People v. New York Edison Co., 159 App. Div. 786, 144 N.Y.S. 707 (1913).

[18] Board of Health v. New York Central R.R., 4 N.J. 293, 72 A.2d 511 (1950); *see* Cowan, *Air Pollution Control in New Jersey*, 9 RUTGERS L. REV. 609 (1955).

[19] 43 Misc. 2d 442, 251 N.Y.S.2d 277 (1964), *modified*, 25 App. Div. 2d 508, 261 N.Y.S.2d 656 (1965).

[20] *Id.* at 447, 251 N.Y.S.2d at 282-83. (Emphasis in original.)

The late Chief Judge Vanderbilt of New Jersey, directly contrasting the inadequacies of the law of public nuisance with the need for effective air pollution control, held:

> The reason for a municipality making unlawful the emission of smoke is readily apparent. The issuance of dense smoke from a single chimney, in and of itself, may be altogether harmless and cause no inconvenience or damage to the public, but if smoke of like density issued from hundreds of chimneys, the contamination of the atmosphere would be substantial and the injury to the public considerable, yet for lack of the requisite elements of a public nuisance at common law, the municipality could obtain no relief by way of indictment. Ordinances making unlawful the emission of smoke are therefore obviously necessary and reasonable and a valid exercise of the local police power.[21]

The conclusion seems inescapable. Modern air pollution control legislation, based upon the need for protection of the public health, must be recognized as independent of the elements of common law nuisance. It is an exercise of legislative police powers and must be judged in accordance with the constitutional standards applicable to those powers. In 1960, the Supreme Court, referring to Detroit's air pollution law, declared:

> The ordinance was enacted for the manifest purpose of promoting the health and welfare of the city's inhabitants. Legislation designed to free from pollution the very air that people breathe clearly falls within the exercise of even the most traditional concept of what is compendiously known as the police power.[22]

B. The Due Process Clause

Recognition that air pollution control legislation is within the proper framework of an exercise of the police power has become standard.[23] The police power is, of course, limited by the fifth and fourteenth amendments to the Constitution of the United States.[24] The question in any analysis of air pollution control legislation is whether the statute is within the limits imposed by the Constitution.

The leading case outlining the constitutional boundaries of air pollution control legislation is *Northwestern Laundry v. Des Moines.*[25] That 1916 case involved a

---

[21] Board of Health v. New York Central R.R., 10 N.J. 294, 306, 90 A.2d 729, 735 (1952).

[22] Huron Portland Cement Co. v. Detroit, 362 U.S. 440, 442 (1960).

[23] City of Rochester v. Macauley-Fien Milling Co., 199 N.Y. 207 (1910); Consolidated Edison Co. v. Murtagh, 280 App. Div. 221, 112 N.Y.S.2d 681 (1952); People v. Bevevino, 202 Misc. 723, 112 N.Y.S.2d 647 (1952); People v. Tatje, 203 Misc. 949, 121 N.Y.S.2d 147 (1953); West Bronx Auto Paint Shop, Inc. v. City of New York, 33 Misc. 2d 29, 223 N.Y.S.2d 984 (1961), *aff'd mem.*, 17 App. Div. 2d 772, 232 N.Y.S.2d 391 (1962), *modified*, 13 N.Y.2d 730, 241 N.Y.S.2d 861 (1963). *See also* City of Utica v. Water Pollution Control Board, 5 N.Y.2d 164, 156 N.E.2d 301, 182 N.Y.S.2d 584 (1959).

[24] "Government hardly could go on if to some extent values incident to property could not be diminished without paying for every such change in the general law. As long recognized, some values are enjoyed under an implied limitation and must yield to the police power. But obviously the implied limitation must have its limits, or the contract and due process clauses are gone." Pennsylvania Coal Co. v. Mahon, 260 U.S. 393, 413 (1922).

[25] 239 U.S. 486 (1916).

challenge to an ordinance similar in many respects to modern control legislation. The ordinance established smoke density limitations measured according to the Ringelmann Smoke Chart[26] and forbade remodeling of new construction without a permit. The standard of efficiency called for by the smoke limitations required, as a practical matter, the remodeling of almost all of the furnaces in operation at the time of the adoption of the ordinance. The law was challenged as violative of both the due process and equal protection clauses of the fourteenth amendment. The Supreme Court held:

> So far as the Federal Constitution is concerned, we have no doubt the State may by itself or through authorized municipalities declare the emission of dense smoke in cities or populous neighborhoods a nuisance and subject to restraint as such; and that the harshness of such legislation, or its effect upon business interests, short of a merely arbitrary enactment, are not valid constitutional objections. Nor is there any valid Federal constitutional objection in the fact that the regulation may require the discontinuance of the use of property or subject the occupant to large expense in complying with the terms of the law or ordinance.[27]

Generally stated, the limitations imposed by the due process clause upon the legislative power to protect the public health are that the exercise of power must not be arbitrary and must not go beyond what is necessary to accomplish the legislative purpose.[28] Since the opposite of "arbitrary" is "reasonable," it has become common judicial practice to determine the constitutional inquiry on the basis of whether the legislation is "reasonable" or "unreasonable."[29] The use of that word in private nuisance cases as an indication of judicial flexibility[30] has led to confusion when the same word is used in a constitutional inquiry.[31] Where there is a legitimate public purpose

---

[26] The Ringelmann Smoke Chart, published by the U.S. Bureau of Mines, is commonly established by statutes as the recognized smoke measurement guide. Its use has been sustained by the courts. *See* People v. International Steel Corp., 102 Cal. App. 2d 935, 226 P.2d 587 (1951); State v. Mundet Cork Corp., 8 N.J. 359, 86 A.2d 1, *cert. denied*, 344 U.S. 819 (1952); People v. Plywood Mfr's of Cal., 137 Cal. App. 2d 859, 291 P.2d 587 (1955); Sittner v. Seattle, 62 Wash. 2d 834, 384 P.2d 859 (1963); People v. Murray, 174 Misc. 251, 19 N.Y.S.2d 902 (1940). For New York City regulations, see A.P.C. Reg. § 9.03.

[27] Northwestern Laundry v. Des Moines, 239 U.S. 486, 491-92 (1916).

[28] Lawton v. Steele, 152 U.S. 133 (1894); Northwestern Laundry v. Des Moines, 239 U.S. 486 (1916); People v. Arlen Service Stations, 284 N.Y. 340 (1940); Sheafer v. Joseph Breen, Inc., 263 App. Div. 135, 31 N.Y.S.2d 543 (1941).

[29] People v. New York Edison Co., 159 App. Div. 786, 144 N.Y.S. 707 (1913); People v. Cunard White Star, Ltd., 280 N.Y. 413 (1939); Health Dep't v. The Rector, etc. of Trinity Church, 145 N.Y. 32 (1895).

[30] *See* cases cited in notes 13, 14 *supra*.

[31] *See* People v. New York Edison Co., 159 App. Div. 786, 144 N.Y.S. 707 (1913); People v. Cunard White Star, Ltd., 280 N.Y. 413 (1939); People v. Peterson, 31 Misc. 2d 738, 226 N.Y.S.2d 1004 (1961); People v. Oswald, 1 Misc. 2d 726, 116 N.Y.S.2d 50 (1952); People v. Savage, 1 Misc. 2d 337, 148 N.Y.S.2d 191, *aff'd mem.*, 309 N.Y. 941, 132 N.E.2d 313 (1955); People v. New York Central & H.R.R., 159 App. Div. 329, 144 N.Y.S. 699 (1913); Dep't of Health v. Philip & William Ebling Brewery Co., 38 Misc. 537, 78 N.Y.S. 13 (1902) (cases applying a judicial "rule of reason") and Dankner v. City of New York, 20 Misc. 2d 557, 194 N.Y.S.2d 975 (1959); Engelshar v. Jacobs, 5 N.Y.2d 370, 157 N.E.2d 626, 184 N.Y.S.2d 640, *cert. denied*, 360 U.S. 902 (1959); Health Dep't v. The Rector, etc. of Trinity

and the legislation is related to its accomplishment, it is inappropriate for a court to "balance" the economic equities of the situation. Where the legislative purpose clearly is the protection of the public health, judicial restraint and the presumption of legislative constitutionality[32] must be the guide. Police power legislation has been referred to as the governmental power that is the least limitable by the courts.[33]

There can be no doubt that these general constitutional principles apply to air pollution control legislation. The New York Court of Appeals stated in *City of Rochester v. Macauley-Fien Milling Co.*:[34]

> The common council is thus the judge as to what ordinances it will pass for the safety and welfare of the inhabitants of the city and the protection and security of their property, and unless an ordinance passed by it is wholly arbitrary and unreasonable it should be upheld. The necessity and advisability of the ordinance is for the legislative power to determine. The presumption is in favor of the ordinance.

The Missouri Supreme Court, deciding the constitutionality of the St. Louis air pollution law in the case of *Ballentine v. Nester*,[35] relied upon an earlier case for the following principle:

> "The methods, regulations, and restrictions to be imposed to attain, so far as may be, results consistent with the public welfare, are purely of legislative cognizance. The courts have no power to determine the merits of conflicting theories, nor to declare that a particular method of advancing and protecting the public is superior or likely to insure greater safety or better protection than others. The legislative determination of the methods, restrictions, and regulations is final, except when so arbitrary as to be violative of the constitutional rights of the citizens."[36]

It can be concluded therefore that whether the constitutional inquiry is phrased in terms of "arbitrariness" or "reasonableness," every advantage should be given to the sustaining of the legislation as long as the statute is related to the control of air pollution for the public health.

C. The Equal Protection Clause

Police power legislation is also limited by the requirements of equal protection of the law. The Constitution precludes an arbitrary system of classification or dis-

Church, 145 N.Y. 32 (1895) (cases applying a "reasonable cost" element). These cases will be discussed in detail in subsequent sections of this paper.

[32] Wasmuth v. Allen, 14 N.Y.2d 391, 200 N.E.2d 756, 252 N.Y.S.2d 65 (1964); Sweeney v. Cannon, 23 App. Div. 2d 1, 258 N.Y.S.2d 183 (1965); People v. Bevevino, 202 Misc. 723, 112 N.Y.S.2d 647 (1952).

[33] Hadacheck v. Sebastian, 239 U.S. 394, 410 (1915); Engelshar v. Jacobs, 5 N.Y.2d 370, 157 N.E.2d 626, 184 N.Y.S.2d 640, *cert. denied*, 360 U.S. 902 (1959).

[34] 199 N.Y. 207, 211 (1910).

[35] 350 Mo. 58, 164 S.W.2d 378 (1942).

[36] *Id.* at 70, 164 S.W.2d at 382, quoting Nelson v. City of Minneapolis, 112 Minn. 16, 18, 127 N.W. 445, 447 (1910). For similar conclusions *see* State v. Chicago, M. & St. P. Ry., 114 Minn. 122, 130 N.W. 545 (1911); Moses v. United States, 16 App. D.C. 428 (1900); Penn-Dixie Cement Corp. v. City of Kingsport, 189 Tenn. 450, 225 S.W.2d 270 (1949); Sittner v. Seattle, 62 Wash. 2d 834, 384 P.2d 859 (1963).

crimination between persons of the same classification. Again, however, every effort will be made by the courts to uphold the legislation. As expressed in the leading case of *Heath & Milligan Co. v. Worst*:[37]

> We have declared many times, and illustrated the declaration, that classification must have relation to the purpose of the legislature. But logical appropriateness of the inclusion or exclusion of objects or persons is not required. A classification may not be merely arbitrary, but necessarily there must be great freedom of discretion, even though it results in "ill-advised, unequal and oppressive legislation." [Citation omitted.] And this necessarily on account of the complex problems which are presented to government. Evils must be met as they arise and according to the manner in which they arise. The right remedy may not always be apparent. Any interference, indeed, may be asserted to be evil, may result in evil. At any rate, exact wisdom and nice adaptation of remedies are not required by the Fourteenth Amendment, nor the crudeness nor the impolicy nor even the injustice of state laws redressed by it.

The cases allow extensive discretion in the establishment of classifications, and most questions of equal protection raised in challenging modern regulatory legislation are directed toward the definition of the established classifications.[38] Just as the decision in an antitrust case becomes predictable once the court has defined the outlines of a "relevant market," judicial definition of the limits of each classification will ultimately control the decision of whether the person affected falls within a certain class or whether all persons within the given class are treated equally. If the classification is interpreted as being very wide, *i.e.*, "all fuel burning equipment," a statute which treats coal burning equipment differently from oil burning equipment will be held to be discriminatory. If the classifications are interpreted as being separate and narrow, *i.e.*, "coal burning equipment" and "oil burning equipment," the law will invariably be found to provide for the required equal treatment within each classification.

> Equal protection is accomplished when all of the same class are treated in a like manner. . . . That one class is treated differently than other classes can give rise to no complaint under the equal protection clause.[39]

The complexities and variations involved in the prevention and control of diversified sources of air pollution requires, as a practical matter, the creation of numerous

---

[37] 207 U.S. 338, 354-55 (1907).

[38] *See* Ballentine v. Nester, 350 Mo. 58, 164 S.W.2d 398 (1942); State v. Chicago, M. & St. P. Ry., 114 Minn. 122, 130 N.W. 545 (1911); City of Rochester v. Macauley-Fien Milling Co., 199 N.W. 207 (1910); Sittner v. Seattle, 62 Wash. 2d 834, 384 P.2d 859 (1963); 7 E. McQUILLAN, MUNICIPAL CORPORATIONS 476 (3d ed. 1949).

[39] Engelshar v. Jacobs, 5 N.Y.2d 370, 157 N.E.2d 626, 184 N.Y.S.2d 640, *cert. denied*, 360 U.S. 902 (1959); People v. Arlen Service Stations, 284 N.Y. 340 (1940); Ballentine v. Nester, 350 Mo. 58, 164 S.W.2d 378 (1942).

classifications and distinctions. Those classifications must be related to the designated purpose for the legislation.[40]

II

LEGISLATIVE PURPOSE: PUBLIC HEALTH EMERGENCY VERSUS EFFICIENT MANAGEMENT OF RESOURCES

The "Findings and Purposes" section of the federal Act[41] contains the foundation for difficult constitutional questions. While the questions have not yet been raised, the trend of new legislation toward "Air Resource Management" indicates that the problems are certain to be raised in the near future. The key congressional "finding" is cast in the following traditional public health terms:

(2) that the growth in the amount and complexity of air pollution brought about by urbanization, industrial development, and the increasing use of motor vehicles, has resulted in mounting dangers to the public health and welfare, including injury to agricultural crops and livestock, damage to and the deterioration of property, and hazards to air and ground transportation . . . .[42]

The enumerated "purpose" clause is as follows:

(1) to protect and enhance the quality of the Nation's *air resources so as to promote* the public health and welfare and *the productive capacity of its population*;
(2) to initiate and accelerate a national research and development program *to achieve the prevention and control of air pollution*;
(3) to provide technical and financial assistance to State and local governments in connection with the development and execution of *their air pollution prevention and control programs* . . . .[43]

It is apparent that the legislative draftsmen had two separate and distinct purposes in mind; one being affirmative in concept—"to promote productive capacity"—and the other being negative in concept—"to prevent and control air pollution." These distinct purposes are now being reflected in new state and local legislation and it is fair to conclude that the trend is toward the affirmative purpose of promoting efficient "Air Resource Management." The city of Chicago is the leading city employing this concept.[44] New York City is the leading city which employs the "prevention and control" concept.[45] Since a comparison of the Chicago Municipal

---

[40] City of Rochester v. Macauley-Fien Milling Co., 199 N.Y. 207 (1910); Ballentine v. Nester, 350 Mo. 58, 164 S.W.2d 378 (1942).
[41] Air Quality Act of 1967, § 101, 81 Stat. 485.
[42] Air Quality Act of 1967, § 101(a)(2), 81 Stat. 485.
[43] Air Quality Act of 1967, § 101(b)(1), (2), (3), 81 Stat. 485. (Emphasis added.)
[44] The entire Chicago program is set out in a series of papers reproduced in *Hearings on H.R. 9509 and S. 780 Before the House Comm. on Interstate and Foreign Commerce*, 90th Cong., 1st Sess. 631-831 (1967). The first paper is Stanley, Air Resource Management in the Chicago Metropolitan Area—Planning for Clean Air. The Chicago legislation (CHICAGO MUNICIPAL CODE ch. 17), with additional explanatory articles, is reproduced in *Hearings on S. 780*, pt. 3, at 1901-92 (1967).
[45] *See* note 9 *supra*, and accompanying text.

Code and the New York City Administrative Code reveals basic similarities, it is pertinent to ask if the distinction between "Air Resource Management" and "Air Pollution Control" is real or just another example of the mysterious language of government experts.[46] I believe that the distinction is real, although it may have its greatest meaning in legal consequences, rather than in the quality of the air.

Two interlocking legal problems are presented when legislative purpose is defined in terms of efficient management of air resources rather than elimination of a public health emergency. The first problem is related to the fundamental question of whether government can dictate or limit the use of private property in the name of "greater efficiency for the general good," without having to pay "just compensation" to the private owner.[47] At least one of the frequently used tests of whether police power regulations have gone so far as to be a compensable government "taking" is whether the legislation simply restrains conduct harmful to others or whether its purpose is positive enrichment of the public at the expense of private property.[48] It has been forcibly argued that legislation of the latter type requires compensation.[49] Coerced sharing for the economic benefit of the majority raises serious questions of an unconstitutional "taking."[50] The "promotion of productive capacity" and "efficient management of resources" indicates that the legislative purpose is collective action for the general *economic* good. Government action of that nature may be socially justified, but compensation may be required for the "donation" of the private property for the public good.[51]

The second legal problem is presented by judicially developed restrictions peculiar to the enforcement of zoning and planning legislation. The gradual shifting of the purpose of air pollution legislation from strict public health concepts is further indicated by the procedure of establishing air quality control regions and air quality

---

[46] The elements of an "Air Resource Management" program are: (a) a continuing air-quality monitoring system; (b) a current and continuing emission inventory; (c) air-quality goals and standards based on air-quality criteria; (d) a thorough knowledge and use of the conditions influencing the transport of air pollutants; (e) urban planning decisions based on air qualilty as well as other environmental factors; (f) air pollution control decisions and resulting ordinances based upon air-quality information and relationships between air quality and effects; and (g) air-use plans. PUBLIC HEALTH SERVICE MANAGEMENT PROGRAM 1-2. Local "prevention and control" legislation starts at item (f), although in fact it usually is based upon information developed from techniques equivalent to (a) through (d).

[47] Michelman, *Property, Utility, and Fairness: Comments on the Ethical Foundations of "Just Compensation" Law*, 80 HARV. L. REV. 1165 (1967).

[48] Sax, *Takings and the Police Power*, 74 YALE L.J. 36, 48 (1964). *See* Mugler v. Kansas, 123 U.S. 623, 669 (1887); Miller v. Schoene, 276 U.S. 272 (1928).

[49] Dunham, *A Legal and Economic Basis for City Planning*, 58 COLUM. L. REV. 650, 663-69 (1958). *See* National Land & Inv. Co. v. Easttown Township, 410 Pa. 504, 529, 215 A.2d 597, 610-11 (1966); Morris County Land Improv. Co. v. Township of Parsippany-Troy Hills, 40 N.J. 539, 555-56, 193 A.2d 232, 241-42 (1963).

[50] Michelman, *supra* note 47.

[51] *See* authorities cited in note 49 *supra*. Various governmental levels have indirectly allowed for compensation, by providing for tax advantages for the person installing air pollution control equipment. A study of the subject is being conducted by federal agencies. *Hearings on H.R. 9509 and S. 780 Before the House Comm. on Interstate and Foreign Commerce*, 90th Cong., 1st Sess. 240 (1967).

standards for each region.[52] This approach has been used to divide New York State into four regional classifications based upon land use: industrial, commercial, residential, and rural.[53] Different air quality standards, generally related to the possibility of practical accomplishment, are established for each regional classification. Thus, rural areas are required to have the cleanest air, and industrial areas are permitted to have dirtier air.[54] While such a classification system projects ultimate "air quality goals," only the minimum levels common to all regions can be related to public health. If it is not unhealthy to breathe a certain quality of air in an industrial region, there is no *health* justification for requiring a stricter standard in a commercial area.

It must be recognized, therefore, that "Air Resource Management" is essentially planning and zoning, and legislation based on that approach may be analyzed and interpreted on that basis. If that is the result, the legislation will be subjected to the problems created by pre-existing non-conforming uses,[55] variances for "practical difficulty" or "unnecessary hardship,"[56] and the rule that zoning statutes are to be strictly construed.[57]

The Public Health Service's recommended legislation, in fact, provides that a variance may be granted upon a finding that "compliance with the regulation or order from which a variance is sought would produce serious hardship without a corresponding benefit or advantage to the people."[58] "Wide discretion in weighing

---

[52] Air Quality Act of 1967, §§ 107, 108, 81 Stat. 490. The country has now been divided into eight "Atmospheric Areas." 33 Fed. Reg. 548 (Jan. 16, 1968).

[53] NEW YORK STATE AMBIENT AIR QUALITY OBJECTIVES—CLASSIFICATIONS SYSTEM (N.Y. State Dep't of Health, 1964).

[54] "Thus, it is illogical to attempt one over-all set of quality objectives to apply to the entire State. It cannot be expected that the board can permit air in a clean area—for example, one used principally for high quality purposes such as recreation—to be degraded to a level that can be attainable in a highly populated and industrialized area. Nor would it be reasonable to expect a highly industrialized area to attain *economically* the level of air quality prevailing in the presently clean areas." *Id.* at § 500.2(c). (Emphasis added.)

[55] Village of Euclid v. Ambler Realty Co., 272 U.S. 365 (1926); Jones v. City of Los Angeles, 211 Cal. 304, 295 P. 14 (1930); People v. Miller, 304 N.Y. 105, 106 N.E.2d 34 (1952).

[56] See generally 2 C. RATHKOPF, THE LAW OF ZONING AND PLANNING ch. 45 (3d ed. 1957).

[57] 440 E. 102d Corp. v. Murdock, 285 N.Y. 298, 34 N.E.2d 329 (1941); Toulouse v. Board of Zoning Adjustment, 147 Me. 387, 87 A.2d 670 (1952); Modern Builders v. City of Tulsa, 197 Okla. 80, 168 P.2d 883 (1946). Public Health legislation will generally be liberally construed. See West Bronx Auto Paint Shop, Inc. v. City of New York, 33 Misc. 2d 29, 223 N.Y.S.2d 984, (1961), aff'd mem., 17 App. Div. 2d 772, 232 N.Y.S.2d 391 (1962), modified, 13 N.Y.S.2d 730, 241 N.Y.S.2d 861 (1963). A distinction between the constitutional limits of legislative zoning power and police power was emphasized in the recent important case of Udell v. Haas, 21 N.Y.2d 463, 288 N.Y.S.2d 888 (1968). Recognizing the heavy presumption of constitutional validity that attaches to police power legislation, basically subjecting it only to a "reasonableness" test, the court held that the zoning power was more limited and that zoning laws not only must meet standards of reasonableness but they must also be consistent with land use policy and a "comprehensive plan" worked out for the community as a whole prior to the adoption of the zoning law.

[58] Proposed Regulation XVI(C), PUBLIC HEALTH SERVICE MANAGEMENT PROGRAM 116. The search for a "corresponding benefit or advantage to the people" would seem to invite the legal argument that the regulation requires the payment of "just compensation." See text accompanying notes 47-51 *supra.*

the equities involved in each case"[59] is recommended, with the only limit being that "no variance may permit or authorize the maintenance of a nuisance, or a danger to public health or safety."[60]

Planning and zoning can be effective weapons for directing future land use and conduct. They are not effective to correct a situation that already exists.[61] As a result, an announced legislative purpose of "Air Resource Management" may inhibit the imposition of new corrective measures upon activities previously considered to be lawful.

III

LEGISLATIVE TECHNIQUES: STATE AND LOCAL CONTROL LEGISLATION

A. Smoke and Other Emission Limitations[62]

Most air pollution legislation has been directed toward limitations upon the density and opacity of smoke. Because of visibility, even where the control law is more extensive, most enforcement efforts have been directed against smoke.

The typical urban smoke control law simply limits the density, opacity, and length of time of smoke emission.[63] The limitations are often not further classified, and they apply to any equipment used in any operation. Such legislation has been sustained many times, and there is no question of its general constitutionality.[64]

In addition to smoke limitations, modern legislation may contain specific limita-

---

[59] Id.

[60] Proposed Regulation XVI(D), id. The use of the terms "nuisance" and "weighing the equities" may cause the legislation to be subjected to some of the limitations developed in the common law private and public nuisance cases.

[61] Dorn C. McGrath, Director of Metropolitan Area Analysis for the U.S. Dep't of Housing and Urban Development, has stated:

"Planning and zoning are fundamentally procedures employed by society to make the business of government, and primarily local units of government, more orderly in response to economic pressures of urban growth. Until enough people to constitute a critical mass of public opinion perceive the gravity of the air pollution problem, it is unlikely that needed remedial action will be taken. When this happens we must remember that neither planning nor zoning, especially zoning, is a very effective remedial procedure. Both can be very effective remedial procedures, however, provided that they have the backing of public commitment."

McGrath, Planning and Zoning—Can They Be Made to Work for Clean Air?, in PROCEEDINGS: THE THIRD NATIONAL CONFERENCE ON AIR POLLUTION 554-57 (Public Health Service Pub. No. 1649, 1967).

[62] The Air Quality Act of 1967, § 211(a), 81 Stat. 503, directs the Secretary of the Department of Health, Education, and Welfare to submit a comprehensive report "on the need for and effect of national emission standards for stationary sources" within two years.

[63] See, e.g., A.P.C. Reg. § 9.03; CHICAGO MUNICIPAL CODE § 17-23 (1967); Cleveland, Ohio, Ordinance 428-A-62, § 4.0502; Los Angeles County Control District, Regulation IV, Rule 50. The Ringelmann Smoke Chart is used as a basis for measurement. See note 26 supra.

[64] Northwestern Laundry v. Des Moines, 239 U.S. 486 (1916); City of Rochester v. Macauley-Fien Milling Co., 199 N.Y. 207 (1910). No distinction will be made if the limitations are promulgated as administrative regulations rather than legislation. West Bronx Auto Paint Shop, Inc. v. City of New York, 33 Misc. 2d 29, 223 N.Y.S.2d 934 (1961), aff'd mem., 17 App. Div. 2d 772, 232 N.Y.S.2d 391 (1962), modified, 13 N.Y.2d 730, 241 N.Y.S.2d 861 (1963); Consolidated Edison Co. v. Murtagh, 280 App. Div. 221, 112 N.Y.S.2d 681 (1952).

tions on the emission of sulfur dioxide, particulate matter,[65] and certain visible contaminants, as well as more general prohibitions. The specific limitations (usually referred to as "emission standards") are detailed and technical and are established according to classifications based upon the general nature of the equipment used and its operating size.[66] Accordingly, the New York City sulfur dioxide emission standard applies to equipment used in a manufacturing process,[67] and the standards for particulate matter are established according to whether the equipment is refuse burning equipment, fuel burning equipment, or manufacturing process equipment, and according to the capacity rating and heat input of fuel burning equipment and the process weight per hour of the manufacturing equipment.[68] The basis for establishing various classifications determined by the nature and size of the equipment used is obvious, for it is one of the most direct ways of determining the characteristics and amount of pollution from an installation. Such classifications have been recognized as valid.[69]

The establishment of emission standards is considered by many to represent the ideal legislative approach, as it theoretically leaves to the owner's discretion the precise type of equipment or fuel to be used. This is the general approach used by the federal government to limit emission from automobiles.[70]

Many legislative and administrative bodies, however, have long recognized that the bare setting of emission standards was not sufficient, and that fuels and equipment should be directly regulated. In enacting Local Law 14,[71] New York City recognized and followed this approach. Among the reasons cited were that there were too many smokestacks to permit constant observation for visible smoke violations, and that no practical scientific equipment was available which was capable of being placed and maintained in every smokestack to constantly record the amounts of invisible gases or particles being emitted.[72] In any event, a strict emission standard has the indirect result of requiring a change in either equipment or fuel in order to meet the standard,[73] for the emission must depend upon what substance goes in and what is done to it.

Particularly in New York, the seeming uncertainty permitted by smoke emission

---

[65] Defined as "Any liquid, other than water, or any solid which is so finely divided as to be capable of becoming wind-blown or being suspended in air." See N.Y. CITY ADMIN. CODE § 892-2.0 (Supp. 1967).

[66] See A COMPILATION OF SELECTED AIR POLLUTION EMISSION CONTROL REGULATIONS AND ORDINANCES (Public Health Service Pub. No. A65-34, 1965).

[67] A.P.C. Reg. § 9.07.

[68] Id. § 9.09.

[69] City of Rochester v. Macauley-Fien Milling Co., 199 N.Y. 207 (1910); Ballentine v. Nester, 350 Mo. 58, 164 S.W.2d 378 (1942).

[70] Air Quality Act of 1967, §§ 201-12, 81 Stat. 499. For the initial regulations, see 31 Fed. Reg. 5170 (1966).

[71] See note 9 supra.

[72] REPORT OF NEW YORK CITY COUNCIL COMMITTEE ON BUILDINGS ON INTRO. No. 49 (N.Y. City Record, at 2621).

[73] This obvious result was particularly recognized in Huron Portland Cement Co. v. Detroit, 362 U.S. 440 (1960), and Northwestern Laundry v. Des Moines, 239 U.S. 486 (1916).

standards alone has enabled some courts, engaged in determining "reasonableness" for due process purposes, to indulge in amateur engineering analyses and declare that the statute must be applied "reasonably" to avoid compelling an "impossible" or "impractical" result or punishment for an "unavoidable necessity." Stretching the concept of "reasonableness" beyond an inquiry into whether the exercise of the police power is arbitrary to whether application of the statute appears "fair" or "practical" in a particular case, is an abandonment of the principles of judicial restraint in favor of flexible private nuisance concepts.

The first of these "rule of reason" cases involved an early smoke control statute which forbade the emission of "any smoke or gas."[74] The extreme prohibition led the court into a simplified engineering analysis that took judicial notice of the "fact" that no fire could be burned without either smoke or gas. The analysis led to the conclusion that "[i]t cannot be supposed that the legislature intended to require the impossible, or to close every furnace in our city for the promotion of a better atmosphere."[75]

If the court had been content with the relatively narrow issue of literal impossibility of compliance, the case would have been unimportant, as the statute was soon amended to prevent "dense smoke." The court, however, went further and expounded:

> It appears further that there is not known any device that can accomplish the absolute combustion of smoke, and that the defendant has adopted a standard pattern of construction; nor does it appear that there is any better device, of tested standing in commercial use, that the defendant has omitted to avail itself of.[76]

The court's general attitude can be observed from the following dicta, sure to bring a sad smile to the face of today's city dwellers:

> We have been so accustomed until lately to the clear atmosphere of our city, as to regard the escape of smoke as constituting in itself a nuisance, forgetting that this is one of but few manufacturing centers where the pall of smoke is not accepted as a necessary incident.[77]

The case was followed by *People v. New York Central & H.R.R. Co.*,[78] which dismissed a conviction for the issuance of dense smoke on the ground that the prosecution had shown no evidence of an excess of smoke over that "necessary" for operation and no evidence that any other method could produce less smoke.

In *People v. New York Edison Co.*,[79] the court acknowledged that smoke control was a proper area for restrictive legislation, but it held:

---

[74] Dep't of Health v. Philip & William Ebling Brewing Co., 38 Misc. 537, 78 N.Y.S. 13 (1902). *But see Ex Parte* Junqua, 10 Cal. App. 602, 103 P. 159 (1909).

[75] 38 Misc. at 540, 78 N.Y.S. at 15.

[76] 38 Misc. at 538, 78 N.Y.S. at 14.

[77] 38 Misc. at 541, 78 N.Y.S. at 16.

[78] 159 App. Div. 329, 144 N.Y.S. 699 (1913).

[79] 159 App. Div. 786, 144 N.Y.S. 707 (1913).

The section should have a reasonable construction which would preclude a conviction for a mere accidental or occasional momentary discharge of dense smoke, but which would insure the prevention of a continuous discharge or a discharge at intervals of large volumes of smoke, such as is caused by the use of soft coal.[80]

The suggestion of a defense of "impossibility" or "unavoidable momentary discharge" lay dormant from 1913 until the 1939 case of *People v. Cunard White Star, Ltd.*[81] That case held the dense smoke emission statute to be an unreasonable obstruction to foreign commerce when applied to a steamship, unless "its scope is limited to prohibition of the discharge of smoke, avoidable by the use of modern appliances and of methods which are practicable."[82]

The facts showed that the S.S. Queen Mary was equipped with modern appliances, but that dense smoke occurred when cold boilers were being started and when demands for steam fluctuated as the ship was entering or leaving port. The prosecution claimed that it was no defense that the steamship was constructed and operated so as to make continued violations a "necessary incident" to the defendant's business. The court answered as follows:

That might be true if construction or operation is improper or if change there were practical. Here, however, there is no suggestion that either operation or construction is not in conformity with the highest standards or that occasional emission of smoke, for a few minutes on the day a vessel enters or leaves port, could be avoided by change which would not unreasonably obstruct the operation of the steamship.[83]

The key phrase, of course, is "change which would not unreasonably obstruct the operation." The dissent claimed that while the defendant's practice of firing the boilers was cheaper, dense smoke could be avoided by firing one boiler at a time.

In *People v. Murray*,[84] the defendant claimed that everything reasonably possible was being done to control smoke at its power plant and that occasional dense smoke was unavoidable, especially when tests of coal were being conducted.[85] The court found, however, that regular operations could be maintained without dense smoke; and as to the "unavoidable necessity" of boiler tests, it stated:

I cannot subscribe to this contention. If the generation of dense smoke by all the power and industrial plants in the City of New York when making tests of coal comes within the category of unavoidable smoke, then we are indeed giving legal sanction to a smoke condition which would be a menace to the health and welfare of the inhabitants of the city. In this situation, economy and efficiency should be subordinated to the general welfare. . . . It would seem reasonable to expect that coal tests could be made outside of New York City under conditions

[80] 159 App. Div. 795, 144 N.Y.S. at 714.
[81] 280 N.Y. 413 (1939).
[82] *Id.* at 417.
[83] *Id.* at 420.
[84] 174 Misc. 251, 19 N.Y.S.2d 902 (1940).
[85] Approximately twelve weeks per year were allegedly used for testing coal.

which duplicate those at defendant's plant. At any rate it rests with science to devise satisfactory and efficient methods of testing coal which do not affect the general health.[86]

The court then went on to limit the "unavoidable" concept to instances not based upon economy or efficiency, but caused by specific reasons beyond the defendant's control.

In *People v. Long Island R.R.*,[87] a claim of "unavoidable discharge" was offered when a coal strike cut off the regular source of low volatile coal and the defendant used reserves of high volatile coal, causing dense smoke. The court rejected the defense on the ground that low volatile coal could be purchased elsewhere, and held that the defense only applied to a momentary discharge and not to a continuing situation.

A series of more recent New York cases indicates a possible swing back toward the theory that if the installation contains properly operated "modern" control equipment and smoke of a prohibited density nevertheless results, then its emission is "unavoidable" and safe from prosecution.[88]

In *People v. Savage*,[89] the issue involved the huge Donner-Hanna coke plant in Buffalo. The court relied upon the claim of "unavoidable necessity" as interpreted by the *Cunard White Star* case and declared:

> It appears from the evidence that the method of storing its coal supply and the precautions taken by the Donner-Hanna plant to eliminate or prevent dust from the coal pile are exceptional in the industry and greatly beyond what is done in most plants.
>
> Also that all its coal and coke piles, ovens, cars, quenchers, buildings, structures, equipment and materials, and methods of care and operation is modern up-to-date and fully in accord with the best coke plants in the coke industry throughout the United States.
>
> The testimony justifies a finding that there is no known method, device or apparatus known to the industry or employed in any other plant in the United States to eliminate or reduce smoke, dust and fumes, or to alleviate this condition, which is not employed and in use at the Donner-Hanna plant, and that its operation, methods and procedures are in accord with the best operational methods employed by the best plants in the industry.[90]

The court held the Buffalo dense smoke statute unconstitutional when applied to the Donner-Hanna plant.

A defense that consists mainly of "My plant is as good or better than anyone

---

[86] 174 Misc. at 260-61, 19 N.Y.S. 2d at 910-11.

[87] 31 N.Y.S.2d 537 (1941).

[88] People v. Oswald, 1 Misc. 2d 726, 116 N.Y.S.2d 50 (1952); People v. Savage, 1 Misc. 2d 337, 148 N.Y.S.2d 191, *aff'd mem.*, 309 N.Y. 941, 132 N.E.2d 313 (1955); People v. Peterson, 31 Misc. 2d 738, 226 N.Y.S.2d 1004 (1961).

[89] 1 Misc. 2d 337, 148 N.Y.S.2d 191, *aff'd mem.*, 309 N.Y. 941, 132 N.E.2d 313 (1955). *See* note 14 *supra* and accompanying text.

[90] 1 Misc. 2d at 340, 148 N.Y.S.2d at 194.

else's plant" should be inadequate in the face of a flat prohibition in a public health statute. Certainly the engineering evaluation of equipment is more a function of the legislature than the courts. It is both conceivable and understandable for one city to require a standard which is stricter than other cities and to require its citizens to do better than those in cities that appear to care or need less.

State v. Mundet Cork Corp.[91] did not reject the theory of "unavoidable necessity" but held that where laboratory experiments had indicated success, the scientific techniques must be actually attempted and have failed before a claim of "impossibility" or "unavoidable necessity" can be considered. Several cases have flatly rejected the defense of "unavoidable necessity."[92] As explained in the early case of *Moses v. United States*:[93]

> The defendant offered evidence tending to show that they had attached to their furnace, at the time, the best known smoke-consuming appliance; but that neither it nor any other, then known, would prevent the emission of such smoke for a brief period upon each occasion that fire might be started, or the furnaces "cooled," or "raked down," provided that soft bituminous coal be the fuel consumed.
>
> That there may be no smoke-consuming appliances that will under all circumstances, prevent the nuisance, is not a matter of relevance. The facts concerning them were presumably within the knowledge of Congress also when it took action; and no provision has been made for their use. The use of smokeless fuel instead may have been expressly contemplated.

Huron Portland Cement Co. v. Detroit,[94] involved a fact situation similar in many ways to that in the *Cunard White Star* case. The shipowner sought to enjoin enforcement of Detroit's smoke emission ordinance. The ship operated pursuant to a federal coast guard certificate which specified and approved the ship's equipment for use on navigable waters. The ship used hand-fired boilers, which, when cleaned, emitted smoke in violation of the Detroit ordinance. In order to meet Detroit's smoke standard, structural alterations were necessary and a different type of boiler had to be installed.

The court found the elimination of air pollution to be a valid purpose for the exercise of a police power determined by Congress to be the primary responsibility of state and local governments. It held that since the vessel was not unconditionally excluded from the Port of Detroit, there was no undue burden upon interstate commerce or federal pre-emption of the field. The defense of "unavoidable necessity"

---

[91] State v. Mundet Cork Corp., 8 N.J. 359, 86 A.2d 1, *cert. denied*, 344 U.S. 819 (1952).

[92] Moses v. United States, 16 App. D.C. 428 (1900); People v. Detroit White Lead Works, 82 Mich. 471, 46 N.W. 735 (1890); Ballentine v. Nester, 350 Mo. 58, 164 S.W.2d (1942). The recent case of Dep't of Health v. Owens-Corning Fiberglas Corp., 242 A.2d 21, 36 (N.J. Super. 1968) upholding recent New Jersey legislation, stated: "We hold that the doctrine of unavoidable necessity is not available to defendant and is not viable in the context of the Air Pollution Code."

[93] 16 App. Div. 428, 440 (1900).

[94] 362 U.S. 440 (1960).

was not even discussed, although the vessel's boilers had to be completely replaced. As expressed by the Michigan court in the same case: "All it costs is money."[95]

Of course, legislation may itself allow a defense equivalent to "impossibility" or "unavoidable necessity." The Air Quality Act of 1967 establishes the following judicial standards in an abatement action:

> The court, giving due consideration to the practicability of complying with such standards as may be applicable and to the physical and economic feasibility of securing abatement of any pollution proved, shall have jurisdiction to enter such judgment, and orders enforcing such judgment, as the public interest and the equities of the case may require.[96]

The administrative enforcement proceedings of the New York State law permit similar defenses of "impossibility, impracticability or financial inability."[97]

While the technique of controlling air pollution by emission standards alone may face the difficulties of an occasional defense of "impossibility" or "unavoidable necessity," the cases sustaining such defenses violate traditional principles of judicial restraint. In the absence of a legislative provision allowing such extremely flexible defenses, the courts should refrain from challenging the technical foundations for the legislative action. It would nevertheless appear desirable for legislation to combine emission standards with more particular equipment requirements so as to avoid judicial relaxation on the grounds that the equipment in use seems to be the best commercially available.

B. Operating Certificates as a Supervisory Technique: Regulation of Equipment

Perhaps the dominant technique of the 1966 New York City law is the regulation and supervision of equipment by the issuance of operating certificates. Under the previous law, most new construction required the filing of plans and a permit before installation and issuance of an operating certificate before operation.[98] Permit systems have been widely used to assure that new construction incorporates the best technical advances and there would appear to be little constitutional question as to the general use of this control technique.[99]

The 1966 New York City law considerably extended the system, by requiring that much *existing* fuel burning equipment, most *existing* refuse burning equipment, all *existing* manufacturing processes emitting a sulfur compound, and certain portable equipment, obtain operating certificates in compliance with various time

---

[95] 355 Mich. 227, 234, 93 N.W.2d 888, 892 (1959).

[96] Air Quality Act of 1967, § 108(h), 81 Stat. 496.

[97] New York Public Health Law § 1282(3). The "hardship" variance provisions of the Public Health Service's recommended legislation would seem to allow the same type of defense. *See* text accompanying note 58 *supra*.

[98] N.Y. CITY ADMIN. CODE § 892-4.0 (Supp. 1967); A.P.C. Reg. §§ 5.11, 5.17. In many instances technical criteria detailing the minimum requirements for the granting of installation permits were issued. A.P.C. Reg. § 511(b).

[99] *See* Northwestern Laundry v. Des Moines, 239 U.S. 486 (1916).

deadlines.[100] In the case of existing fuel burning and refuse burning equipment, certain improvements are specifically required before an operating certificate will be issued, and in all cases, the equipment must incorporate the best advances in the art of air pollution control.

It is, of course, pertinent to examine the constitutionality of requiring lawfully operated equipment to be upgraded in order to continue to operate lawfully.

In the leading case of *Hadacheck v. Los Angeles*,[101] the ordinance in question prohibited the operation of any brickyard within certain limits of Los Angeles. The defendant had begun brickmaking prior to enactment of the ordinance on land that had not then been a part of the city. The area later became predominantly residential and was annexed to the city. The ordinance was based upon the city's power to halt the emission of fumes, smoke, soot, steam and dust resulting from the brickmaking. Referring to the police power, the Supreme Court declared:

> It is to be remembered that we are dealing with one of the most essential powers of government, one that is the least limitable. It may, indeed, seem harsh in its exercise, usually is on some individual, but the imperative necessity for its existence precludes any limitation upon it when not exerted arbitrarily. *A vested interest cannot be asserted against it because of conditions once obtaining.* [Citation omitted.] *To so hold would preclude development and fix a city forever in its primitive conditions. There must be progress, and if in its march private interests are in the way they must yield to the good of the community.*[102]

In *Health Department v. The Rector etc. of Trinity Church*,[103] legislation required running water to be made available on each floor of a tenement house. The argument was made that the requirement could not legally apply to pre-existing buildings. The court rejected the argument and held:

> Anyone in a crowded city who desires to erect a building is subject at every turn almost to the exactions of the law in regard to provisions for health, for safety from fire and for other purposes. He is not permitted to build of certain materials within certain districts because though the materials may be inexpensive they are inflammable, and he must build in a certain manner . . . in carrying out all these various acts the owner is subjected to an expense much greater than would have been necessary to have completed his building if not compelled to complete it in the manner, of the materials and under the circumstances prescribed by various acts of the legislature. . . . I do not see that the principle is substantially altered where the case is one of an existing building and it is to be subjected to certain alterations for the purpose of rendering it either less exposed to the danger from fires or its occupants more secure from disease.[104]

---

[100] N.Y. CITY ADMIN. CODE §§ 892-4.2, 4.3 (modified and amended in 1968), 4.4, 4.5 (Supp. 1967).
[101] 239 U.S. 394 (1915).
[102] *Id.* at 410. (Emphasis added.) *See also* People v. Detroit White Lead Works, 82 Mich. 471, 46 N.W. 735 (1890).
[103] 145 N.Y. 32 (1895).
[104] *Id.* at 44-45.

The principle has been recently endorsed as follows:

It is clearly settled that "in no case does the owner of property acquire immunity against the exercise of the police power because he constructed it in full compliance with existing laws."[105]

While it would therefore appear to be settled that a challenge to the "retroactive" provisions of the New York City law on the grounds of prior lawful operation would be unsuccessful, "Air Resource Management" legislation containing such provisions would be vulnerable to attack. This vulnerability exists because the latter is based upon planning to pre-existing, non-conforming uses which would seem to prevent "retroactive" correction or forced upgrading of equipment.[106]

Naturally any required upgrading of equipment will result in an owner's expenditure of funds. Since the legislature can inquire into the matter of prospective costs, the usual rule is that questions of cost are left by the courts to legislative discretion.[107] Some cases have stated in dicta, however, that the cost of improvements required by legislation must be "reasonable." In the *Trinity Church* case, the court, after holding that the law applied to pre-existing buildings, proposed:

In both cases the object must be within some of the acknowledged purposes of the police power and such purpose must be possible of accomplishment *at some reasonable cost*, regard being had to all the surrounding circumstances.[108]

This reference to "reasonable cost" has been recently repeated by the New York Court of Appeals.[109] Such references are another instance of confusing the use of the word "reasonable" in the due process test of arbitrariness, with its application in private nuisance cases.

In the case of *Adamec v. Post*,[110] the New York Court of Appeals followed the retroactivity principle of the *Trinity Church* case, but went on to reject the "cost" challenge as follows:

The imposition of the cost of the required alterations as a condition of the continued use of antiquated buildings for multiple dwellings may cause hardship to the plaintiffs and other owners of "old law tenements" but, in a proper case, the Legislature has the power to enact provisions reasonably calculated to promote the common good even though the result be hardship to the individual. . . .

Certainly the proportion of cost of the alteration to the assessed or even market value of the old law tenement can be no criterion of whether the Legislature has acted reasonably in requiring the alteration. . . .

---

[105] Engelshar v. Jacobs, 5 N.Y.2d 370, 375, 157 N.E.2d 626, 628, 180 N.Y.S.2d 640, 643, *cert. denied*, 360 U.S. 902 (1959). *See also* Dankner v. City of New York, 20 Misc. 2d 557, 194 N.Y.S.2d 975 (1959).
[106] *See* cases cited note 55 *supra*.
[107] Northwestern Laundry v. Des Moines, 239 U.S. 486 (1916); Sittner v. Seattle, 62 Wash. 2d 834, 384 P.2d 859 (1963); Huron Portland Cement Co. v. City of Detroit, 362 U.S. 440 (1960).
[108] 145 N.Y. at 45. (Emphasis added.)
[109] Engelshar v. Jacobs, 5 N.Y.2d 370, 157 N.E.2d 626, 184 N.Y.S.2d 640, *cert. denied*, 360 U.S. 902 (1959).
[110] 273 N.Y. 250 (1937).

Because the State has tolerated slum dwellings in the past it is not precluded from taking appropriate steps to end them in the future.[111]

The only time that the cost of complying with public health legislation should be a factor for judicial consideration is when standards are so completely arbitrary and oppressive as to be a patent legislative disguise for requiring absolute termination of the basic activity.[112] The fact that economic hardship in a particular instance may cause a termination of activity will not sustain a constitutional challenge.[113]

When the question was recently raised by a municipality contesting a water pollution classification, the New York Court of Appeals declared:

Appellants contend that if the fiscal and economic aspects of water purification cannot properly be raised at the time of classification, then they can never influence a particular classification, since the municipality is legally bound to abide by the classification made, subject only to such deferment as the Board may allow. The obvious answer to this is that the Legislature well knew that a comprehensive water purification program would impose a financial burden upon the municipalities of the State, but determined, by enacting the Pollution Control Act, that the pressing need for water purification outweighed any financial hardships incident thereto.[114]

As long as the legislature studies the costs involved and does not expressly provide for the issue to be considered in a particular case, a reopening of the inquiry by a court would appear to be an unjustified interference with the legislative power.[115]

Requirements for operating certificates for existing equipment necessarily involve numerous classifications. These classifications must meet the constitutional requirements of the equal protection clause. Separate classifications are established in New York City for fuel burning equipment using residual fuel oil, fuel burning equipment using coal, refuse burning equipment and manufacturing equipment emitting sulfur compounds. Each of the classifications is based either on the use of the equipment, the fuel used in the equipment, or the nature of the emission.

The St. Louis ordinance challenged in *Ballentine v. Nester*,[116] approached that city's smoke problem by regulating the kinds of coal that could be used and the types of furnaces in which certain coals could be burned. The court maintained:

We hold that as Section 5340, supra, classified coal to be used according to its ash, sulfur, and volatile contents, and the type of furnace in which these various classi-

---

[111] *Id.* at 259-60.

[112] Lawton v. Steele, 152 U.S. 133 (1894).

[113] Sittner v. Seattle, 62 Wash. 2d 834, 384 P.2d 859 (1963). In State v. Mundet Cork Corp., 8 N.J. 359, 86 A.2d 1, *cert. denied*, 344 U.S. 819 (1952), the court's inquiry was as to whether the expense of compliance was "insuperable."

[114] Town of Waterford v. Water Pollution Control Board, 5 N.Y.2d 171, 180, 156 N.E.2d 427, 431, 182 N.Y.S.2d 785, 791 (1959).

[115] *See* text accompanying notes 96, 97 *supra*. A court will, however, always have open to it the question of whether the legislation constitutes a "taking" without just compensation.

[116] 350 Mo. 58, 164 S.W.2d 378 (1942).

fications of coal may be burned bears a reasonable relation to the dense smoke nuisance, the ordinance is not an arbitrary classification as it applies equally to all users of coal of the same classification.[117]

Accordingly, there would appear to be little chance of a successful challenge to operating certificate requirements such as those in New York City, on the basis of a denial of equal protection of the law.

C. Regulation of Fuels

Among the control techniques receiving the most attention are direct limitations upon the kind and nature of fuels permitted to be burned, even in otherwise correctly operated equipment.[118]

The first known direct limitations upon fuel use were, as might be expected, limitations on the use of various coals. In 1895, the then city of Brooklyn passed a statute which provided, in part:

> No factory, engine-room or electrical station shall use what is known as soft coal for fuel in the furnaces of such factories, engine-room or electrical station within a radius of four miles of the city hall in the city of Brooklyn. . . .[119]

It was quickly concluded that the statute was a valid exercise of the police power, and a conviction for violation was upheld.[120] The statute was later held to prevent the use of a mixture containing only twenty per cent soft coal regardless of whether the mixture would burn without smoke.[121]

The main thrust of the pioneering St. Louis legislation consisted of direct limitations on the volatile matter, sulfur, and ash contents of coal, as well as limitations upon the type of equipment to be used. In *Ballentine v. Nester*, the constitutional challenge was based upon a claim that the statute was not a bona fide health regulation because it regulated the *manner* of burning, rather than the gases or particles emitted.[122] In upholding the statute, the court declared:

> There can be no doubt that under the above sections that the legislative department of the City of St. Louis has the power to abate the smoke nuisance in the city by any reasonable method. To accomplish that object, it enacted Section 5340, supra. This section sought to obtain that object by regulating the kind of coal that can be burned in that city. . . . The public policy or wisdom of a regulation in regard to the use of soft coal is for the legislature to determine and not the

---

[117] *Id.* at 72, 164 S.W.2d at 383.

[118] N.Y. CITY ADMIN. CODE § 893-1.0(a) (Supp. 1967); New York State Rules and Regulations, Title 10 (Health), Chapter IV, Subchapter A, Part 200 (effective April 18, 1968); Los Angeles County Air Pollution Control District, Regulation IV, Rules 62, 62.1; St. Louis, Mo., Ordnance 50163, § 11(a).

[119] Ch. 322, Laws of 1895, City of Brooklyn, New York.

[120] City of Brooklyn v. Nassau Electric R.R., 44 App. Div. 462, 61 N.Y. 33 (1899).

[121] City of New York v. H.W. Johns-Manville Co., 89 App. Div. 449, 85 N.Y.S. 757 (1903).

[122] For proof of the versatility of the legal profession, see Oswald v. Christy, 112 N.Y.S.2d 913 (1952), where a challenge to an emission standard system was based upon the statute's failure to directly regulate the fuel and manner of burning.

courts. . . . The courts have no power to determine the merits of conflicting theories, nor to declare that a particular method of advancing and protecting the public is superior or likely to insure greater safety or better protection than others.[123]

In *State v. Chicago, M. & St. Paul Ry.*,[124] the challenge was to a Minneapolis ordinance limiting the volatile content of coal used in certain types of engines. The limitation effectively prohibited the use of soft coal in those engines. The court upheld the statute and stated:

A legislative requirement that locomotives shall burn coal other than the kind that produces the smoke nuisance is directly and substantially related to the prevention of annoyance and discomfort incident to dense smoke. The public policy or wisdom of such a prohibition is for the Legislature to determine.

The courts cannot undertake to decide whether the means adopted by the Legislature are the only means, or even the best means, possible to attain the end sought. . . .

Counsel for defendant urges that careful firing in locomotives will prevent the nuisance. Existing conditions suggest strongly either that such is not the fact, or that careful firing cannot, in general practice, be obtained.[125]

The 1966 New York City law prohibits the burning of soft coal for heating purposes and permits other uses of soft coal (primarily for the generation of steam and electricity) only if particulate control equipment of a certified ninety-nine per cent efficiency is installed.[126]

In view of the many instances of judicial recognition of the relationship between bituminous coal and air pollution and the obvious basis for the separate classifications of soft coal used for space heating and soft coal used for other purposes, a constitutional challenge to New York's restrictions on the use of bituminous coal would appear to have little chance of success.

Another controversial provision of the New York City law established a new schedule of limitations upon the sulfur content of coal and residual fuel oil.[127] The limits resulted primarily from a study of serious health episodes in New York City and elsewhere.[128]

Since both coal and oil vary in natural sulfur content, and since it is obvious that other fuels can be substituted for high sulfur fuel oil and high sulfur coal, the primary issue involved in the application of the sulfur limitations is economics. High sulfur residual fuel oil and high sulfur coal command the cheapest price

---

[123] 350 Mo. 58, 70, 164 S.W.2d 378, 382 (1942).

[124] 114 Minn. 122, 130 N.W. 545 (1911).

[125] *Id.* at 127-28, 130 N.W. at 547.

[126] N.Y. CITY ADMIN. CODE § 893-2.0 (Supp. 1967). Previous law limited the volatile content of coal used in mechanically fed equipment not equipped with a combustion controller. *See* People v. Prince Jagendorf Greene, Inc., 7 N.Y.2d 42, 163 N.E.2d 323, N.Y.S.2d 498 (1959).

[127] N.Y. CITY ADMIN. CODE § 893-1.0(a) (Supp. 1967).

[128] Interim report of New York City Council Special Committee, in *Hearings on S. 780*, pt. 3, at 1500.

among today's commonly used fuels. Fuel oil can be further refined so as to reduce the sulfur content; the question is solely one of competition.[129]

Some aspects of damage from sulfur were recognized in the following 1952 dicta:

> Bituminous coal contains from one percent to two percent of sulfur, most of which is evolved in the gaseous form but some is found in the soot. Its sticky nature causes it to adhere tenuously to objects with which it comes into contact and since it usually contains free sulfuric acids, it has a destructive action upon stone, fabrics, metals and vegetation apart from the widespread dirt and discoloration which it causes. Aside from the damage it causes, it does in addition entail greatly increased expense in general maintenance, washing, cleaning and artificial lighting. These damages are further made visible when we note the contrast between gardens maintained in the city with those in the country.[130]

The fact that many experiments are now being conducted for methods of removing sulfur dioxide from the stack[131] led to a novel provision in the New York City law. It permits an exemption from the sulfur limitations for an operator whose equipment has control apparatus capable of continuously preventing the emission of sulfur dioxide greater than would be the result of the direct sulfur content limitations.[132] Continuous monitoring equipment and other detailed safeguards are required. This alternative was established even though no existing method was considered economically feasible for commercial operation in this country. Systems for stack gas removal are in limited operation in England and Germany and detailed scientific and mechanical information is available. This exemption provision was obviously designed to stimulate industry into channeling research and development efforts toward new methods of air pollution control. There would seem to be no legal objection to this type of legislation since it is in the form of a permissive exemption, and the standards required are specifically described.

Despite the many technical advances that can be expected as attention to the problem of air pollution increases, the basic control technique of directly limiting the type or content of fuels will probably dominate for many years.

D. Regulation of Equipment Operators

The New York City law requires instruction for all operators of fuel burning equipment using residual oil and all operators of refuse burning equipment.[133] The completion of a course of instructions in air pollution control techniques is required and a certificate evidencing completion of the course is required to be posted adjacent to the equipment. The course of instruction may be maintained by educational insti-

---

[129] Id. at 1522-23.

[130] People v. Consolidated Edison Co., 116 N.Y.S.2d 555, 560 (1952).

[131] Interim report of the New York City Council Special Committee, in *Hearings on S. 780*, pt. 3, at 1523.

[132] N.Y. CITY ADMIN. CODE §§ 893-1.0(b)-(e) (Supp. 1967).

[133] Id. § 896-1.0.

tutions, industry or labor organizations; but the course must be approved by the City's administering agency.

Since the competence and knowledge of operators of equipment directly related to air pollution affect the control of air pollution, the constitutionality of requiring a program of instruction appears certain. As stated in *Wasmuth v. Allen*:[134] "The imposition of a new requirement for the continued practice of a profession previously carried on without the need of such requirements does not violate the Constitution."

As other statutory provisions require the installation of new devices for residual oil burning equipment and refuse burning equipment, the requirement that operators receive instruction in the use and purpose of this equipment is related to the "continuing regulation and correction" envisaged by New York City's control program.[135]

E. Direct Prohibition of Specific Activities

The complete prohibition of an activity detrimental to the public health has long been a standard legislative technique.[136] New York City, for example, has long-standing regulations banning such business activities as the burning of bones and the skinning of animals.[137]

The direct abatement of a particular activity is subject to the same constitutional limitations as other air pollution control techniques.[138] The legislation may be general, such as a complete ban of all open burning activities,[139] or may have reference to a specific industry.[140] Legislative intention to flatly prohibit an activity should be clear and specific. An attempt to achieve the same object, by establishing performance standards not truly designed to be achieved, will inevitably involve a defense of "impossibility."[141]

F. Enforcement Techniques

The enforcement techniques utilized by state and local legislation are as varied as the methods of creating air pollution. Criminal sanctions are the most frequently used enforcement approach with violation of any provision of the law or regula-

---

[134] 14 N.Y.2d 391, 398, 200 N.E.2d 756, 759-60, 252 N.Y.S.2d 65, 70 (1964).

[135] West Bronx Auto Paint Shop, Inc. v. City of New York, 33 Misc. 2d 29, 223 N.Y.S.2d 984 (1961), *aff'd mem.*, 17 App. Div. 2d 772, 232 N.Y.S.2d 391 (1962), *modified*, 13 N.Y.2d 730, 241 N.Y.S.2d 861 (1963).

[136] *See* 3 BLACKSTONE, COMMENTARIES 215 (16th ed. 1825).

[137] N.Y. CITY HEALTH CODE § 135.21.

[138] Lawton v. Steele, 152 U.S. 133 (1894). *See also* Hadacheck v. Los Angeles, 239 U.S. 394 (1915).

[139] N.Y. CITY ADMIN. CODE § C19-148.0 (Supp. 1967); CHICAGO MUNICIPAL CODE §§ 17-30, 17-31 (1967); PUBLIC HEALTH SERVICE MANAGEMENT PROGRAM 99-100. *Cf.* Pennsylvania v. Toth, 189 Pa. Super. 552, 152 A.2d 284 (1959); Shearing v. City of Rochester, 51 Misc. 2d 436, 273 N.Y.S.2d 464 (1966).

[140] *See* Highway 100 Auto Wreckers, Inc. v. City of West Allis, 6 Wis. 2d 637, 96 N.W.2d 85 (1959) (burning of junked automobiles).

[141] *See* text accompanying notes 74-90 *supra*.

tions being a misdemeanor or an offense for which criminal penalties may be imposed in a criminal court proceeding.[142] While the time-honored method of abating a nuisance is the securing of a civil injunction, most legislatures have apparently determined that such a procedure is not fast enough for effective air pollution control.[143]

Although criminal sanctions are used, criminal intent is not necessary for conviction. As described in *People v. Consolidated Edison Co.*:[144]

> In an action as the present one, good faith is no defense. The criminal intent of mens rea essential to a conviction in the case of true crimes need neither be alleged or proven with respect to violations of municipal ordinances which forbid the commission of certain acts as contra y to the general welfare and make them malum prohibitum. Proof or admission of the doing of the forbidden thing, regardless of intent, good faith or wilfulness, must bring a conviction.

Questions of evidence in air pollution control enforcement cases are no different than those presented in any other case.[145] The use of mechanical equipment to measure smoke only goes to the weight of the evidence, and electronic smoke indicator records may in one case be insufficient to overcome the observations of inspectors,[146] while in another case they may be sufficient.[147]

In addition to usual enforcement procedure, summary powers to shut down offending equipment may be granted, primarily to deal with emergency situations.[148]

Many statutes employ initial administrative enforcement techniques.[149] The use of a permit requirement system is the most typical administrative enforcement method. Final enforcement, of course, must rest with the courts in either criminal or civil injunctive proceedings.

CONCLUSION

The varied and technical nature of air pollution has caused legislatures to adopt multiple and varying legal techniques in an attempt to achieve realistic control. Experience has shown that most carefully drafted public health related control techniques are within the legal boundaries established by the U.S. Constitution.

[142] N.Y. CITY ADMIN. CODE § 894-3.0 (Supp. 1967); CHICAGO MUNICIPAL CODE § 17-79 (1967); CAL. HEALTH & SAFETY CODE §§ 24253, 24277-82 (West 1967).

[143] For the Los Angeles, California experience, see Kennedy, *The Mechanics of Legislative and Regulatory Action*, in PROCEEDINGS: NATIONAL CONFERENCE ON AIR POLLUTION 306 (Public Health Service Pub. No. 1022, 1962). *But see* Leone v. Paris, 43 Misc. 2d 442, 251 N.Y.S.2d 277 (1964), *modified*, 24 App. Div. 2d 508, 261 N.Y.S.2d 656 (1965) (water pollution).

[144] 116 N.Y.S.2d 555, 560 (1952).

[145] *See* People v. Prince Jagendorf Greene, Inc., 7 N.Y.2d 42, 163 N.E.2d 325, 194 N.Y.S.2d 498 (1959).

[146] *See, e.g.*, People v. Murray, 174 Misc. 250, 19 N.Y.S.2d 902 (1940).

[147] *See, e.g.*, City of Chicago v. Butler Bros., 350 Ill. App. 550, 113 N.E.2d 210 (1953).

[148] *See* N.Y. CITY ADMIN. CODE § 892-6.0 (Supp. 1967); CHICAGO MUNICIPAL CODE §§ 17-75, 17-76 (1967).

[149] *E.g.*, N.Y. State Public Health Law § 1282; Air Quality Act of 1967, § 108, 81 Stat. 491.

The legal tools are available for the job that has to be done, although no one could honestly claim that effective air pollution control has been achieved. Modern and comprehensive state and local prevention and control statutes are relatively new, and their economically harsh effects have deterred dynamic enforcement. The frustrations incident to enforcement should not, however, cause a change of direction away from the present control techniques to the more remote aims of planning and zoning legislation. Centralized desires for efficient utilization and management of resources are tightly circumscribed by the protections of the free enterprise system guaranteed by the Constitution. The efficiencies of "cost-effectiveness analyses"[150] as interpreted by government, cannot be imposed upon private property without just compensation.

Air pollution is a current public health problem. The need for elimination of that problem *now* provides a sound constitutional basis for corrective legislation. The need for future land-use planning, no matter how genuine, should not be allowed to dominate the purposes and directions of state and local legislative efforts to prevent and control air pollution at its source.

---

[150] Air Quality Act of 1967, § 107(c), 81 Stat. 491.

INCENTIVES TO AIR POLLUTION CONTROL

PAUL H. GERHARDT[*]

"Should it be the carrot or the stick?" That is the metaphorical question economists often ask about pollution abatement programs. In the debate which has ensued between economists, legislators, administrators, and businessmen, adversaries have cloaked the substantive issues in a shroud of public rhetoric. It is the purpose of this article to help cut away this shroud, and to lay out the basic policy alternatives available to those who would control air pollution.

I

WHAT IS THE PROBLEM?

There is small if any doubt that air pollution can and has caused substantial social and economic losses. Its role is well documented in experiments, tests, and experience gathered from major episodes. Air pollution contributes to the corrosion of metal and stone; it discolors and makes buildings dirty outside and inside; and in general it contributes to the blight of the neighborhood.[1]

Air pollution also damages and destroys plant life—leading to agricultural and aesthetic losses. It places real restrictions on the types of vegetation that may be raised in many areas of the country. In New Jersey, for example, pollution injury to vegetation has been observed in every county and damage has been reported to at least thirty-six commercial crops.[2] Air pollution may also limit plant growth and production, impair quality, and may even reduce vigor to a degree where plants are predisposed to further losses as from biotic pathogens.[3]

More importantly, air pollution imposes costs in terms of human health. In testimony before the Subcommittee on Air and Water Pollution of the Committee on Public Works of the United States Senate, Dr. William Stewart, Surgeon General of the Public Health Service, unequivocally stated that air pollution is "unquestionably a factor in the development of not one, but many, diseases affecting literally millions of our people."[4]

The sharply rising incidence of lung cancer, emphysema, bronchitis, and asthma

---

[*] Chief, Economic and Social Studies Section, Office of Legislative and Public Affairs, National Center for Air Pollution Control, U.S. Public Health Service, Department of Health, Education, and Welfare.

The author is especially indebted to R.J. Anderson, L.B. Barrett, and Allen Kneese for more than just editorial assistance, and to Marion Van Landingham for the latter.

[1] R. RIDKER, ECONOMIC COSTS OF AIR POLLUTION 57, 115 (1967).

[2] Middleton, *Air Pollution Threat to Flora and Fauna Doubles Threat to Man*, CONSERVATION CATALYST, December 1967, at 1, 3.

[3] Treshow, *Plant Communities Menaced by Polluted Air, id.* at 7, 9.

[4] *Hearings on S780 (Air Pollution—1967) Before the Subcomm. on Air and Water Pollution of the Senate Comm. on Public Works*, 90th Cong., 1st Sess., pt. 3, at 1131 (1967).

has been associated with air pollution. Epidemiological surveys reveal that death rates from cardiorespiratory diseases in general are noticeably higher in urban than in rural areas, and that rates increase with city size, as does air pollution.[5]

Dr. Dubos observes that whatever its apparent selectivity, any biologically active substance is likely to react with more than one function. Above and beyond the direct toxic effects that occur rapidly and which are easily detected, there are others that develop more slowly and indirectly.[6]

Government cannot eliminate these economic and social costs by cleaning the air stream as it can purify water for public use. The only practical solution is to reduce substantially the uncontrolled disposal of pollutants to the atmosphere. Air pollution control involves political, economic, and social considerations. The economist's contribution to the discussion of the problem is to attempt an evaluation of some alternative ways in which society might restructure the market process to bring about improved air quality and how these alternatives might compare with direct regulation and enforcement approaches.

II

WHY IS AIR POLLUTION AN ECONOMIC PROBLEM?

The economist sees air pollution as a classic case of an *external diseconomy*. External diseconomies arise whenever market forces alone are insufficient to make an individual bear the full costs including the social costs that result from his actions. If these costs can somehow be internalized so that the economic unit generating pollution is required to pay for its elimination, then the diseconomy is removed.[7]

In a profit-motivated economy profits are maximized to the extent that the cost of waste disposal is minimized. Profits are also maximized to the extent that waste is turned into valuable by-products or recovered products. When the value of such products exceeds the costs of producing them, waste reduction, like the practice of honesty, is its own reward. When the costs of waste reduction and disposal are not offset, the costs of disposal are borne by others than the producer of the wastes. The costs are clean-up and disposal costs. Or they are personal, material, and esthetic damages that are suffered in tolerating polluted air, putrid water, and a trash-littered landscape.

The producers of pollution are generally unaware of the total effects of the pollution they produce. No one producer has an incentive to eliminate his pollution entirely; his incentive, commonly, is limited only to the elimination of that part which adversely affects his own operation. The arguments against going farther are that it will cost too much, that prices will have to be increased, that consumers will not

---

[5] R. DUBOS, MAN ADAPTING 216 (1965).

[6] *Id.* at 222-23.

[7] *See generally* Kneese, *Air Pollution—General Background and Some Economic Aspects*, in THE ECONOMICS OF AIR POLLUTION 23, 29-30 (H. Wolozin ed. 1966).

buy it, and that there is no proof that air pollution is damaging anything anyway, so why pick on me.

It can be asserted that, for survival, producers are obligated to provide a product of value. It can be asserted further that, for social efficiency, value includes product safety and minimum social costs. There can be no question that pollution will be reduced if appropriate incentives can be identified and provided which force producers to account for product safety and social costs.

A manufacturer calculating private costs of production will include raw materials, labor, equipment, facilities, overhead, advertising, and taxes. He will annualize costs based on useful life of capital. He may or may not include the costs of disposing of waste gases and dust. A large portion of these by-products of the manufacturing process are still dispersed into the air and justified on the ground that it is an economic function of the atmosphere to assimilate such wastes.

If there are only a few stacks, only a few automobiles, and a limited number of heating units sending pollutants into the air over a community, and if atmospheric conditions are such that these pollutants are soon gone with the wind, the disposal of wastes to the atmosphere may seem efficient. But, if there are many stacks, many automobiles, and thousands of heating units within a limited geographic area all contributing their respective wastes to the surrounding pool of air, the resulting pollution may not be assimilated and costs will be imposed on society.

III

POSSIBLE ECONOMIC INCENTIVES

It should be obvious that internalizing costs does not necessarily mean that producers must bear the total burden. Since the public benefits from both clean air and a productive industrial sector, it is reasonable to expect that the public will pay something for the control of pollution. The question is how.

Examination of alternatives suggests that there are basically two types of incentives that may be used to encourage polluters to reduce or eliminate the emission of pollutants into the atmosphere: economic incentives and enforcement of regulations—the carrot and the stick.

The economic incentives involve the public's sharing the costs of control in a rather direct way. One simple form of economic incentive would take the form of tax credits and fast write-offs for the initial purchase and installation of control equipment. Other forms of economic incentive would include award payments, emission charges, or combinations of payments and charges. These might be useful in stimulating reduction of emissions over the long run. Award payments might be geared to a percentage reduction from total potential emissions, to an absolute reduction in terms of certain amounts of pollutants, or to the attainment of an emission standard set by a government regulation.

With a system of emission charges, a company might pay a low charge if the damage caused by its emissions were low, and a high charge if the damages were high. There would be nothing except the economic motivation provided by the incentive scheme to force control of emissions.

In a system combining award payments and emission charges, companies exceeding emission standards might receive payments to offset the cost of control and to keep them from relaxing to the required levels. Companies emitting large amounts of pollution might be charged as an incentive for them to approach the standards. Charges could be geared so that it would be noticeably cheaper for polluters to meet emission standards than to pay emission fees. Charges could conceivably be structured to pay the costs of awards.

The principal alternative to using financial or economic incentives to change the behavior of a polluter would be for a government to enact legislation requiring that certain emission standards be met. Failure to comply could entail the payment of a comparatively steep fine for each day a company is in violation of standards.

A. The Provision of Incentives Through Equipment Tax Credits

Equipment tax credits might appear to be the most attractive economic incentive from the viewpoint of industry. This is a tentative conclusion based on the fact that some forty-odd bills have been brought before Congress which would provide tax credits, rapid write-offs, or both, for the purchase and installation of air pollution control equipment.

A typical bill would offer a twenty per cent tax credit for capital investment instead of the seven per cent credit now allowed for new facilities and equipment. It would also offer a write-off for depreciation purposes of from one to five years instead of the standard useful life basis, which could be twenty years or more. If enacted, such legislation could provide a benefit to industry of roughly $300,000 to $400,000 above present rates for every $1 million it spends on the purchase and installation of air pollution control equipment.

It has been estimated that, under the present seven per cent investment tax credit, perhaps $10 to $25 million of assistance is given each year to manufacturing firms investing in air and water abatement equipment combined. Air and water pollution control equipment is also included under the accelerated depreciation allowance for capital equipment—such as double declining balance and sum-of-the-years-digits. The effect is roughly similar to an interest-free loan for the amounts involved. The current annual subsidy through this provision may be $15-30 million.[8]

There are a number of possible problems associated with tax credits and rapid write-offs as an incentive to air pollution .,batement. In the first place, it may be difficult from a practical administrative standpoint to determine how much of a

---

[8] WORKING COMMITTEE ON ECONOMIC INCENTIVES, FEDERAL COORDINATING COMMITTEE ON THE ECONOMIC IMPACT OF POLLUTION ABATEMENT, COST SHARING WITH INDUSTRY? 6 (1967) [hereinafter cited as FEDERAL COORDINATING COMMITTEE].

plant's investment should be charged to pollution control and how much to process changes undertaken primarily for increased productivity that incidentally may affect a significant reduction in the production of air pollutants. If pollution control means buying a specific piece of equipment, such as an electric precipitator, and installing it to trap escaping and valueless pollutants, then it is comparatively easy to assign costs. But when pollution control is not limited to such simple, end-of-the-line devices, the assignment of costs is considerably more complicated and would depend heavily on engineering and economic judgments.

The problem is further complicated when air pollution control produces valuable by-products. A producer of carbon black, for example, uses a highly sophisticated filtration system to prevent the loss of a product worth several cents per pound.

A recent issue of *Mill and Factory* magazine cited other examples which illustrate the importance, for any economic incentive scheme, of relating incentives to net costs.

> A steel company has developed a smoke-cleaning process which traps most of the iron dust particles and, after putting them through a sintering process, recharges them for use in its open hearths.
>
> A chemical company has a plant with a dust collection system that accumulates about 4000 tons of fly ash a year. This "waste" material contains about 70% carbon, and its re-use as fuel brings the company substantial savings. Another plant of this same company used to emit foul smelling benzothiazole. Control equipment costing $85,000 was installed and now the company recovers about $50,000 worth of benzothiazole a year.
>
> A chlorine user with air pollution controls is now recovering "waste" chlorine that had formerly cost him $60 a liquid ton. The recovery costs are now down to only $19 a ton.[9]

A second difficulty involves the possibility that a policy of tax credits for capital expenditures would encourage industry to commit resources to control hardware approaches instead of looking for possibly lower cost approaches. If this were the result, equipment tax credits would be an inefficient subsidy from an economic point of view.

This bias was succinctly stated by the Working Committee on Economic Incentives of the Federal Coordinating Committee on the Economic Impact of Pollution Abatement in its recent report:[10]

> The subsidy is in a small part illusory because the assistance would be given for a higher level of expenditures caused by the subsidy creating an incentive to overuse of capital to the neglect of operating and maintenance expenditures. This would arise because capital costs are made artificially cheaper by virtue of a tax write-off. Tax write-offs are handicapped because they are incapable of providing assistance to all of the costs of abatement. The capital cost accounts for roughly one-third of the total cost for water pollution abatement and one-eighth for air

[9] *The Case for Clean Air—A Special Report*, MILL & FACTORY, April 1967, at 41, 56.
[10] FEDERAL COORDINATING COMMITTEE 27.

pollution abatement. Of course, with subsidies given to capital alone, the capital cost proportion will tend to rise and unnecessarily consume more resources. The addition of chemicals or supervisory personnel often times is less costly than building additional capacity in order to treat larger waste loads. Fuel substitution alone is estimated to be the least-cost alternative in over 60 percent of the cases involving air pollution abatement.

Fuel substitution may be a particularly practical approach to the reduction of sulfur oxide emissions for many coal burning power plants. They may switch from high-sulfur to low-sulfur content coal, to low-sulfur residual oil, to natural gas, to desulfurized coal or fuel oil or to atomic energy—usually at somewhat increased costs. The technology for desulfurization of fuel oil already exists and continuing research and development continues to make such approaches appear increasingly economical. A comprehensive economic incentive system would not discourage such approaches.

In addition to prejudicing polluters in favor of control equipment instead of seeking lower cost alternatives, tax credits and fast write-offs would create additional loopholes in tax laws, which, some would hold, are already riddled by special exceptions. Every time aid takes such form, it tends to become a precedent for still more such programs.

Another argument against tax credits and other financial type incentives is the belief that the costs of pollution control will probably be low and incentives will not really be necessary. It is currently estimated, for example, that for a number of existing industries (including steel, utilities, foundries, petroleum refining, kraft paper, cement, and chemicals) when capital costs are annualized on a ten-year life, including an imputed ten per cent interest, the full additional cost of particulate control will be roughly one-half of one per cent of value added by manufacture. It would appear that such a relatively low cost could be successfully absorbed by most sections of industry.

Some assistance is already available for hardship cases. The Small Business Administration (SBA) has authority to make loans to approximately ninety-five per cent of all non-farm industry in the United States. A small business is defined as a company which is independently owned and operated and is not dominant in its field. Among manufacturing industries facing the greatest abatement costs—foods, paper, chemical, petroleum refining, and primary metals—over ninety per cent are eligible. Under the Small Business Act of 1958, SBA can make direct loans either by itself or in participation with banks and can guarantee loans made by banks.[11] Direct loans may be up to $100,000, $150,000 for SBA participation loans, and $350,000 on guaranteed portion of loans made by private banks. Interest is set at five and one-half per cent on SBA funds and up to eight per cent on bank funds. The maximum term is ten years except for that part of the loan used for facilities construction, which may run up to fifteen years.[12]

---

[11] 15 U.S.C. § 636(a) (1964).

[12] FEDERAL COORDINATING COMMITTEE 31.

Economic Development Administration (EDA) assistance (financial and technical) can be offered any company, regardless of size, "if pollution abatement actions should 'tend to limit modernization, expansion or solvency of the facility.' Usually such a plant must be in a county which is designated as a 'depressed area.' Nearly one-third of the land area in the United States is currently designated as depressed."[13]

Even in areas

> outside of "depressed areas," EDA can pay all the cost of technical studies for the purpose of identifying least-cost methods of abating pollution for plants in towns or sections of cities threatened by reduced economic activity. The only condition is that the pollution abatement actions against the affected plant can potentially or actually cause an increase in unemployment. Such a broad mandate allows adequate latitude for assisting any hardship plant which is otherwise economically viable except for the short-term burden of pollution abatement expenditures.[14]

If some kind of additional tax incentive system were to be insisted upon, a somewhat flexible scheme might be developed along the following lines. A government might pay some share (say, fifty per cent) of the full additional costs of meeting governmentally imposed pollution control standards. The capital cost would be the annual amortization of required anti-pollution capital investments, plus imputed interest. Operating costs would include the direct additional costs of energy, water, operating labor, and proper maintenance of the control effort. The calculated payment could be added to income for tax purposes.

Tax credits or cost sharing payments might be limited to the extent that annualized pollution control costs exceed some share (say, one per cent) of value added on a plant basis. The share of value added is used here as a proxy for burden, but it is not identical with burden.

A guiding rule of such an incentive system would be that pollution control costs must be defined as those incurred in meeting specific requirements imposed on the firm pursuant to government regulations. Government revenue officers could presumably determine the full additional annualized costs of pollution control on the basis of statements and other information provided by the affected firm.

B. Award Payments

Emission reduction payments could, theoretically, be geared to the amount of abatement achieved (*i.e.*, pounds of pollutants recovered), or they could be geared to achieving and maintaining a particular standard of performance (*i.e.*, a power plant reaching a ninety-five per cent reduction of potential sulfur oxide emissions). Payments could be adjusted to produce various levels of performance. For example, when weather forecasts indicate a severe temperature inversion which would trap pollution over a metropolitan area and create an air pollution episode, performance payments

---

[13] *Id.* at 32.
[14] *Id.*

could be raised to reduce emissions and the resulting concentrations of air pollutants. Industries might respond by switching to low sulfur fuels or curtailing operations until the episode danger had passed. Award payments would help offset both the higher costs of fuel and the shutdown expenses.

While all of this is theoretically possible, a major problem with emission payments at the present time is that a technology for economically and effectively measuring emissions is not available. It is questionable, furthermore, whether engineering estimates of emission volumes would satisfy the measurement needs of an emission reduction payment system or of the legal requirements such a system might impose.

C. Emission Fees

With an emission fee system, a firm could choose to abate pollution to meet emission standards or pay a relatively high emission charge. An analogous system of effluent fees has been applied in the Rhine Valley for water pollution control with some success. Emission charges for air pollution control, however, appear less well suited to the pollution control problem.

In water pollution, it may make sense to give a large polluter like an industrial plant a choice between treating its own effluent or paying a fee for a government agency to do a job of stream cleaning from multiple sources. But the air cannot be stream-cleaned by such secondary off-site treatment systems. Once pollutants leave factory stacks or automobile exhausts they are in the air until dispersed by natural forces. As Allen V. Kneese has observed,

> . . . we are in somewhat the same position in regard to polluted air as the fish are to polluted water. We live in it. Accordingly, control of air pollution is largely a matter of preventing pollutants from escaping from their sources, eliminating the source, or shifting location of the source or the recipient.[15]

In water, a polluter who decides to pay an effluent fee rather than control emissions at the source is, in essence, making a payment for a service—which cannot be rendered for polluters of air.

Another difficulty is that a fee system could be exceedingly difficult and costly to administer. As mentioned above, emission measurement technology is presently inadequate to meet the requirement that a regulatory agency be able to determine with some precision just how much an individual polluter is contributing to the atmospheric burden. It might be equally difficult to decide how to determine what the fee structure should be in order to attain a satisfactory level of air quality.

IV

REGULATION

The obvious alternative to purely economic incentives would be to legislate emission standard regulations and enforce them with fines and other penalties. New

---

[15] Kneese, *supra* note 7, at 33.

Jersey is one example of a state that has recently passed air pollution legislation that combines a system of regulations with fines for violations and rebates for compliance. The 1967 amendment to the Air Pollution Control Act of 1954 provided that:[16]

> Any person who violates the provisions of this act or any code, rule, regulation or order promulgated or issued pursuant to this act shall be liable to a penalty of not more than $2,500 to be collected in a civil action by a summary proceeding under the penalty enforcement law (N.J.S. 2A:58-1 et seq.) or in any case before a court of competent jurisdiction wherein injunctive relief has been requested. If the violation is of a continuing nature, each day during which it continues after the date given by which the violation must be eliminated in accordance with the order of the department, shall constitute an additional, separate and distinct offense.
>
> The department is hereby authorized and empowered to compromise and settle any claim for a penalty under this section in such amount in the discretion of the department as may appear appropriate and equitable under all of the circumstances, including a rebate of any such penalty paid to the extent of 90% thereof where such person satisfies the department within 1 year or such other period as the department may deem reasonable that such violation has been eliminated or removed or that such order or injunction has been met or satisfied, as the case may be, by the installation of air pollution control apparatus.

In such a situation a polluter will try to find the least costly method of control (including methods that produce salable by-products). Process controls and fuel substitution will be used in many instances instead of heavy investment in control equipment.

Net costs of control may be passed on to consumers, equity holders, employees, or suppliers—a less direct but still effective sharing of costs. There may, of course, be instances where price increases result in customers substituting other products, or investors choosing among alternative investments if their returns are reduced by the added costs of pollution control.

Where a system of regulation is used, there should always be adequate provision for assisting companies particularly hard-hit by the cost of controls.

V

PRESENT TRENDS

Present trends in the United States indicate greater use of regulations than of direct cost-sharing incentives. In its report, the Working Committee on Economic Incentives stated:[17]

> Across-the-board cost-sharing in the form of tax write-offs is not recommended because it distorts the tax structure, causes the total cost of pollution abatement to rise significantly, promotes excessive use of capital equipment and waste treatment facilities, and discourages selectivity in environmental quality management. Across-the-board use of grants and loans is similarly handicapped and, in addition, is subject to fluctuations in Congressional appropriations.

---

[16] Ch. 105, § 1, [1967] N.J. Laws (1967 N.J. SESS. LAW SERVICE 357).
[17] FEDERAL COORDINATING COMMITTEE 5.

Except for the control of automobile emissions, the establishment of regulations or other incentives is, however, a state and local responsibility. Both the Clean Air Act of 1963 and its subsequent amendments and the Air Quality Act of 1967[18] encourage states to take this responsibility. Under the Clean Air Act, for instance, federal grants have helped to produce a substantial expansion of state and local control programs. Prior to passage of this act only sixteen states had air pollution control legislation; today the number is forty-six. In addition, federal abatement actions in a number of interstate areas have paved the way for state and local agencies to cooperate across territorial boundaries. The Clean Air Act also helped stimulate a much greater effort to develop new and improved control technology.

The Air Quality Act of 1967 reaffirms that state and local governments have a primary role in protecting air quality,[19] but gives the federal government increased authority to act in emergency situations,[20] increased responsibility for reviewing and approving state and regional control programs,[21] and finally, authority to establish federal controls in states or regions which fail to establish needed controls.[22]

Since air pollution is no respecter of geographical boundaries, the Air Quality Act is designed to deal with air pollution on a regional basis. The act requires the Department of Health, Education, and Welfare to designate *specific air quality control regions*.[23] These regions will be designated on the basis of factors that suggest that a group of communities should be treated as a unit for the purpose of setting and implementing *air quality standards*. At the same time, the Department is required to develop and publish air quality *criteria* for a pollutant or group of pollutants,[24] together with information on available control techniques applicable to the various sources of that pollutant or group of pollutants.[25] Air quality criteria are derived from the best available scientific knowledge of the effects of air pollutants on health and welfare. Still another requirement is that the Department publish information on control techniques that will identify the best methods available for reducing pollutant emissions at their various sources and the costs thereof—whether these techniques involve the application of control equipment, changes in fuel use or industrial processes, or any other practical approach.

As soon as a criterion and the related information on control techniques is published for a pollutant, the act begins to have a direct effect on those states responsible for the air quality control regions that have been designated. The act sets up a timetable which states must follow in developing air quality standards and implementation plans for the designated regions. It is possible that the implementation plans will

---

[18] The earlier legislation has been replaced by the Air Quality Act of 1967, 81 Stat. 485.

[19] *See, e.g.*, § 102(a), 81 Stat. 485 (1967); H.R. Rep. No. 728, 90th Cong., 1st Sess. 1 (1967).

[20] § 108(k), 81 Stat. 497 (1967).

[21] *See, e.g.*, § 108(c)(1), 81 Stat. 492 (1967).

[22] §§ 108(c)(2)-(4), 81 Stat. 492 (1967).

[23] § 107(a)(2), 81 Stat. 490 (1967).

[24] § 107(b), 81 Stat. 491 (1967).

[25] § 107(c), 81 Stat. 491 (1967).

offer financial incentives as well as regulations to encourage application of controls. If the Secretary of Health, Education, and Welfare finds that the air quality standards and plans for their implementation are consistent with criteria and related control technology information, then those standards and plans will take effect.[26] If a state fails to establish standards, or if the Secretary finds that the standards are not consistent with the criteria, he can initiate action to insure that appropriate standards are set.[27] States may request a public hearing on any standards developed by the Secretary; in such cases the hearing board's decision will be binding.[28] States will be expected to assume the primary responsibility for application of the air quality standards. If a state's efforts prove inadequate, the Secretary is empowered to initiate abatement action.[29]

Backed by a federally-supported research and development effort enlisting the support of industry,[30] and by federal grants for state and local control programs,[31] the national drive to control air pollution should be considerably accelerated. There should be the concentration of interest, money, and talents that will allow us to lower the emission of pollutants which exact such high economic and social costs today and threaten to exact even higher costs tomorrow. While the major vehicle for this progress may continue to be the establishment of emission regulations, it is entirely possible that the development of improved instrumentation for measuring emissions will make other forms of incentives attractive.

---

[26] § 108(c)(1), 81 Stat. 492 (1967).
[27] § 108(c)(2), 81 Stat. 492 (1967).
[28] § 108(c)(3), 81 Stat. 492 (1967).
[29] § 108(c)(4), 81 Stat. 493 (1967).
[30] See §§ 103-04, 81 Stat. 486 (1967).
[31] § 105, 81 Stat. 489 (1967).

LEGISLATING FOR AIR QUALITY MANAGEMENT: REDUCING THEORY TO PRACTICE

GEORGE HAGEVIK*

INTRODUCTION

Air pollution is more or less representative of the nation's increasing environmental problems in that while it has been with us for some time it has only recently grown to a scale where differences in degree have begun to become differences in kind. Up to some level of concentration, disposal of wastes is for the most part a local irritation. But, at a certain threshold, costs to society start to increase significantly. This phenomenon has resulted in a considerable redefinition of air pollution problems. For example, the concern is no longer so much with smoke damage as with harm from photochemical smog and other synergistic effects. Also, a higher aspiration level on the part of the population of metropolitan areas has resulted in a reduced tolerance for anything impairing the quality of the environment. These and other changes in the nature of the air pollution problem suggest a new or at least a broader view of planning for air quality management.

The regulatory machinery for dealing with the air pollution problem is still for the most part of a primitive variety. The Air Quality Act of 1967 assigns primary responsibility for devising the regulatory mechanism to state governments, subject to review by the Department of Health, Education, and Welfare (HEW),[1] and appears to contemplate that new legislation or regulatory action will appear at the state and local level as soon as HEW provides the data and criteria for which it is responsible under the act.[2] The resultant need for review of laws and standards, coupled with changing perceptions of the problem, suggest that a new generation of legislative responses at the state and local level is to be both hoped and looked for. In the formulation of this new response, greater sophistication will be needed if the considerable costs involved in air pollution abatement are to be minimized, and it is not clear that existing air quality management efforts are yielding the experience necessary to guide the legislatures in this direction. Perhaps greater assistance will come from economists and other experts who can recognize that the legal attack on air pollution requires a new strategy, not just further adaptations of old approaches originally designed to deal with zoning and nuisances.

* B.A. 1960, M.A. 1963, University of Washington; M.R.P. 1966, University of North Carolina; Ph.D. candidate, University of North Carolina. Assistant Professor of City and Regional Planning, Rutgers University (effective January 1969).

The author gratefully acknowledges the assistance of the editor in the preparation of portions of this article.

[1] § 101(a)(3), 81 Stat. 485.

[2] §§ 101(b), 106, 107, 81 Stat. 485.

This paper first attempts to set down some basic social science theory about the economics of air pollution and about decision making in general. It then seeks to apply this understanding in the development of a hypothetical regulatory program for dealing with stationary sources of pollution. This hypothetical program owes little to existing control efforts and is conceived in the understanding that regulatory officials must be enabled to operate effectively even in the dim light of partial knowledge defining and relating the social and technological aspects of air pollution. Since the program is merely sketched, it will not serve as a blueprint but only as a stimulus to new thinking about air quality management and the organization for carrying it out.

I

THE ECONOMIST'S VIEW—EFFLUENT FEES

Readings in welfare economics published during the last thirty years are replete with references to smoke damage as a classic instance of what are called negative externalities.[3] Such discussions, however, have been of more value to economists interested in the further theoretical development of welfare economics than to the air pollution control officer concerned with actual abatement and control activities. Unfortunately, in this instance the spillover from theory to practice has been minimal. Why is this the case? For one thing, the economic theory requires limiting conditions and large assumptions about the data available, neither of which can be fulfilled in practice. The problems of collecting data on such subjects as air pollution damage and the contribution of each emitter to existing concentrations are staggering, to say the least, and economists have not had the fortitude or the means to tackle the measurements necessary to make concrete control proposals. Sheer complexity has discouraged interest, and, until very recently, there was apparently less investment by government and private funding agencies in this field of economic research than the need seems in retrospect to have warranted. In any event, the theory has proved not too difficult to master, but attention is only beginning to focus on the need for data and practical means of developing these data or compensating for the lack thereof. The 1966 volume, *The Economics of Air Pollution*, edited by Professor Harold Wolozin, is probably the best single indicator both of economists' increased interest in the problem and of the gulf remaining between theory and practice.

The practitioner looking for practical answers in the Wolozin volume will be disappointed for it is little more than a summary—albeit an excellent one—of the state of the art. The primary contribution of the book is that it brings relevant economic theory to bear on the problem, explicitly or implicitly reveals the advantages and weaknesses of the economist's approach, and suggests data deficiencies and research needs. The consensus of the participants in the forum from which the

---

[3] *E.g.*, A. PIGOU, THE ECONOMICS OF WELFARE 160-61 (1932).

book was drawn seems to be that the problem has been defined and that the task for the next few years is to gather data and do research that might lead to estimates of the necessary answers. If an analogy to water quality management holds, the estimate of a few years seems optimistic. For, even though economists have been concerned with water resource development for some time, Allen Kneese's seminal work on water quality, *The Economics of Regional Water Quality Management*, did not appear until 1964.

The economist's views on air quality management can be usefully reviewed in a brief manner. Most economists would state the problem in this way: The discharge of pollutants into the air imposes on some people costs which are not adequately borne by the sources of the pollution due to the failure of the market mechanism, resulting in more air pollution than would be desirable from the point of view of society as a whole. The "classical" economic theorist's distinctive approach to the problem is manifested in his belief that the objective of pollution abatement programs should be to minimize the total of (*a*) air pollution damage costs and (*b*) the costs incurred in any program to alleviate that damage. Any given level of pollution abatement should be reached by the least costly combination of means available, and the costs of any decrement of pollution should not exceed the benefits obtained by the reduction. Thus, the standard theoretical approach would be to calculate the damage to each receptor from polluted air containing various amounts and kinds of effluents. Such a calculation would permit measurement of the benefits to be expected from proposed abatement projects. Next, one would calculate the cost to each pollutant source of abating its emissions in varying degrees. The optimal allocation of the air resource would then require that pollutants be prevented from entering the atmosphere at levels which would inflict more marginal damage on receptors than the marginal cost to the source of preventing the pollution.[4]

The operational procedure which economists would recommend for achieving this optimal condition would include an evaluation of the damage done by the emission of incremental amounts of pollutant into the air at any given location and time and an assessment of a corresponding charge against the emitters. The charge would thus reflect the marginal costs that the sources impose on others. It would be determined by relating ambient air quality to rates of emission, using air monitoring networks and relatively simple atmospheric diffusion models.

The principal advantage from the economist's point of view of "internalizing" the cost by means of a government-levied charge on the source is that the economic units involved can decide on the best adjustment to be made in light of the costs

---

[4] A detailed statement of this approach is found in Crocker, *The Structuring of Atmospheric Pollution Control Systems*, in THE ECONOMICS OF AIR POLLUTION (H. Wolozin ed. 1966) [hereinafter cited as WOLOZIN]. For a refinement of the problem of determining which abatement expenditures are justifiable, *see* notes 69-70 *infra* and accompanying text.

and benefits they perceive. Those firms which can reduce emissions at a cost that would be less than the charge will do so to avoid being assessed the charge. Those firms which *cannot* reduce emissions at a cost that would be less than the charge would elect to pay the fee but would nevertheless have a continuing incentive to reduce emissions. Thus, the optimal level of pollution abatement will be approached by the method that is least costly to society as a whole.

Under this system, management rather than government officials would bear much of the burden of investigation and decision making, and management is said to be better able to evaluate the advantages and disadvantages of the various ways of dealing with the effluent problem and to choose the best mix. This is held to be preferable to being restricted to any one abatement technique. Implicit in the economist's view is recognition that the optimal level of air pollution abatement is closely tied to the technological processes involved, with the least-cost solution being in many cases a complex combination of process changes and treatment of effluent; in some cases, moreover, the least-cost solution might involve partial abatement and payment of the lower effluent fees associated with the remaining emissions. The continuing incentive provided by the effluent fee to search for additional or alternative ways of abating discharges involves a much different response than that compelled in a straight enforcement action. Enforcement by criminal proceeding or by injunction or cease and desist order, for example, would provide no real alternative to incurring the abatement costs, whatever they might be. Moreover, enforcement programs that would compel the adoption of specific technology would altogether destroy the incentive to explore alternative abatement techniques or to combine approaches to achieve the maximum efficiency in pollution reduction.

A system of effluent fees has additional theoretical appeal because of its adaptability to changing or variable circumstances. Fees can be varied up or down in accordance with weather conditions, the time of day, the season of the year, and other factors in order to correlate emitters' costs even more closely with the damage caused. The theoretical advantage of this flexibility may be difficult to realize in practice, however, and indeed may even prove a liability. Given the vast inadequacy of data and the probabilistic character of the factors that might be reflected in variable fees, the schedule would take on an appearance of arbitrariness that might be difficult to dispel. We have here one key to the unlikelihood that effluent fees will soon play a major role in air quality control.

The primary problems with effluent fees are simply the shortage of data and the lack of agreement on many of the theoretical problems that are presented. The major information deficiency is in the measurement of damages attributable to particular pollutants, and myriad conceptual and informational problems inhere in the allocation to individual polluters of the share of the total damages for which they are "responsible." Perhaps most difficult of all is the theoretical problem of allocating damages to specific polluters when synergistic effects occur—that is, where the combination of two or more pollutants, such as sulfur oxides and particulates, causes greater damage than either pollutant could cause alone. Problems of equity are also presented by the need to allocate damage costs between new and existing industries. Finally, there are also doubts that monitoring technology is adequate to permit effective enforcement of an effluent fee system. Especially where there are numerous small polluters to be monitored, such a system would be costly to administer.

Another problem, which must be faced in any regulatory system, with or without effluent fees, has to do with the determination of who should benefit from the use of the air resource. If air is to be treated as a free good for the receptors, including humans, plants, and animals, certain costs are thus imposed on others who may wish to use the air for waste disposal. Theoretical discussions seldom deal with why these costs should not be allocated according to "practical" considerations such as the supposed ability of industry to pass on added costs to consumers and the apparently greater ability of industrial firms to select and apply the least-cost solution (including the possibility of paying adjoining landowners to move or take protective measures). An effluent fee program might be designed to encourage such flexibility, but administrative problems would again seem to be overwhelming in the short run.

While these many problems and data shortages will handicap any program of enforced abatement which purports to compare abatement costs and the benefits derived therefrom, an effluent fee program would also have to survive legal attacks based on arguments of apparent discrimination and abuse of the taxing power. As understanding of the nature of air pollution and pollution damage costs increases, effluent fees may become more feasible and may ultimately fill an important role in air pollution control. But today, while the assignment or sale of emission or receptor rights has theoretical appeal, the pricing of such rights still requires some sort of centralized decision-making system. Such a system, as it might now be constituted in our political and institutional environment, would yield only a few of the advantages that a fully market-oriented system, from which it is conceptually derived, would produce.

Finally, a basic complaint against the theoretical underpinnings of the effluent fee approach has been raised by Wolozin, who states,

My skepticism is based on the unfortunate fact that we do not know enough in an empirical way about the effects of taxation on business policies and human behavior to be at all certain about the outcome of any scheme of tax like effluent fees. Even the underlying theory can be questioned.[5]

This questioned theory is, of course, the conventional neoclassical microeconomic model, which depends upon the postulate of rationality and the concept of the firm as a profit maximizer. Since these assumptions have often been criticized as un-

---

[5] Wolozin, *Discussion*, in PROCEEDINGS: THE THIRD NATIONAL CONFERENCE ON AIR POLLUTION 580 (Public Health Service Pub. No. 1649, 1967) [hereinafter cited as THIRD NAT'L CONF. PROCEEDINGS].

realistic, Wolozin suggests that a more useful approach might be to view the goals of the firm in relation to its position as an organization in a political and social system.[6] Wolozin's point is not well taken, however, for it seemingly ignores three fundamental considerations. First, many significant polluters will in fact be entrepreneurs in the traditional sense rather than firms in which management has become independent of ownership, the condition usually cited as having undermined the profit-maximization postulate. Second, the proposition that management generally prefers lower costs to higher is a principle which has never been directly criticized, and it holds largely true even in regulated public utilities where "regulatory lag" permits realization of profits wherever unanticipated cost savings can be accomplished.[7] Finally, Wolozin misses the notable fact that management's presumed social responsibilities, which are so strongly emphasized by those who would contest the profit-maximization postulate, are also at work in this field, assisting in the achievement of the social goal of a cleaner environment. One might predict, therefore, that effluent fees, by raising the cost of *not* fulfilling a perceived social responsibility to abate, will yield dividends *greater* than traditional theory would anticipate.

In sum, effluent fees have a solid theoretical foundation, but the practical problems associated with establishing and enforcing a fee schedule appear so great that immediate adoption of this approach seems unlikely. Understanding of the air pollution problem and the regulatory challenge it poses nevertheless requires a grasp of effluent fees' potentiality, since a system of fees may be the ultimate goal toward which regulation should evolve. Vickrey's advocacy of an effluent fee program rests in part on the consideration that it would force the regulator "to bring the problem into perspective, and tends to put something of a restraint on the pure air enthusiast who might at times be inclined to impose standards that would entail too high a cost relative to benefits."[8] One premise of the hypothetical regulatory program developed below is that the cost-benefit principle can also be implemented in a program of direct regulation and that the lesson Vickrey wants taught can be learned without opting for effluent fees as the dominant regulatory approach.

II

CHOICE OF A CONTROL PHILOSOPHY

A. Alternative Approaches to Control

In addition to the effluent fee approach, payments and direct regulation are other approaches to environmental quality management problems.[9] Direct regulation is

---

[6] *Id.*

[7] *But cf.* comments by Linsky, Mills, and Wolozin, *id.* at 589.

[8] W. Vickrey, Theoretical and Practical Possibilities and Limitations of a Market Mechanism Approach to Air Pollution, a paper presented at the Air Pollution Control Ass'n Conference, Cleveland, Ohio, June 1967.

[9] *See generally* A. KNEESE, THE ECONOMICS OF REGIONAL WATER QUALITY MANAGEMENT 193-95 (1964); Mills, *Economic Incentives to Air Pollution Control*, in WOLOZIN 40.

somewhat different from the other two in that it is nonfiscal. The payments approach includes not only subsidies but also reductions in taxes that otherwise would be collected. Common examples include the subsidization of particular control equipment, accelerated depreciation, and tax credits for investment in control equipment. Direct regulation includes a mixed bag of licenses, permits, registration, zoning, air quality and effluent standards, and the enforcement of standards through regulatory bodies and the courts.

1. Payments

One possible payment system might rely on selective payments to waste contributors for the purpose of motivating them to restrict emissions to an optimal degree. These payments would in principle be equivalent to the off-site costs imposed by increments of waste discharge and would vary with atmospheric conditions and effluent location, as well as with the quantity and quality of effluent. Since this sort of payment would be similar in theory but opposite in approach to the effluent fee scheme, the criticisms and difficulties mentioned above would apply here also.

The more typical proposal under the payments heading, however, relates to tax relief or subsidies. Such proposals are a popular topic these days, particularly among industry representatives and members of Congress, but they have only one substantial argument in their favor—there is less resistance to a program of subsidies than to programs of regulation. There are, however, a number of problems with the payments approach. As Mills states,

> [T]here is a strong practical argument against most of the policies under the payments heading. They are simply payments for the wrong thing. The investment credit proposal will illustrate the deficiency that is common to others. An investment credit on air pollution abatement equipment reduces the cost of such equipment. But most such equipment is inherently unprofitable in that it adds nothing to revenues and does not reduce costs. To reduce the cost of such an item cannot possibly induce a firm to install it. The most it can do is to reduce the resistance to public pressure for installation. Common sense and scattered bits of evidence suggest that these payments policies are costly and inefficient ways to achieve abatement.[10]

More specifically, it would be difficult to decide how much to pay to whom for any level of pollution abatement since there is no commonly accepted level of air quality from which payments could be computed. The taxpayer's feelings of equity might also be violated since the industrial firm, in not having to consider pollution abatement as a cost of production in the same sense that labor and capital are, would rely on payments raised at least partially by higher taxes on other taxpayers.[11]

Payment schemes, tax credits, or accelerated depreciation may also bias the tech-

[10] Mills, *Federal Incentives to Air Pollution Control,* in THIRD NAT'L CONF. PROCEEDINGS 575-76.
[11] *See* Mills, *supra* note 9, at 45-46.

nique used for control in an uneconomical direction because they tend to promote construction of treatment facilities when adjustments in production processes, products, or inputs might achieve the same result at lower cost and might even increase productivity. Tax writeoffs of capital cost are also at a disadvantage because they are not capable of reducing all abatement costs. It has been estimated that capital cost accounts for only about one-eighth of the air pollution abatement costs for a typical firm.[12] Indeed, fuel substitution alone is estimated to be the least-cost alternative in over sixty per cent of the cases involved in air pollution abatement.[13]

Grants and loans have the same objectives as tax writeoffs in that they lower the cost of capital expenditures. Thus the criticisms suggested above apply. However, it has been suggested that if grants were made for both capital and operating costs and administered through regional air quality management organizations this particular criticism would lose much of its bite. But it must be remembered that extensive reliance on grants and loans suffers from the uncertainty of fluctuations in legislative appropriations.

2. Direct Regulation

Although the ideal method for dealing with the effects of the unidirectional external diseconomies associated with air pollution would be a system of effluent charges, it is often suggested that the best operational method for dealing with practical problems is direct regulation. Existing federal policies on air pollution abatement mostly fall in the category of regulation and enforcement activities.[14] The advantage of this approach is that it permits the government to take interim steps even though it has almost no idea of relevant measurements. For example, if people's eyes were burning because of obvious emissions from an industrial plant, it would be logical to require filtration of these emissions even if one had no way of measuring the amounts of the emissions. Such regulation can be justified since, as a report of the staff of the Senate Committee on Public Works states, "Whatever yardsticks are employed, it is clearly evident that the cost of property damages alone from air pollution is great—far greater than the amounts devoted to its abatement by industry and all levels of government."[15] The implication seems to be that there is little chance of the costs of such a program exceeding the benefits.

Not all economists view direct regulation with complete suspicion. Crocker states,

---

[12] WORKING COMM. ON ECONOMIC INCENTIVES, FEDERAL COORDINATING COMM. ON THE ECONOMIC IMPACT OF POLLUTION ABATEMENT, COST SHARING WITH INDUSTRY? 27 (Summary Report 1967) [hereinafter cited as FEDERAL COORDINATING COMM.]

[13] Id.

[14] For a full discussion of federal powers under the statute, see Martin & Symington, A Guide to the Air Quality Act of 1967, in this symposium, p. 239.

[15] STAFF OF THE SENATE COMM. ON PUBLIC WORKS, 88TH CONG., 1ST SESS., A STUDY OF POLLUTION— AIR 20 (Comm. Print 1963).

Given the uncertain quality of available physical, biological, and economic information, and the potentially high costs associated with the gathering of additional information about atmospheric pollution problems, the control authority, in order to impress receptors and emitters with the necessity of regarding the air's two value dimensions as scarce economic resources, appears to be justified in setting minimal standards.[16]

A greater commitment to standards is evident in the writings of Paul Gerhardt, an economist with the National Center for Air Pollution Control. He states,

A polluter faced with the necessity to comply with a law or suffer punishment will generally find the least cost set of controls or have no one to blame but himself. He will pass cost increases along to customers in the form of price increases or to equity holders in the form of reduced profit shares. Optimum allocation will be preserved as the public makes new choices about their spending and investing patterns. Administrative costs could be less than for some alternatives as there would be no complicated tax revenue emission charge or payment system to operate.[17]

But, as expected, relative simplicity is not achieved without certain costs. One objection to direct regulation is its allegedly extreme inflexibility which results in considerably higher costs than would more selective abatement. To use an example from water pollution, the Federal Water Pollution Control Administration found in the Delaware River Basin that simple equal-proportional reduction of all waste loads would cost fifty per cent more than achieving the same quality standard by requiring firms to reduce their waste loads in proportion to their harmful effects.[18] In the case of air quality management, the Federal Coordinating Committee on the Economic Impact of Pollution Abatement suggests that the cost of achieving a specific air quality standard could increase by 200 to 400 per cent if equal-proportional reduction on a year-round basis were attempted.[19]

The argument over the desirability of direct regulation cannot be resolved on the merits here. It is perhaps more important, however, to note that government already appears to be committed to direct regulation as the preferred means of dealing with the air pollution problem, although subsidies and tax concessions will continue to appear. While Congress did not see fit in the Air Quality Act to enact the President's proposal for a program of national emission standards for all polluting industries, such standards are still under consideration.[20] Moreover, most state and local abatement programs are based on strict prohibitions of the emission of specified concentrations of pollutants. Against this background, the final section of this article, in developing a hypothetical program of direct regulation, is premised on

[16] Crocker, *supra* note 4, at 79.

[17] P. Gerhardt, Some Economic Aspects of Air Pollution, a paper presented at the Mid-Atlantic States Section, Air Pollution Control Ass'n Conference, Oct. 4, 1967.

[18] FEDERAL COORDINATING COMM. 14.

[19] *Id.*

[20] *See* Air Quality Act of 1967, § 211(a), 81 Stat. 485.

these judgments, among others: (1) that government has already opted for a direct regulation approach, (2) that such an approach holds fewer dangers of resource misallocation and inequity than would a payments or subsidy program, (3) that direct regulation would be more likely to operate effectively with necessarily imperfect data than would an effluent fee approach, and (4) that its legal status might be somewhat less open to question than an effluent fee program simply because it is somewhat less of a novelty in the spectrum of public policies. Finally, while it is believed that there is already a commitment to regulation, the shape of the regulatory machinery, the details of the policies to be implemented, and the decision-making methodology to be employed do not seem to be finally determined. The hypothetical program is thus framed to encourage maximum flexibility in pursuit of least-cost solutions, which economic theory tells us are important and can help us to find.

B. A Larger View of Decision Making

To this point the review has been over what should be familiar ground. Unfortunately for many practitioners in the field of air quality management, knowledge relating to benefit-cost ratios, marginal cost pricing, and optimal taxing schemes has been secondary to the necessary concern with temperature inversions, wet scrubbers, filters, and the like. This is the case even though air pollution is in a fundamental sense a social and economic problem the solutions to which have to be worked out within a complex political and institutional framework. Technological means are currently available to purify the air to any desired degree, but costs increase significantly as more control is desired.[21] The economist's view of air quality management is important because we are finally perceiving a condition of scarcity so central to his thinking. Air is now viewed as a congested facility, and without the attempt at evaluation he provides, the desirable objective of reducing the level of pollution in the atmosphere by the least costly means possible would be difficult to achieve.

Since pollution abatement is primarily a matter of avoiding costs, programs need to be initially evaluated from an economic point of view for, as Turvey has noted, "even though an economic calculation of gains or losses is often not sufficient to reach a well based decision, it is nearly always an essential preliminary."[22] This determination of sound economic policy in air quality management requires an accurate and continuing evaluation of the costs of abatement relative to air pollution damages. Viewing costs avoided as benefits, decisions need to be sought that maximize the present value of net benefits.[23] Ideally, this analysis would be

---

[21] The main technological problem that remains to be solved is the development of a method of monitoring levels of emission accurately and at low cost.

[22] Turvey, *Side Effects of Resource Use*, in ENVIRONMENTAL QUALITY IN A GROWING ECONOMY 52 (R. Jarrett ed. 1966).

[23] This is essentially a benefit-cost view of air quality management since one may alternatively refer to (1) damages (costs) avoided as benefits and (2) costs incurred for abatement as costs, and say that

directed toward finding abatement efforts that equate incremental abatement costs and the value of incremental damage costs reduced.[24] But even a less sophisticated approach could measure abatement costs so that they include both administrative costs of control and capital and process change costs associated with abatement. Tools of evaluation, whether in sophisticated or crude form, need to be applied not only to the theoretical ideal of effluent fees and charges but also to the actual or potential use of payments and continuous and noncontinuous emission standards under a program of direct regulation.

While direct regulation seems to be emerging as the dominant control philosophy, the regulation to be undertaken may nevertheless comprise subsidies, licenses, permits, effluent charges, emission standards and variances therefrom, emergency powers, and some reliance on market forces. Experimentation with regulatory approaches to determine the best mix of such control techniques is desirable, and this need should be recognized by HEW in its review of state enforcement plans under the Air Quality Act. Such experimentation can be accomplished most readily by a control agency that is given broad powers with discretion to choose the tools needed for particular purposes. The hypothetical regulatory program described below contemplates such experimentation.

The overriding decision-making issue in this field is simply the difficulty of regulating an activity requiring prompt and decisive regulatory attention under conditions of imperfect knowledge, information, and understanding. The need for experimentation stems from these uncertainties. Ridker, commenting favorably on the need to get on with the job of regulating and the desirability of regulatory experimentation, quotes a British air pollution control official as follows:

> You Americans behave as if you have sufficient time and money to investigate a problem to death before you decide to act. In Britain we take note of a problem we do not like, take some action to correct the problem, and then do research after the fact to determine whether we were right.[25]

Such a purely seat-of-the-pants approach might not be politically feasible in this country and might be open to legal attack. Nevertheless, regulation must proceed with only partial knowledge, and if sensible and progressive regulation is to be achieved, substantial decision-making powers must be delegated to control agencies along with the discretion to experiment and innovate control approaches. The challenge becomes one of devising an effective decision-making process, with the

---

waste reduction up to but not beyond a certain point will maximize benefits minus costs. Cost minimization (including damages as a cost) and net benefit maximization are in this case identical.

[24] It is significant, as Gerhardt points out, that there has been far more interest in assessing the value of the damage by air pollution than in the costs of control. The costs of recent attempts at control have generally been accepted as a fraction of total damages. The interest in incremental costs of control will increase as the point of equality between incremental control costs and incremental damages is approached. *See* Gerhardt, *supra* note 17. For an argument suggesting that abatement costs should be a matter of immediate concern, *see* notes 69-70 *infra* and accompanying text.

[25] Ridker, *Strategies for Measuring the Cost of Air Pollution*, in WOLOZIN 87, 100.

decision maker's discretion structured and guided by legal principles, growing technical understanding, and clearly defined legislative goals, and with opportunities for
participation by affected parties in the decision-making process. Social science theory
can again be turned to, this time for guidance in the shaping of such a regulatory
program.

III

THE ROLE OF BARGAINING

Social scientists have developed a plethora of overlapping and competing theories
and models of the decision process. The literature on the subject is vast, and any
attempt at synthesis here would only result in confusion for the reader.[26] What is
needed at this stage is a theoretical framework that relates social, political, and
economic behavior to the institutional structures under consideration in a program
of air quality management. Such a framework, concerned with the actors in the
decision process, the strategies they pursue, the nature of the information available
to all parties, and the environment in which decisions are made, would be of
great assistance to legislators attempting to develop more rational regulatory institutions for securing pollution abatement. The following discussion may help to
provide a conceptual approach to the formulation of an effectively functioning control
program.

A. Theory of Conflict Resolution

Significant public policies originate in the conflict of group interests.[27] The peaceful resolution of these conflicts is generally achieved through reconciliation, compromise, or an award process in which both parties agree to accept the verdict of an
outside person or agency.[28] Reconciliation relies on discussion to lessen the differences of opinion between the participants. Compromise uses the mediation and
conciliation aspects of bargaining, while an award is achieved through arbitration
or legal trial. In air quality management or in any other environmental management program none of the three types of resolution can be considered as an independent technique for pollution abatement, although one form might predom-
inate. Indeed, Boulding asserts that reconciliation and compromise might occur
simultaneously, that some reconciliation may be necessary before compromise is
possible, that there are likely to be elements of discussion and propaganda in bargaining situations, that in arbitration cases or in court proceedings there are often elements of bargaining and reconciliation before the award is announced, and that an

---

[26] For a useful review of the major contributions in the area of decision theory, *see* Robinson &
Majak, *The Theory of Decision-Making*, in CONTEMPORARY POLITICAL ANALYSIS 175 (J. Charlesworth ed
1967).

[27] *See, e.g.*, J. ANDERSON, POLITICS AND THE ECONOMY (1966).

[28] *See* T. SCHELLING, THE STRATEGY OF CONFLICT 3-20 (1966).

award might not be accepted unless it has been preceded by informal reconciliation and bargaining.[29]

Game theory has become one principal avenue for research on conflict resolution, and it is usually defined as the formal study of rational decisions in situations
where "two or more individuals have choices to make, preferences regarding the
outcomes, and some knowledge of the choices available to each other and of each
other's preferences."[30] It is concerned with situations—games of strategy—in which
the best course of action for each participant depends on what he expects the other
participants to do, with the outcome a function of what choices are made by the
other actors. The individual decision units have only partial control over the
strategic factors affecting their environment, since the essence of the game is that
it involves adversaries whose fates are intertwined. In a sense each group or individual faces a cross-optimization problem in which plans must be adjusted not only
to one's own desires and abilities but also to those of others.

Bargaining, which is defined as the process by which a tolerable settlement for
all participants is reached,[31] falls within the theory of games but is a species of game
in which relatively little progress has been made, partly because it includes situations involving common interest as well as conflict between opponents.[32] Cooperation is useful in this type of game because within some range of possibilities both
parties will be better off with a solution, i.e., bargain, than without one. Conflict
is involved because within this range of solutions the participants compete for the
most favorable distribution of benefits. Thus, while both parties are interested in
the adoption of some solution, they have divergent interests with regard to the
particular solution that is adopted.[33]

Although bargaining has been widely studied and discussed, it is not always
clear, as McKean has pointed out,[34] just how bargaining works. Because of this lack
of knowledge, bargaining is often viewed as a constraint in decision making rather
than as a variable that could be manipulated to achieve a least-cost solution.[35] The

[29] K. BOULDING, CONFLICT AND DEFENSE: A GENERAL THEORY 310-13 (1962).

[30] Schelling, *What is Game Theory?*, in CONTEMPORARY POLITICAL ANALYSIS 213 (J. Charlesworth
ed. 1967).

[31] *See* Banfield, *Notes on a Conceptual Scheme*, in POLITICS, PLANNING AND THE PUBLIC INTEREST 307
(M. Meyerson & E. Banfield ed. 1953).

[32] In the terminology of game theory, bargaining is a positive-sum (as opposed to zero-sum), frequently nonsymmetrical game between participants with a mixture of conflict and cooperation. Zero-sum
games are those in which one player's loss is the other's gain. The sum of gain plus loss is zero—hence
"zero-sum." A positive-sum game is one in which the gain of one party is not equal to the loss of the
other. For example, a gain for A of one unit of value may only cause a loss to B of one-half unit.
A nonsymmetrical game results when B's loss varies from move to move even though A's gain with
each move is constant. These variations from the zero-sum prototype make the mathematics of a game
extremely complex.

[33] This dichotomy gives the bargaining game its unusual character and raises issues quite different
from pure conflict or pure cooperation games.

[34] McKean, *The Unseen Hand in Government*, 55 AM. ECON. REV. 494 (1965).

[35] *See* R. CYERT & J. MARCH, A BEHAVIORAL THEORY OF THE FIRM 31 (1967).

usual explanation for this situation is that there are no generally accepted operational criteria for determining economic efficiency, that there are many competing groups with diverse interests and values seeking to influence policy making, and that a variety of political, social, and ethical as well as economic considerations are involved in the making of public economic policy. The policy process involves the striking of balances and the making of compromises more often than the finding of "correct" policies or the choice between "right" and "wrong" in any absolute sense. Given the suggested importance of bargaining in the decision-making process, bargaining should no longer be viewed as a constraint within which one attempts to optimize. There are obvious costs and benefits associated with shifts in bargaining behavior that can be identified. Current and anticipated research on decision making in air quality management needs to take cognizance of the role of bargaining, and the researcher should seek to identify the costs and benefits attached to any bargaining solution.

While economists and mathematicians have developed highly sophisticated approaches to game theoretic decision making, such methodology might be only tangentially relevant to decision making in air quality management. For the social scientist that which is conceptual and rudimentary in game theory is the most valuable.[36] Rather than being thought of as a formal "theory," it is now viewed as a framework for analysis which can be adapted and modified according to specific needs. In essence, it provides a point of reference for examining a problem and gaining needed insights without accepting the often unrealistic rules of the game. With this in mind, the following section reviews some of the insights gained in the study of the bargaining aspects of game theory that might have potential application in devising a regulatory framework for air quality management. Because it is within the legislative power to change the rules and context within a particular "game" situation, understanding of the forces at work would assist in making institutional and substantive adjustments that will contribute to more nearly optimal outcomes.

B. Some Insights from Bargaining Theory

1. Continuous Games

Research on conflict situations clearly shows that negotiation and bargaining operate best in situations where the subject in contention can be divided into parts that can be dealt with sequentially. This incrementalism, whether achieved by changes in moves or in value systems, is of considerable importance.[37] To draw the analogy of chess, players move in turn, each moving a piece at a time; the game proceeds at a slow tempo by small increments and is of an indeterminate length. The game changes character in the course of play by a succession of small changes

[36] See, e.g., Schelling, supra note 30, at 219; Shubik, The Uses of Game Theory, in CONTEMPORARY POLITICAL ANALYSIS 260 (J. Charlesworth ed. 1967).

[37] See T. SCHELLING, supra note 28, at 170.

that can be observed and appreciated, with plenty of time for mistakes of individual players or mutual mistakes which can be noticed and adapted to in later play. In an uncertain situation, a person is often saved from making a strategic error if he hesitates, so the capacity to make future decisions is not relinquished.[38]

The decomposition tactic in bargaining can be applied to either threats or to promises, and can be viewed as a necessary prerequisite for making a bargain enforceable. This is so since there is a perception on the part of the participants that future possibilities for agreement will not develop unless mutual trust is created and maintained. The participants need to be confident that each of them will not jeopardize opportunities for future agreement by destroying trust near the start of the game.[39] Such confidence is naturally not always in evidence, so decomposition serves to encourage the same expectations on the part of all participants. An aspect of building mutual expectations is that if a threat can be decomposed into a series of consecutive threats, there is an opportunity to demonstrate to an opponent during his initial reaction to a threat that you "mean business," thereby making the continuous game a learning experience.[40] Although it is possible that future opportunities for bargaining are not anticipated, a semblance of a continuing game can be created by separating the issue at stake into consecutive components. The principle is also apparent that it is poor strategy to require compliance in terms of some critical amount or degree that would be deemed mandatory, for action geared to increments has a greater chance of success than one that has to be carried out either all at once or not at all once some particular point has been reached.

This is a concern of some importance in environmental management situations since they are structurally "lumpier" than chess games. There is no continuous range of choices open to the polluter and the abatement officer. Due to the initial administrative and psychic costs and the initial and marginal capital costs, moves have a considerable impact, and it is usually difficult to project a control situation more than a move or two ahead. The pace of the game can bring things to a head before much experience has been gained or much of an understanding reached unless ways are found to increase the number of possible moves. The use of incrementalism in structuring pollution abatement progress eases the impact of each move and allows the participants to acquire both knowledge of each other and experience with the particular problem at hand. Costs are spread over a longer period of time, and the slower pace of the process and the indeterminate length of the "game" reduce the possibility of crisis. Because of these advantages gained through the use of incrementalism, one would expect that conscious attempts would be made to increase the number of "moves" and extend the life of the game. It is of interest that the Air Quality Act specifies that multiple actions must take place before final regulatory

[38] See K. BOULDING, THE IMPACT OF THE SOCIAL SCIENCES 43 (1966).

[39] See T. SCHELLING, supra note 28, at 45.

[40] This learning process is detailed in A. RAPPAPORT & A. GHAMMAH, PRISONER'S DILEMMA (1965).

action occurs.[41] These steps make the process more incremental in nature, thus gaining for the participants the advantages described above.

Another aspect of the continuous game which must be considered is that negotiating processes develop certain rituals, and attempts to bypass or reduce these rituals may destroy the negotiating process itself.[42] For example, the parties begin the proceedings with somewhat bombastic statements that set the initial boundaries to the negotiations. There is a period of withdrawal designed to make it appear that the commitments are genuine. The parties know, however, that the commitments are not absolute; otherwise the negotiations would break down. There may follow a process of trading by which mutual concessions are made, and there may have to be a period during which, even though no visible progress occurs, the incipient settlement is in fact developing. The resolution of conflict through bargaining thus involves the difficult institutional problem of arranging these ritual elements in the proper order and proportion.[43] Because legal procedures may be too inflexible to permit the proper mix of ritual elements required by the bargaining and reconciling processes, a formal legal proceeding may often be a poor way of handling a conflict in air pollution control.

2. Focal Point Solutions

In bargains that involve quantification of solutions, such as the setting of emission and ambient air standards, there seems to be some appeal in mathematical simplicity. Outcomes tend to be expressed in even numbers since they provide good "resting places."[44] Thus a compromise at forty-seven per cent is much less likely than at fifty per cent. Just as the mathematical properties of a game can influence its outcome, the perception by the participants of the historical, cultural, legal, and moral properties of the game can serve to focus expectations on certain solutions. A "focal point"[45] solution has characteristics that distinguish it qualitatively from surrounding alternatives. Unlike the numerical scale, which is too continuous to provide good resting places, qualitative principles are more difficult to compromise, and focal points thus generally depend on qualitative principles. But a commitment to a principle that provides the basis for a numerical calculation which comes out at a specific number may provide the support for a stand at that point.

The outcome of any game can best be characterized by the notion of converging expectations.[46] A good example is the remarkable frequency with which long negotiations over complicated quantitative formulas or shares in some benefits and costs are ultimately influenced by a seemingly irrelevant previous negotiation. Prece-

---

[41] See § 108, 81 Stat. 485 (1967). See Martin & Symington, supra note 14, at 244-47.

[42] See Douglas, The Peaceful Settlement of Industrial and Intergroup Disputes, 1 J. CONFLICT RESOLUTION 69 (1957).

[43] See K. BOULDING, supra note 29, at 311.

[44] T. SCHELLING, supra note 28, at 114.

[45] Id. at 111.

[46] See id. at 114.

dent seems to exercise an influence that considerably exceeds its logical importance since both parties recognize it as a focal point. Past bargains become precedents for present situations in that they often remove from conscious consideration many agreements, decisions, and commitments that might well be subject to renegotiation as conditions change.[47]

If the outcome of a game is seemingly already determined by the participants' perception of the configuration of the problem itself and where the focal point lies, it would seem that the scope of bargaining skill would be insignificant. But it can be argued that the obvious outcome depends greatly on how the problem is formulated, on what analogies or precedents the definition of the bargaining issue calls to mind, and on the kinds of data that may be available to bring to bear on the question in dispute. Thus bargaining skill in air pollution control can be seen to be important before bargaining actually begins by being able to give prominence to some particular outcomes that would be favorable.

C. Conclusions on Bargaining Theory

Several aspects of the many facets of bargaining have been reviewed. These aspects—incrementalism, ritualization, continuing negotiation, and focal point solutions—all suggest that rationality in bargaining outcomes is a function of basically psychic phenomena. At first this view may appear to run contrary to the accepted economic notion that "rationality" is evident only in the minimum-cost solution. But a broader view of decision making may suggest that the least-cost solution is most readily approximated through procedures which take full cognizance of the psychic elements in any bargaining situation and which channel these elements in the direction of a mutually sought, economically sound goal.

V

THE ON-SITE INCINERATION EXAMPLE

An example of decision making in air quality management that helps to illustrate the discussion of bargaining is the attempt to reduce particulate emissions in New York City. During the mid 1960s the heightening concern of the public in New York City with air pollution was focused on visible suspended particulates. During this time, more than ninety per cent of the 50,000 complaints received per year by the Department of Air Pollution Control were related to visible emissions. Public attention was particularly focused on the approximately 12,000 apartment house and commercial incinerators which emitted an estimated 8,400 to 9,000 tons of particulates per year into the atmosphere. These incinerators became the first important issue in air quality management to face the city administration.

In 1966, responding to public pressure, the City Council passed, in some haste,

---

[47] See R. CYERT & J. MARCH, supra note 35, at 33.

a local law dealing with the reduction of sulfur dioxide emissions from fuel burning, the use of bituminous coal, the upgrading of municipal incinerators, the upgrading of existing private on-site incinerators, and the banning of incineration in new buildings. Of particular interest is the section of the law prohibiting construction of residential and commercial on-site incinerators after May 1968 and requiring the upgrading of all existing ones.[48] The first deadline under the law was May 20, 1967, a year after its passage. At that time the owners of an unknown number of incinerators in buildings of seven or more stories were to have completed construction of unspecified control equipment to meet criteria for levels of emissions which had at that time not yet been defined. Local Law 14, as it was called, also had a May 20, 1968, deadline for the upgrading of buildings under seven stories. The law states that the process of upgrading includes the "installation and use of an auxiliary gas burner regulated by automatic firing clocks, an overfire air fan and nozzle system and control apparatus as may be defined by the [Commissioner of Air Pollution Control]."[49] Basically the required procedure involved the installation of a firebox that burns the refuse efficiently and a scrubber system—a motor-driven device to force the smoke through a special water bath that will remove the heavy particulates. Only compactors would be permitted in new multiple dwellings. This fairly direct attempt at controlling particulate emissions, although not an ideal approach, might seem to some people a useful first step in the direction of cleaner air. Unfortunately it was not.

Why was this the case? The initial problem was that the Department of Air Pollution Control had relatively little time to develop specific criteria for upgrading as required under the law. As a result, the criteria were not formally adopted by the Board of Air Pollution Control until five months before the actual upgrading of the first group of apartment houses was to have been completed. A second problem was that the Department of Air Pollution Control had no enforcement powers to require compliance before the May 20, 1967, deadline. The options were to seal every noncomplying incinerator on or after that date or expedite compliance later. The first deadline came and passed with few completed upgradings. At one time about sixty incinerators were under seal by the Department. This state of affairs was partially due to questions that were raised as to who would *not* be required to upgrade their equipment. In an interpretation of Local Law 14 the City Corporation Counsel ruled that the law permitted every incinerator which had been installed before on-site incinerators became mandatory in 1951 to be closed down voluntarily rather than upgraded. Then, in August 1967, the Corporation Counsel interpreted the absence of any incinerator provision in the new city housing maintenance code to mean that almost all existing incinerators were now "volun-

---

[48] Local Law 14, May 20, 1966, N.Y. CITY ADMIN. CODE §§ 892-2.0 to 897-2.0 (Supp. 1967-1968).
[49] N.Y. CITY ADMIN. CODE § 892-4.3 (Supp. 1967-1968).

tary" and could close down rather than upgrade, which meant that the owner might convert to refuse chutes and handle raw or compacted refuse.

An additional complication was a virtual moratorium that was declared on public statements on the issue by the city administration on the ground that the Commissioner of Air Pollution Control was being sued by the New York Real Estate Board and some private real estate interests for imposing a law that was deemed to be "arbitrary and capricious." Another factor was that the Department of Sanitation was not prepared to collect an unknown amount of refuse that formerly was burned. Although there were other reasons why the Sanitation Department could not be counted on to collect the refuse, the Department cannot be blamed for viewing with alarm the prospect of picking up some unspecified amount of refuse that was previously burned in on-site incinerators.

As a result of these developments the city administration finally decided that the law in its original form was unworkable. On the basis of the experience gained, the law was amended in two ways that are more in agreement with the minimum cost approach and bargaining theory. These amendments related to the generation of alternatives to upgrading and the timing of compliance dates.

Before the amendments were introduced, a cost study of the alternative ways of approaching the problem of reducing particulate emissions from on-site incinerators was carried out.[50] The study considered the varying size of buildings, operating expenses, labor costs, capital investment, and the distribution of unit costs among a number of apartments. The results of this research indicated that the larger buildings would find it most economical to upgrade and that middle-sized buildings could be left to decide for themselves whether it would be cheaper to compact or to upgrade. It was predicted that only buildings which had about fifty units or less per incinerator would find it more economical to shut down. Using these data, the Department of Air Pollution Control estimated the refuse output from the projected shutdowns and determined that the Department of Sanitation could handle the additional volume over a three-year period. Although the actual amendment to the law as passed by the City Council did not include giving the option to every landlord to choose the method which he considered to be the cheapest, the option to shut down for buildings with forty or fewer dwelling units per incinerator was passed as a direct result of the economic analysis.

Another amendment provided a deadline for submission of compliance plans six months prior to the completion deadline. Various strategies of noncompliance that were so successful under the original law have a much lower probability of success now that the Department of Air Pollution Control can use an incremental approach to pollution abatement, which will avoid unexpected reactions and smooth

---

[50] Task Force 2 of the Comm. for Implementing Local Law 14, Economics of Upgrading or Discontinuing Incineration (mimeo., Oct. 3, 1967).

out the "lumpy" features of compliance programs. In keeping with bargaining theory, the "game" is spread out over a longer period of time.

The on-site incinerator example did not, of course, involve bargaining except in a very general sense, since the behavior that was observed involved noncompliance on the one hand and frustrated attempts at enforcing an unrealistic ordinance on the other. The example does, however, clearly convey both the relevance of decision theory to explain the way decisions are made and the importance of comprehending the least-cost principle in a program of direct regulation. Some further reflection on the role of bargaining as it is apt to evolve in air pollution control programs and other environmental management programs should suggest that the least-cost solution can and should be sought in a regulatory program, both by explicit recognition of the cost-benefit nexus and by giving bargaining a chance to function in conjunction with market forces. Indeed, it is possible to assert that regulation strategically employing cost-benefit analysis and market forces can yield solutions to particular pollution control problems that the regulators themselves are not wise enough to devise.

VI

DEVISING A HYPOTHETICAL REGULATORY SCHEME:
BARGAINING AND THE LEAST-COST SOLUTION

A. The Shape of Regulatory Programs, Present and Future

New York City's amended incinerator rules represent an across-the-board legislative attempt to control gross pollution from a very common type of emitter. While bargaining theory explains in some measure the experience with the original attempt and the evolution of the amendments, no opportunity for individual bargaining was actually observed. However, control of other types of pollution will almost necessarily involve ad hoc regulation of individual industrial polluters who cannot appropriately be dealt with by general legislation or rule-making.[51] In these circumstances face-to-face bargaining will be almost essential as a means of dealing with individual polluters.

As local air pollution control ordinances and statutes are now formulated, bargaining does not have a clear chance to operate, though practice almost inevitably opens some opportunities for give and take between polluters and the control agency in both the standard setting and compliance stages. Most of the legislation, which appears to have been modeled after zoning legislation, either establishes fixed emission standards or delegates the setting of the contemplated standards to the control

---

[51] Holden notes the inadequacies of state water pollution control legislation for this purpose. M. HOLDEN, POLLUTION CONTROL AS A BARGAINING PROCESS: AN ESSAY ON REGULATORY DECISION-MAKING (1966).

agency. Because fixed standards not only conflict with the least-cost principle but may raise potental constitutional problems, the statutes generally provide for variances to be granted by the agency. A typical variance provision is this one from the Illinois statute:

> The Board may grant individual variances beyond the limitations prescribed in this Act, whenever it is found, upon presentation of adequate proof, that compliance with any provision of this Act, or any rule or regulation, requirement or order of the Board, will result in an arbitrary and unreasonable taking of property or in the practical closing and elimination of any lawful business, occupation or activity, in either case without sufficient corresponding benefit or advantage to the people.[52]

The hardship required to be shown is a considerable one, though much is left to agency and court interpretation. One would have to conclude that, while the typical statutory language appears to permit variances only in extreme cases—perhaps only in those having constitutional dimensions[53]—an agency might, by seizing on the requirement that there be a "corresponding benefit or advantage," indulge in as much comparison of benefits and costs as it might wish. On balance, however, existing legislation appears to give less than sufficient sanction to methods of finding least-cost solutions.

The Air Quality Act of 1967 provides that states shall give effect to federally determined air quality criteria and control techniques once they are promulgated by HEW, which is also granted power to review the standards established and the proposed plan of enforcement.[54] It was apparently contemplated by Congress that new state and local legislation would be forthcoming, and this expectation, coupled with a fairly clear congressional mandate that pollution control be undertaken selectively in light of technological and economic feasibility,[55] suggests that new thought should be given to devising machinery that will be capable of doing this job most effectively. Indeed, if the concepts of "technological and economic feasibility" are equated with cost-benefit analysis, the question arises whether many existing regulatory schemes might fail to meet the approval of HEW. The issue that is raised is whether the federal act would justify HEW disapproval of state

---

[52] ILL. REV. STAT. ch. 111½, § 240.11 (1967).

[53] The reference to the constitutional problem simply refers to the general principle that the state cannot curtail one's use of his property without paying "just compensation." The concept of "taking," which appears in the statute, is a constitutional concept which defines whether or not compensation must be paid, and it is applied rather inconsistently. Still, it is possible that curtailment of the property owner's rights to pollute may be classified as a "taking" unless a strong case can be made based on regulation for public health and use of the police power. When aesthetic and generalized environmental quality goals are emphasized, constitutional doubts are increased. See Pollack, *Legal Boundaries of Air Pollution Control—State and Local Legislative Purpose and Techniques*, in this symposium, p. 331; see also Michelman, *Property, Utility, and Fairness: Comments on the Ethical Foundations of "Just Compensation" Law*, 80 HARV. L. REV. 1165 (1967).

[54] §§ 107(c), 108(c)(1), 81 Stat. 485. See Martin & Symington, *supra* note 14, at 259.

[55] The Air Quality Act of 1967, § 107(c), 81 Stat. 485, provides, "Such recommendations shall include such data as are available on the latest available technology and economic feasibility of alternative methods of prevention and control of air contamination including cost-effectiveness analyses."

and local legislation on the ground of heavyhandedness, or lack of willingness to discriminate among polluters on the basis of the many economic and administrative factors that are comprised in an optimal, least-cost solution. The act suggests that review is limited to assuring only that maximum effectiveness is achieved,[56] and HEW may be motivated to review only for weakness and not for potential economic hardship on polluters.

The remainder of this article, drawing on these speculations, sets forth some ideas about the shape and function of air quality management programs that can best approximate least-cost solutions. As noted earlier, the outlook is for programs of direct regulation rather than for the sort of effluent fee approach advocated by the welfare economist. While the data shortages that prevent implementation of effluent fees will also plague programs of direct regulation, the latter approach is more familiar and, as noted earlier, can probably sustain a greater amount of regulation in relative ignorance than could a more novel system. But in keeping with the "new federalism," which is often praised as lending itself to experimentation and innovation in ways of attacking particular problems, HEW should not, in exercising its supervisory powers, restrict states to traditional patterns of regulation. Indeed, the regional approach to regulation specified by the Air Quality Act would seem to anticipate and encourage new departures. Such innovation and experimentation at the regional level might produce significantly improved regulatory procedures.[57]

B. Structuring a Regulatory Program to Facilitate Bargaining

The regulatory setup we conceive of in the following discussion is the one most common in other systems of direct economic regulation. It features an independent regulatory body (the "commission") supported by a staff of legal and technical experts. Membership on the commission is for a relatively long fixed term, and, because of the nature of the issues to be encountered, the members might be required to have expertise of specified types. Thus, a three-member commission might comprise a lawyer, an economist, and a pollution control engineer. The commission

---

[56] The state control plan will be approved if the Secretary finds, among other things, "that such State *standards* are consistent with the air quality criteria and recommended control techniques issued pursuant to section 107." § 108(c)(1), 81 Stat. 485. (Emphasis added.) Section 107(c) provides that control techniques should be based on technological and economic feasibility. *See* note 55 *supra*. But the state enforcement *plan* need only be "consistent with the purposes of the Act insofar as it assures achieving such standards of air quality within a reasonable time," and must provide "a means of enforcement by State action, including authority comparable to" certain emergency powers provided in the act. § 108(c)(1), 81 Stat. 485. Thus the emphasis arguably is on achieving prompt compliance and not on cost effectiveness.

[57] One possible, perhaps even a likely, evolution from the present system would require polluters to *pay* for the variances they seek, the fee to be set in accordance with damage estimates. If variances were purchased rather than granted, the system would change profoundly, with variances becoming more palatable to the public and the control agency. Bargaining over the fees would yield some of the benefits sought in the program hypothesized below.

would operate as an independent decision maker, and its final rulings would be subject to judicial review. The agency staff bears the major enforcement burden and provides the evidence and expertise which guides the commission's efforts.

Any attempt to hypothesize about the outlines of an enforcement program that attempts to approach a least-cost solution through administrative means must recognize the desirability of avoiding the use of litigation before either judicial or administrative tribunals as the primary means of achieving abatement in individual cases. The limitations of both legal and technical staff resources, the importance of achieving prompt relief, the difficulty of resolving difficult and highly uncertain technical issues in an adversary proceeding, and the considerable administrative costs involved, all point to the need for minimizing the use of litigation whenever possible.[58] The approach that would be most helpful in achieving this objective would be to structure regulation to encourage the use of bargaining and settlements as the primary means of accomplishing regulatory objectives. Such a structuring would most likely include the following conditions:

(1) The control agency's regulations should provide for establishment of formal communication with both actual and potential polluters. Thus it might be required that all polluters within the agency's jurisdiction file reports with the agency on their present emission levels and perhaps a ten-year estimate of anticipated increases or decreases in these emissions. Other continuing contact would also be desirable, and informal conferences could be called that would bring the agency staff, trade associations, and other interest groups together to discuss the local problems. The author's interviews with Los Angeles Air Pollution Control District personnel confirm that informal conferences have been a key element in successfully controlling stationary sources of pollution.

(2) The agency's potential sanctions must be substantial but flexible enough so that they could be adjusted to the nature and magnitude of each particular problem confronted. Massive fines for emitting a small amount of pollution, for example, would be a poor agency strategy since it would distort the credibility of the agency's image as an arbiter of the public interest.

(3) The sanctions must put no premium on delay. Thus, a retroactive effluent charge, perhaps accumulating from the date of the agency's complaint, might be provided as a means of compelling a polluter to engage in bargaining in good faith. Filing of a complaint would thus constitute in itself a significant sanction and would most likely lead to bargaining before a formal proceeding was initiated, much as the Federal Power Commission and the Federal Communications Commission have tended to bargain for rate reductions without starting a formal rate

---

[58] The inadequacies of a litigation-oriented approach are detailed in NAT'L RESEARCH COUNCIL, NAT'L ACADEMY OF SCIENCES, WASTE MANAGEMENT AND CONTROL 203-221 (Pub. No. 1400, 1966).

case.[59] With this strategy, bargaining would also be encouraged after a complaint was filed.

(4) Paradoxically, although the agency's sanctions must be strong enough to encourage polluters to bargain in good faith, they should probably not be so strong as to allow the agency to enforce its will without some recourse to bargaining. This surprising condition—that weaker sanctions may be desirable—is dictated by the conclusion of studies of mixed conflict and cooperation situations that the "game" will not be constituted in good faith unless each side has something to win and something to lose, and that both must be in a position to lose if an outcome is not achieved. The final sanction of formal proceedings can and should be costly to both the agency and the polluter. Both this and the previous condition reflect the fact that inequality or imbalance in the strength of each party's sanctions will bias the outcomes of bargaining. The proper balance may be difficult to achieve but must be sought if something approximating the optimal, least-cost solution is to be arrived at.

(5) If informed bargaining is to operate to the public's advantage, the agency must be adequately staffed so that it is known that its sanctions will not go uninvoked if agreement is not reached or if bargaining is not conducted in good faith. The abatement of ninety per cent of the emissions from stationary sources of air pollution in Los Angeles County, for example, was achieved in part through the efforts of several hundred Air Pollution Control District employees. The New York experience recited above also illustrates the importance of credibility of sanctions.

(6) Public utility regulation points to the fact that the public's representatives at the bargaining table must be neither altogether free of nor unduly subject to political influence, in order, first, that excessive zeal or laxness can be checked and, second, that polluters may not accomplish through influence what they are unable to achieve by negotiation. Judging with respect to this one point, one might argue that the regulatory framework has been more effective in Los Angeles County than in New York City. California legislation authorizes any county to set up its Air Pollution Control District by resolution of the County Board of Supervisors declaring the need for the District to function. The districts are granted the power to "make and enforce all needful orders, rules, and regulations,"[60] and Los Angeles County was given considerable latitude in attacking its local problems. New York City, like Los Angeles County, has the power to adopt and enforce rules and regulations and authority to require permits and control devices on pollution-generating equipment,[61] but experi-

---

[59] See generally Welch, Constant Surveillance: A Modern Regulatory Tool, 8 VILL. L. REV. 340 (1963). See also note 65 infra.

[60] CAL. HEALTH & SAFETY CODE §§ 24260 (West 1967).

[61] N.Y. CITY ADMIN. CODE §§ 894-2.0, 892-3.0, 892-5.0 (1966); CAL. HEALTH & SAFETY CODE §§ 24261-63 (West 1967).

ence to date as was revealed by the on-site incinerator study, has been that the City Council has actively intervened in the Department's regulatory program. A comparative study of the two agencies shows that Los Angeles Air Pollution Control District has had much more freedom in the development of rules and regulations.[62]

(7) Experience with other types of regulation also suggests the desirability of maintaining public control of administrative discretion through openness in decision making. Thus, the data submitted by both the polluter and the agency staff, the terms of the settlement itself, the staff's reasons for accepting it, and the commission's approval should be on public file.[63] Also useful might be annual or more frequent reports of settlements, together with underlying data, which could be used by the legislative body to which the agency is responsible.[64]

(8) A final precondition for effective bargaining is a clearly defined legal framework within which bargaining can operate. This is essential so that the bargainers— the agency staff and the individual polluter—can largely avoid differences on questions of legal principle while concentrating on the development of the technical and economic data needed to reach a judgment about potential least-cost solutions.[65] Included among the many issues that ideally need to be resolved and eliminated from dealings with individual polluters are as many of the overriding facts as possible about the air pollution problem in the particular airshed. Such questions as estimates of pollution damage in general and attribution of this damage to particular pollutants would be best resolved authoritatively after public hearings open to all interested parties. Bargaining with individual polluters could then proceed without calling these matters back into question. Further discussion below considers how certain specific issues are better resolved in general agency rule-making proceedings than in case-by-case bargaining or adversary proceedings.

If conditions such as the foregoing could be created, face-to-face bargaining could be made to serve an important function in the administration of an effective air pollution control program. It is argued that the advantages would be many, including the establishment of cooperative attitudes between regulators and industry, which would encourage a joint search for solutions to problems; a de-emphasis of

---

[62] Hagevik, Decision Processes in Air Quality Management (unpublished dissertation, forthcoming in 1969).

[63] The Air Quality Act of 1967, § 108(c)(5), 81 Stat. 485, states that in connection with hearings conducted under the act, "no witness or any other person shall be required to divulge trade secrets or secret processes." Some confidentiality must be provided by any regulatory scheme.

[64] Evaluation of agency performance by the legislature is one of the more important aspects of a rational decision process. See A. MAASS & M. HUFSCHMIDT, DESIGN OF WATER RESOURCE SYSTEMS ch. 15 (1962).

[65] Testimony to the importance of establishing such a framework appears in an opinion of the FCC defending the decision to commence the first full-scale rate case against AT&T. In response to Bell's stated preference for bargaining as a rate-making method, the Commission stated, "Indeed, we believe that the standards and criteria developed on the record here will enable us to employ continuing surveillance [i.e., bargaining] even more effectively in the future." Re American Tel. & Tel. Co., 61 P.U.R.3d 554, 559-60 (1965). The words "even more" are self-serving.

fact finding through quasi-judicial processes and the avoidance of "swearing contests," which are characteristic of adversary proceedings requiring expert testimony; speed, flexibility, and efficiency in the sense that appellate proceedings and time-consuming judicial review would be avoided; and a more efficient use of technical, administrative, and legal staffs.

C. Toward a Least-Cost Solution

There is an axiom among engineers that one can "go slow by running too fast." Although this statement can be interpreted by control officials with some justification as a polluter's excuse for doing nothing, the establishment of the preconditions for an effective control program is a case where the axiom applies. The structuring of the process that will produce efficient resource allocation depends in large part, as we have noted, on the decisions of the legislators who create the sanctions and provide the enforcement staff and on the establishment of a clear legal and factual framework within which to operate. Since a prime objective is to keep as many issues as possible out of litigation, the agency needs the authority to negotiate concerning factual uncertainty. Given the state of the art in environmental management, the legislators need to realize that the "best guess" approach requires that some substantial degree of discretion be given to the agency and its technical staff.

The commission will begin developing the necessary legal and factual framework by holding public hearings as a prelude to authoritative findings on these factual issues:

(1) the total damages attributable to air pollution in the airshed.

(2) the allocation of these damages to each pollutant or each major group of sources. The findings on these first two points need not be sufficiently detailed to satisfy a welfare economist, and it is obvious that the goal is simply the best estimates possible.

(3) an inventory of emissions, including the total amount of each pollutant emitted at particular times and in particular areas.

(4) the relationship of emission levels to the assimilative capacity of the ambient air. This would be determined by using a relatively simple atmospheric diffusion model and air quality monitoring devices. Thus, New York City is now putting into operation an aerometric system of monitoring stations which record and transmit data on levels of sulfur dioxide, dustfall, suspended particulates, and smoke shade on a continuous basis to the Department of Air Pollution Control; New York has also developed a simple model which fairly accurately describes the complex diffusion of pollutants in the city.

(5) the objectives of the abatement program, stated in terms of air quality and the level of damages anticipated as optimal for the airshed as a whole.[65a]

[65a] *See* note 70 *infra* on the derivation of such objectives.

Some of the foregoing factual judgments would be based in part on the air quality criteria to be issued by HEW under the Air Quality Act.[66] Additional evidence would be required, and the agency's conclusions should be buttressed by subsidiary findings and a reasoned opinion. All such findings would be subject to periodic review and revision, each time following the procedures employed in the initial formulation. Taken all together, these findings should give a sufficiently clear picture to allow our decision-making and bargaining framework to begin functioning.

An additional matter that the agency would probably find it appropriate to resolve in a rule-making proceeding is the development of a generalized technique for determining a polluter's contribution to the region's over-all concentration of pollutants. Once this issue was settled in principle, the questions at issue with each polluter would be (1) his respective contribution of pollutants to concentrations in the ambient air, which would probably be fairly close to the proportion of total emissions for which he was responsible, adjusted for such factors as wind, timing of emissions, and stack height; and (2) the polluter's costs associated with varying levels of abatement.

Ideally the agency staff would be able to negotiate effectively within this framework of settled legal and economic principles and authoritative general findings of fact concerning the extent and danger of pollution. The issues at stake in the bargaining with individual polluters would be almost exclusively factual and would be susceptible to quantified solutions, thus facilitating some compromise in areas of valid doubt. Focal point bottlenecks could be largely avoided since matters of legal and economic principle would have been eliminated for the most part by rule making; where legal questions did arise they could be set aside for separate authoritative decision by the commission. Such procedures would allow time for incrementalism to operate to narrow gradually the range of possible results, and the continuing negotiating machinery, which would be focused primarily on technical issues, would provide a hospitable climate for the resolution of these issues.[67]

The strategy of a least-cost solution within a bargaining framework suggests that the legislative body to which the control agency is responsible must clean its own house first by upgrading or abandoning any municipal incinerators it operates and reducing the emission levels from governmental heating and generating plants. This is necessary to avoid the embarrassing—and legitimate—charge that a governmental jurisdiction is forcing the private sector to clean up its pollution while continuing to pollute the air itself. This has been a continuing accusation in New York

[66] § 107, 81 Stat. 485 (1967). *But see* note 70 *infra* on the theoretical deficiencies of the HEW criteria.

[67] One of the reasons given for the success of the Los Angeles Air Pollution Control District is that there has been a great deal of cooperation between the technical staff of the District and the technical staffs of the regulated industries.

City where the municipal incinerators had not been upgraded by the time private on-site incinerators were to be upgraded.

The agency's next move would be to tackle the sources of air pollution which can have their levels of pollutant emissions reduced in fairly straightforward ways that clearly yield greater benefits than costs. This might mean that the agency should proceed against those polluters who are perceived by both the control agency and the public at large as the most significant polluters of the atmosphere in the jurisdiction, but not always. For example, it is now recognized in New York City that the formulators of Local Law 14 made a strategic error in the structuring of the legislation by requiring that initial action be taken against on-site incinerators even though they were a source of easily visible localized particulate concentrations.

Initial agency action, in addition to avoiding potential charges of being "arbitrary and capricious," must consider the impact of highly localized costs in relation to diffuse benefits and whether the technological and administrative solutions to problems are at hand. In the New York case, it can clearly be argued that a much greater reduction of air pollution could have been achieved at a lower cost to individual polluters by proceeding initially against the emissions of sulfur oxides and particulates resulting from the burning of fuel oil. A technical solution—switching to low-sulfur fuel oil—was available which could be implemented without too much difficulty.[68] In fact, due to difficulties involved in getting thousands of on-site incinerators upgraded or shut down, the program to change to a low-sulfur fuel, which was initiated after the incinerator upgrading, yielded tangible benefits much sooner.

Selecting the initial target in this manner has considerable implications in terms of later control efforts. A demonstrated success gives the agency a good image, reflects positively on the elected officials who give the agency support, and lessens the opposition of businessmen to control efforts aimed at them. The stage is also set for conflict resolution procedures such as negotiation and bargaining rather than for the polarization of attitudes that results in litigation.

One of the more important matters that should concern a control agency operating under our system is the establishment of a method of determining the maximum abatement expenditure—or level of abatement—that could be required of an individual polluter. This complex question has practical importance because all polluters cannot be attacked at once and the marginal unit abatement costs apparently justified when pollution levels are high will seem inappropriate when more nearly tolerable concentrations have been achieved.[69] All polluters should be subject to the

---

[68] Although making the use of low-sulfur fuel mandatory is in conflict with the economists' rational model, it can still be viewed as a sound decision in keeping with our strategy, which would allow mixing of necessary approaches. At a later stage another approach should probably be substituted.

[69] Since the aggregate cost curve for damage abatement within an airshed is almost certainly nonlinear—costs increase as the more obvious sources of pollution are controlled and as the more serious damage is eliminated—an estimate of the amount of damage reduction obtainable from a unit of abate-

same maximum, however, and the derivation of this maximum is extraordinarily difficult. A very rough figure can be derived, however, if air quality standards or goals—indicators of the level of air quality desired within a given jurisdiction— have been developed from objectives and constraints specified in the legislative process and in HEW's air quality criteria. Beginning with these goals, which will necessarily include estimates of the abatement outlays required to achieve them,[70] the agency can arrive at a general estimate of the theoretical emission level at which all marginal expenditures would equal marginal benefits. No polluter should be required to abate below that emission level which he would be permitted to maintain under such optimal conditions, or, in other words, to pay more for a unit of abatement than would yield a net gain if optimal conditions prevailed.

CONCLUSION

Optimizing methods are a guide to decisions, not a philosopher's stone that substitutes for decision. With a view to achieving practical results, it has been pointed out how bargaining might contribute to finding a least-cost solution. Although bargaining is often viewed as a distributional device rather than one that promotes efficiency, it has been shown that the latter view can also be taken. Having been directed, or having found it expedient, to adopt a cost-benefit approach, the control agency would be responsive within our framework to polluters' arguments based on a comparison of marginal benefits and costs associated with alternative emission reduction techniques. The polluter would most likely be inclined to hold out for the lowest-cost remedy and to develop and advance in the negotiations alternative ways of accomplishing the objectives being sought—an advantage, it will be recalled, usually associated exclusively with effluent fees as a control mechanism. Market forces will thus aid the controllers in seeking the most efficient approach to pollution damage reduction. For these reasons the outcome of a properly structured bargaining process should not deviate too far from economic rationality.

The hypothetical regulatory program we have outlined probably represents an ideal difficult to achieve in our society today. Why it may be so is a matter for

---

ment by the first polluter proceeded against might be high if this polluter was considered as an isolated source. This would apparently justify imposition of equally high abatement costs. Such a view of marginal control expenditures and benefits is deceptive, however, in that if other firms or groups of firms were forced to abate sequentially, their positions on the curve would be lower and their expenditures would yield a lower return, thereby decreasing the amount of required investment. Thus, a simplistic comparison of marginal costs and benefits is not enough, since this would result in applying a different standard to each polluter depending on the sequence in which they are attacked.

[70] See Thomas, *The Animal Farm, A Mathematical Model for the Discussion of Social Standards for Control of the Environment*, 77 Q. J. ECON. 143 (1963). Thomas points out that to set a quality criterion is to impute a cost-benefit ratio. *Id.* at 147. Thus the starting point for pollution abatement programs should be cost-benefit analysis and not arbitrarily determined quality criteria or emission standards. *But see* H.R. REP. No. 728, 90th Cong., 1st Sess. 16 (1967), which states that economic considerations are to have no place in the development of HEW's criteria.

conjecture and concern, and the most pessimistic conclusions one might draw is that the law and the legal system are in many respects incompatible with the scientific pursuit of optimal conditions under constraints of uncertainty.[71] We have proposed a scientific approach to pollution control requiring gross estimates of pollution damage and abatement costs. A problem of concern in this framework is the difficulty of making damage and cost estimates having enough objective validity to withstand legal attack when viewed as the product of a hearing record which must contain "substantial evidence" to support the result reached. In many respects informed guesses will be all that the control commission can show, and honesty should compel the commission to admit the depth of human ignorance on the questions in issue and to acknowledge frankly that its findings are made for the purpose of getting on with the abatement job. Courts would then be faced clearly with the problem of allowing regulation to proceed in the dim light of partial knowledge or to cease until science can provide light enough to satisfy the judicial sense of what due process requires.

Experience with the regulatory process in general suggests, however, that agencies do not as a rule confess ignorance but rather pretend to omniscience. While often not disclosing the true basis for their decisions and allowing their opinions to be written in "judge proof" boilerplate by their legal staffs, the agencies assume an air of knowledgeability that belies more than it reveals. This attitude might work in air pollution control as well, and the temptation to adopt it will be great. Control commissions may prefer to fill their opinions with statistics and data and to conclude by solemnly declaring, "Having considered all of the evidence and the relevant legal principles . . . ." The results may be unimpeachable for the simple reason that the underlying principles relating such items as costs to benefits are not stated and thus not subject to review. The alternative may be unattractive in administrative circles because the necessary estimates are of such precariousness that they can be defended only by candor about the depth of the problem and by apparent conscientiousness in approaching it. Nevertheless, the courts should learn to insist on full disclosure in lieu of obfuscation. Once this is obtained, judicial review should then require only the exercise of the agency's expert judgment on the best information and data available, incomplete and unsatisfying as it may seem. In no event should the courts prevent effective regulatory action solely because science has not yet yielded the secrets needed to realize the the regulatory ideal.

---

[71] For a more optimistic view, see National Research Council, supra note 58, at 204, 207-09, 214-17.

OBTAINING BOILER FUEL GAS TO REDUCE AIR POLLUTION: THE POLICY OF THE FEDERAL POWER COMMISSION

BARRY D. REIN*

INTRODUCTION

Public utilities, particularly those operating steam-electric generating plants, contribute substantially to atmospheric pollution. The extent of their contributions may be affected in any given instance by the location of the plant, the type of generating unit, the particular fuel or fuels burned, the existence of pollution control equipment, and the scheduling of particular fuels in multi-fuel plants. One or more of these factors may fall within the purview of regulatory agencies of the federal, state, and local governments. This article deals with an aspect of utilities regulation of particular importance: the jurisdiction of the Federal Power Commission (FPC) over the use by steam-electric generating utilities of natural gas for boiler fuel, for the purpose of reducing air pollution produced by burning alternative fuels.

In 1938 the FPC was given responsibility for administering the federal part of a comprehensive federal-state regulatory scheme intended to assure that natural gas, a wasting asset, would be allocated to uses consistent with the public interest at minimum cost to the consumer. Through the years this broad directive has been narrowed to an inquiry into particular criteria which purport to embody the public interest. Attempts in recent years to add to this list of criteria the impact of a requested fuel use change on air pollution have met with less than complete success. The problem sought to be mitigated by these attempts—utilities' contributions to atmospheric pollution—is not likely to be solved in the immediate future other than by increased allocations of gas to replace coal and oil as boiler fuel. However, other solutions, particularly nuclear power generation, are visible somewhat further ahead. Consequently, until these alternative solutions are found or implemented, it is likely that increasing pressure will be brought to bear upon the Commission to certificate boiler fuel gas. Where certification can be shown to have a significant impact on air pollution, such pressure may ultimately result in a reversal of the Commission's present unreceptiveness to air pollution arguments.

* B.S. 1961, Massachusetts Institute of Technology; LL.B. 1965, Georgetown University. Associate in the firm of Pennie, Edmonds, Morton, Taylor & Adams, New York City. Counsel, Citizens for Clean Air, Inc., New York City.

The writer wishes to express his appreciation to Robert F. Ebin, Esq., of counsel for Citizens for Clean Air, Inc., before the Federal Power Commission in *Transcontinental Gas Pipe Line Corp. (Phase II)*, for his valuable assistance in the preparation of this article.

I

THE EFFECT OF STEAM-ELECTRIC GENERATION ON AIR POLLUTION

Generation of electrical power by fossil fuels invariably produces pollutants; the particular pollutants produced and their rates of production vary with different fuels. The important fossil fuels (burned under boilers to make steam used to run turbine generators) are oil, coal, and natural gas.[1]

Coal and oil in burning produce fly ash, soot, and grime (euphemistically known collectively as "particulate matter"), hydrocarbons, carbon monoxide, sulfur oxides (sulfur dioxide and sulfur trioxide), nitrogen oxides, and other pollutants. Sulfur oxides and particulates, primarily, are relevant to the present discussion since they are the significant pollutants produced by burning coal and oil. Natural gas, in contrast, produces no particulates, is virtually sulfur-free, and yields no significant amounts of other pollutants. This fact has resulted in pressure upon the FPC, which has jurisdiction over interstate transportation and sale of natural gas, to license the provision of quantities of gas to replace coal and oil as boiler fuel. However, in the several proceedings which have been brought to obtain gas for boiler fuel, the Commission has generally taken the position that the advantage to be gained by way of reducing air pollution does not outweigh other factors militating against granting the gas.

For an indication of the potential benefit to be obtained by substituting gas for coal or oil, consider that in 1965 the average sulfur oxide emissions of Consolidated Edison Company ("Con Ed") in New York City[2] amounted to 789 tons per day—361.9 tons due to coal burning and 427.1 tons due to oil.[3] In total, Con Ed contributed about half (300,000 tons) of the total sulfur dioxide emitted into New York's atmosphere in 1965. Of slightly over 95,000 tons of particulates emitted into New York City's atmosphere in 1966, power generation accounted for twenty-one per cent.[4]

The importance of the utilities' role in polluting a given atmosphere depends upon the importance of sulfur oxides in the area's over-all pollution picture. Climate, topography, meteorology, industrial concentration, and many other factors affect a city's pollution mix. In Los Angeles, for example, where space heating (a major

---

[1] A small amount of steam is generated by some utilities for direct delivery through insulated pipes to customers for heating and air conditioning. Steam generation presents certain problems over and above those associated with electrical generation, namely, that steam generating plants cannot be relocated outside the cities served by them, since the steam cannot be transported over appreciable distances.

[2] Much of the data used herein relates to New York City because this data is readily available to the author.

[3] These figures are based on New York City in 1965. Percentage ranges for the sulfur content of coal and oil burned by Con Ed are approximated: coal, 1-2.5%; fuel oil, 2.15-2.40%. MAYOR'S TASK FORCE ON AIR POLLUTION IN THE CITY OF NEW YORK, FREEDOM TO BREATHE 117 (1966) [hereinafter cited as TASK FORCE REPORT].

[4] G. CHALMERS, AIR POLLUTION CONTROL IN SOLID WASTE MANAGEMENT IN THE NEW YORK CITY METROPOLITAN REGION, table 2 (Resource Paper prepared for Citizens for Clean Air, Inc., New York City, 1968) [hereinafter cited as SOLID WASTE MANAGEMENT REPORT].

contributor of sulfur oxides) is almost nonexistent, the primary problems stems from the community's heavy reliance on the automobile, which produces large quantities of oxides of nitrogen that react with ozone to form a brownish haze over the city. In New York, while nitrogen oxides are a problem, the inordinate quantities of sulfur oxides from space heating, industry, and utilities dominate the pollutant mix.

The physiological harm to the human body from sulfur compounds and particulates is thoroughly documented.[5] Oxides of sulfur are emitted into the atmosphere, predominantly as sulfur dioxide; a small percentage is, or is oxidized to, sulfur trioxide, which combines with water vapor in the air to form sulfuric acid. Minute particles of soot in the atmosphere act as condensation nucleii for the oxides and the acid. Respirable because of their size, these carrier particles transport the sulfur compounds into the passages in the lungs, causing pulmonary emphysema as well as lesser lung ailments. The particulates which serve as carriers are generally less than five microns in diameter and are emitted into most urban atmospheres from space heating and industrial plants as well as from power generating utilities. The utilities' contribution to the finer particulates—those especially harmful to health— is moreover greater than their over-all share of net particulate emissions. The reason for this is that relatively efficient control devices on the utilities' stacks preferentially remove larger particles; power plant emissions are consequently entirely in the dangerous under-five-micron range.[6]

Further complicating an analysis of the utilities' contribution to pollution is a lack of understanding of the relationship between emissions and atmospheric concentration. Emissions of a particular pollutant from one kind of source can be measured. However, there is no known method for quantitatively translating an emission from a particular source or type of source into the pollutant concentration in the atmosphere caused directly by that source or source type. Qualitative conclusions, necessarily imprecise, can be drawn but they are not very satisfactory as hard evidence.

Still other factors, none of which are susceptible of mathematically precise description, enter into any attempt to prove or disprove the effect of a utility's emissions on air pollution. Cities often generate atmospheric inversions—a layer of air which traps a bubble of stagnant air beneath it. Utilities usually have high smoke-stacks, and their emissions to some extent "punch through" the inversion layer; to that extent

---

[5] E.g., McCarroll, Measurements of Morbidity and Mortality Related to Air Pollution, a paper presented at the 59th Annual Meeting of the Air Pollution Control Ass'n, San Francisco, Cal., June 20, 1966; Winkelstein, The Relationship of Air Pollution and Economic Status to Total Mortality and Selected Respiratory System Mortality in Men, a paper presented at the American Medical Ass'n Air Pollution Medical Research Conference, Los Angeles, Cal., March 2-4, 1966; prepared testimony of Dr. Stephen M. Ayres, Record at 8597-8610, Transcontinental Gas Pipe Line Corp. (Phase II), 38 F.P.C. No. 532, 71 P.U.R.3d 161 (Nov. 6, 1967). See also Cassell, The Health Effects of Air Pollution and Their Implications for Control, in this symposium, —.

[6] In the New York City metropolitan area, power plants contribute about 20% (13,000 tons in 1966) of the total particulates but about one-third of the respirable particulates. SOLID WASTE MANAGEMENT REPORT 3.

their emissions do not contribute to the city's pollutant concentration. But the extent of this "punch-through" effect can never be known, even to a good approximation.[7]

The advocate's burden of demonstrating to the FPC that, with all of the above factors considered, the requested certification will have a substantial beneficial impact on the local pollution problem, is not an easy one. Moreover, the art and rules of legal advocacy are not the best tools for arriving at scientific truth. Nevertheless, if sufficient expert opinion is mustered on the side of those seeking the gas, all that the opposition can do is present a negative defense, attempting to show a lack of hard scientific evidence for the experts' conclusions. This is not a very persuasive type of case.

II

THE SCOPE OF THE FPC's JURISDICTION UNDER THE NATURAL GAS ACT— CONSERVATION OF GAS AND THE "END USE" DOCTRINE

Jurisdiction over interstate transportation and sale of natural gas, bottomed on the Commerce Clause of the Constitution, is granted to the FPC by the Natural Gas Act of 1938.[8] Section 1 of the act, defining its scope, provides in part

(a) . . . that the business of transporting and selling natural gas for ultimate distribution to the public is affected with a public interest, and that Federal regulation in matters relating to the transportation of natural gas and the sale thereof in interstate and foreign commerce is necessary in the public interest.

(b) The provisions of this chapter shall apply to the transportation of natural gas in interstate commerce, to the sale in interstate commerce of natural gas for resale for ultimate public consumption for domestic, commercial, industrial or any other use, and to natural-gas companies engaged in such transportation or sale. . . .

A "natural gas company" is defined by section 2 of the act, as "a person engaged in the transportation of natural gas in interstate commerce, or the sale in interstate commerce of such gas for resale."[9]

The regulatory power of the Commission is comprehensive, extending to rates and classifications; regulations, practices, and contracts affecting rates; extension, improvement, or abandonment of facilities; making connections with customers to be served; and the transportation or sale of gas[10]—all subject to the interstate and foreign commerce restrictions of section 1(b) of the act.[11] Section 4 empowers the Com-

---

[7] Their effect at some distant point downstream from the emission is another matter. *E.g.*, TASK FORCE REPORT 12 ("Dirty air drifts into New York from hundreds of miles away—especially from nearby New Jersey, with its relatively uncontrolled industrial complexes and incinerators.") *See* note 58 *infra*.

[8] 15 U.S.C. § 717 (1964).

[9] *Id.* § 717(a)(6).

[10] *Id.* §§ 717d, 717f. The Commission is empowered to and does delve deeply into the cost economics underlying any rate which it may properly regulate.

[11] The Commission was not granted comprehensive power over all incidents of gas production, transportation, and sale. Certain incidents were left for state regulation. *See* Panhandle Eastern Pipe Line Co. v. Public Service Comm'n, 332 U.S. 507, 514 (1947). Its jurisdiction was materially expanded,

mission to review and regulate rates charged by natural gas companies in connection with the transportation or sale of all gas subject to its jurisdiction, and to declare unlawful any rates which are not "just and reasonable."[12] Section 7(c) requires that[13]

> No natural gas company . . . shall engage in the transportation or sale of natural gas, subject to the jurisdiction of the Commission, or undertake the construction . . . of any facilities therefor, or acquire or operate any such facilities . . . unless there is in force with respect to such natural gas company a certificate of public convenience and necessity issued by the Commission authorizing such acts or operations.

The movement of gas in foreign (as distinguished from interstate) commerce is broadly and simply covered by section 3 of the act, requiring Commission sanction of all exports and imports of natural gas. That sanction is assured unless the export or import would "not be consistent with the public interest."[14]

This bird's-eye view of the broad federal regulatory power over natural gas, extending to most gas currently being produced, indicates that air pollution considerations might be urged upon the Commission in any number of situations. However, such considerations have figured importantly only in one context—attempts by public utilities to obtain gas as boiler fuel for electrical power generation. Non-boiler-fuel gas intended for resale by utilities to consumers has been obtained or refused based upon the usual economic and market factors historically relevant to "public convenience and necessity," as that term is used in section 7 of the act. It has apparently not been necessary for petitioners to advance arguments based on air pollution to obtain resale gas, even though such arguments might conceivably be made.

Attempts to obtain boiler fuel gas, however, have run headlong into the FPC's "end use" policy, bottomed on the Commission's asserted duty to conserve gas, a wasting asset, by limiting its expenditure to end uses adjudged to be in the public

however, by the 1942 amendments to the Natural Gas Act, 56 Stat. 83, 15 U.S.C. § 717f(c)-(g) (1964); see FPC v. Transcontinental Gas Pipe Line Corp., 365 U.S. 1 (1961).

[12] 15 U.S.C. § 717c. §§ 717c(a) and (b) state,
"(a) All rates and charges made, demanded, or received by any natural-gas company for or in connection with the transportation or sale of natural gas subject to the jurisdiction of the Commission, and all rules and regulations affecting or pertaining to such rates or charges, shall be just and reasonable, and any such rate or charge that is not just and reasonable is declared to be unlawful.
"(b) No natural-gas company shall, with respect to any transportation or sale of natural gas subject to the jurisdiction of the Commission, (1) make or grant any undue preference or advantage to any person or subject any person to any undue prejudice or disadvantage, or (2) maintain any unreasonable difference in rates, charges, service, facilities, or in any other respect, either as between localities or as between classes of service."
[13] Id. § 717f(c).
[14] Id. § 717b. Its foreign commerce jurisdiction, insofar as it concerns facilities located at any United States border, is exercised by the Commission in conformity with Exec. Order No. 10,485, 3 C.F.R., 1949-1953 Comp., at 970, 15 U.S.C. § 717b (1964).

interest. Such uses are, according to the Commission, those for which no other fuel is equivalent to gas or provides the same technical and economic advantages. Other end uses—including use as boiler fuel—are deemed to be inferior, that is, the necessity to conserve gas outweighs any advantage to be gained from the "inferior" use.

The end use doctrine and its application by the Commission are central to an understanding of past attempts to obtain boiler fuel gas and to the probable outcome of future attempts. The doctrine is not new; decisions of the Commission alluded to and weighed end use beginning as far back as 1944.[15] There was at that time some question whether matters of conservation, upon which its inquiry into end use is founded, were properly the subject of the Commission inquiry. Conservation was clearly not placed within the Commission's purview by the 1938 act.[16] To correct what it believed to be an undesirable limitation, preventing inquiry into the social and economic ramifications of fuel use, the Commission argued as follows:

> The Natural Gas Act as presently drafted does not enable the Commission to treat fully the serious implications of such a problem. The question should be raised as to whether the proposed use of natural gas would not result in displacing a less valuable fuel and create hardships in the industry already supplying the market, while at the same time rapidly depleting the country's natural-gas reserves. Although, for a period of perhaps 20 years, the natural gas could be so priced as to appear to offer an apparent saving in fuel costs, this would mean simply that social costs which must eventually be paid had been ignored.
> Careful study of the entire problem may lead to the conclusion that use of natural gas should be restricted by functions rather than by areas. Thus, it is especially adapted to space and water heating in urban homes and other buildings and to the various industrial heat processes which require concentration of heat, flexibility of control, and uniformity of results. Industrial uses to which it appears particularly adapted include the treating and annealing of metals, the operation of kilns in the ceramic, cement, and lime industries, the manufacture of glass in its various forms, and use as a raw material in the chemical industry. General use of natural gas under boilers for the production of steam is, however, under most circumstances of very questionable social economy.[17]

The 1942 amendments to the act, enacted at the Commission's urging,[18] at least partially closed this gap in its regulatory authority. The uncertainty of the impact in this area of the 1942 amendments, however, is illustrated by the fact that in *FPC v. Transcontinental Gas Pipe Line Corp.* (hereinafter called the *X-20* case),[19]

---

[15] Memphis Nat. Gas Co., 4 F.P.C. 197 (1944), *aff'd sub nom.* Department of Conservation v. FPC, 148 F.2d 746 (5th Cir. 1945), *cert. denied,* 326 U.S. 717 (1945).

[16] This was recognized by the Commission in its Annual Report for 1940. 20 FPC ANN. REP. 79-80 (1940). The 1938 act, § 7(c), ch. 556, § 7(c), 52 Stat. 825, *as amended,* 15 U.S.C. § 717f(c) (1964), authorized the Commission to determine public convenience and necessity only in cases where application was made to transport gas into areas already being served by another natural gas company.

[17] 20 FPC ANN. REP. 79 (1940).

[18] H.R. REP. No. 1290, 77th Cong., 1st Sess. 3 (1941); S. REP. No. 948, 77th Cong., 2d Sess. (1942).

[19] 365 U.S. 1 (1961).

which in 1961 finally confirmed the legitimacy of the end use doctrine, each successive tribunal decided this question oppositely to the previous one. The Supreme Court ultimately found inquiry into end use by the Commission to be a proper exercise of its duty to consider all factors, including gas conservation, bearing on the public interest. But this, the Court ruled, did not go so far as to empower the Commission "to formulate a flat rule against direct sales [of gas] for use under industrial boilers."[20] This limitation on its authority appears at least to require the Commission in a section 7 proceeding to examine the particular factors surrounding the end use at issue and to make them part of the equation for determining the public interest. Thus there are no end uses which per se warrant denial of certification; there is no statutory authority for any per se rule based on end use categorizations.

Aside from putting to rest arguments over the extent of the Commission's power to consider end use, the X-20 case was the first instance in which air pollution arguments were advanced in an attempt to obtain boiler fuel gas. The precise issue before the Commission and, subsequently, the Court, was whether Transcontinental should be permitted to sell to Con Ed certain gas for use as boiler fuel. Unfortunately (by way of precedent) for those who have since sought to obtain certification of boiler fuel gas, the particular sale proposed by Con Ed was a "direct," or nonjurisdictional, sale. That is, the proposed X-20 service involved a sale by the producer directly to Con Ed, who then contracted with Transcontinental to have it transported to New York.[21] This raised in the Commission's mind the spectre of a vast increase in nonjurisdictional sales, over which it exercises no rate-making power, possibly leading to a sizable increase in field prices.

Aside from the jurisdictional factor the Commission's attention was focused primarily on so-called "conventional requirements" of public convenience and necessity.[22] As the court of appeals' opinion pointed out, this phrase

> is a vague one, something like "due process of law," out of which one can get what he cares to put in. It is, obviously, the kind of a phrase where experience through the years builds up criteria which must be met in determining its content. Such experience-built criteria were what the Commission looked at when it saw that the "conventional requirements" for convenience and necessity had been met.[23]

[20] Id. at 17. The Court felt compelled to draw this line because the Commission had admitted a lack of "complete and comprehensive authority" over end uses in its 1944 Annual Report to Congress. FPC, THE FIRST FIVE YEARS UNDER THE NATURAL GAS ACT 15 n.14 (1944), quoted in 365 U.S. at 15.

[21] A "direct" sale is one in which, as in this case, the contract of sale expressly prohibits the vendee from reselling the gas; the sale is consequently not for resale in interstate commerce and therefore not within the Commission's jurisdiction. As the presiding examiner candidly pointed out, had Con Ed been able to liquefy the gas and ship it to New York other than by pipeline, the entire transaction would have been outside the scope of federal regulation. Transcontinental Gas Pipe Line Corp., 20 F.P.C. 303, 316 (1958).

[22] 21 F.P.C. 138, 141 (1959).

[23] 271 F.2d 942, 946 (3d Cir. 1959).

Measured by these conventional tests—adequate gas reserves, adequate market, and sufficient pipeline capacity—the requested service should have (and admittedly would have) been certificated. However, the Commission staff, opposing Transcontinental's application along with economically interested groups, argued that (in addition to being a potential threat to field price structure) burning the gas under utilities' boilers was an "inferior" end use, and further that direct sales of gas to large industrial users would pre-empt pipeline capacity to the detriment of small consumers.

The hearing examiner ruled against the staff, since in his opinion the "policy" arguments underpinning its position were not cognizable by the Commission in a section 7 proceeding. However, he added that if cognizable, they merited a ruling in favor of Transcontinental. The full Commission reversed, holding the policy considerations properly within the scope of a section 7 inquiry. The Supreme Court agreed,[24] finding both the end use and price[25] factors underlying the staff's arguments proper considerations. Chief Justice Warren, speaking for the Court, explained the rationale of the end use doctrine in the following words:

> No one disputes that natural gas is a wasting resource and that the necessity for conserving it is paramount. As we see it, the question in this case is whether the Commission, through its certification power, may prevent the waste of gas committed to its jurisdiction. One apparent method of preventing waste of gas is to limit the [end] uses to which it may be put, uses for which another, more abundant fuel may serve equally well. Thus the Commission in this case, as it often has in the past, has declared that the use of gas under industrial boilers is an "inferior" use, the assumption being that other fuels, particularly coal, are an adequate substitute in areas where such other fuels abound.[26]

The Court rejected arguments that considerations of natural resource conservation had been left by Congress exclusively to the states.

In X-20, for the first time, one argument urged upon the Commission was that the requested gas was necessary to combat air pollution. However, the advantage to be gained by certification was merely the removal of a smoke plume from Con Edison's Waterside plant, which blocked the view from the United Nations building. The specific air pollution evidence adduced in X-20 was merely thirteen pages of testimony by New York City's Air Pollution Control Commissioner, concluding that there might not even be a causal relationship between emissions from the Waterside station and injury to health. The air pollution considerations of the case were clearly secondary to the basic question of whether the so-called policy considerations raised by the Commission staff were cognizable in a section 7 proceeding, and the

---

[24] 365 U.S. 1 (1961). The Court reversed a decision of the court of appeals, which had reversed the Commission.

[25] The "end use" factors were the wasteful use of gas and its pre-emption of pipeline capacity; the "price" factor was that the nonjurisdictional (and therefore non-price-controllable) sale, since it was at a field price higher than that approved by the Commission, would drive the price up generally.

[26] 365 U.S. at 8-9.

Supreme Court was concerned with whether the legislative history of the act supported the Commission's authority to examine those considerations. Yet the Supreme Court's approval of the conservation argument in the face of an asserted air pollution problem has remained the nemesis of those seeking gas for the purpose of alleviating air pollution.

III

PROCEEDINGS BEFORE THE COMMISSION TO OBTAIN BOILER FUEL GAS TO ALLEVIATE AIR POLLUTION

In the wake of *X-20*, the Commission has been called upon on three occasions[27] to certificate gas for boiler fuel in order (among other reasons) to reduce air pollution in the area to be served. Two of these proceedings have involved the country's largest, most populous, and most notoriously polluted cities—New York and Los Angeles. In each of the three cases, the Commission refused to find that the asserted air pollution benefits warranted certification of the requested service. However, in two of the three proceedings the service was certificated on the basis of other considerations. The third case involved the approval of a proposal for the development of the Los Angeles market and the denial of a competing proposal which contemplated substituting gas for other fossil fuels for power generation in order to reduce pollution.

- In only two of these three cases was there a relatively complete exposition of (*a*) the harmful effects of the existing air pollution condition, and (*b*) the reduction in those harmful effects which the requested gas substitution was expected to bring about. In neither case were the Commission members unanimous in their evaluation of the air pollution evidence of record. Yet examination of the record and the reasoning in both cases indicates that before the Commission will approve a proposal involving increased use of gas for air pollution abatement, it will require the proponents of the proposed service to meet a higher burden of proof than that previously required to justify allocations of gas for other, even "inferior," end uses. In fact, it may not be going too far to suggest that a majority of the Commission would prefer to sweep air pollution under the rug as a factor in determining whether a proposed use is consistent with the present or future public convenience and necessity.

A. The *Gulf Pacific* Case

The Commission's first full-scale consideration of air pollution (unlike its brief consideration in *X-20*) as an attempted justification for obtaining increased quantities

---

[27] The Los Angeles area was involved in Transwestern Pipeline Co., 36 F.P.C. 176 (1966), *rehearing denied*, 36 F.P.C. 1010 (1966) [hereinafter cited as *Gulf Pacific*]; service to Florida's lower east coast was considered in Florida Gas Transmission Co., 37 F.P.C. 424 (1967); and New York City's air pollution was extensively reviewed in Transcontinental Gas Pipe Line Corp. (Phase II), 38 F.P.C. No. 532, 71 P.U.R.3d 161 (Nov. 6, 1967) [hereinafter cited as *Transco*].

of boiler fuel gas came in 1966 in the *Gulf Pacific* case. *Gulf Pacific* involved two competing proposals for the development for the expanding Los Angeles market, one of which, that of the Gulf Pacific Company, contemplated burning increased quantities of gas under boilers for power generation in order to abate Los Angeles' considerable air pollution. Extensive evidence was received documenting the adverse effects of Los Angeles' particular air contaminants on health and property and the partial alleviation of these effects to be obtained by substituting natural gas for sulfur-containing fuels. The hearing examiner, deciding that the gas should be granted, concluded that the atmospheric pollution existing in the Los Angeles area presented a "health problem"[28] and that

> The Los Angeles air pollution problem will not be eliminated by the use of gas under boilers but the reduction in tonnage of pollutants in the magnitude here under consideration will affect the concentration of contaminants and aid in the program of the APCD [Los Angeles county Air Pollution Control District] to reduce air pollution to the benefit of the people in the Los Angeles basin.[29]

On appeal the Commission disagreed. Reviewing the evidence, the Commission concluded that air pollution in Los Angeles did indeed constitute some threat to health but that the evidence was insufficient to draw any conclusions as to the extent of the danger. It stated,

> It is plain on this record that Los Angeles has an acute air pollution problem. We also accept the considerable medical evidence that this air pollution may have *some deleterious effect upon the health* of the residents of Los Angeles as contended by the Los Angeles County Medical Society, the APCD, and others, *although the extent of the deleterious effect is a matter of dispute.* While common sense tells us that any actual or potential danger from air pollution will be decreased if there is a substantial reduction in the concentrations of pollutants in the Los Angeles atmosphere, our resolution of this issue would be heavily influenced by a clear indication that the existing levels are either well within levels of tolerance or well above such levels. The many health experts who participated in this proceeding have not defined any such standard with respect to the various aspects of the air pollution question with which this record deals, and it does not lie within the competence of this Commission to do so.[30]

The Commission found that the use of greater volumes of natural gas in Los Angeles would not have "an appreciable effect upon the area's smog problem," which it found was the area's major pollution problem. While recognizing the existence of sulfur oxides in Los Angeles' air, the Commission took issue with the alleged severity of the problem, noting that the 0.1 ppm (parts per million) level[31] had been

---

[28] 36 F.P.C. 262, 294 (Initial Decision of the Presiding Examiner, 1965).

[29] *Id.* at 295.

[30] *Id.* at 186. (Emphasis added.)

[31] One-tenth part per million (ppm) is the maximum acceptable level of SO_2 concentration according to standards set by the U.S. Department of Health, Education, and Welfare (HEW); this level is not to be exceeded more than 1% of the time. *See* text accompanying note 47 *infra.*

exceeded at monitoring stations only a maximum of five days in the four years 1960-1963, compared with 42 days in Washington, 75 days in Philadelphia, 186 days in Chicago, and 196 days in New York during 1963 alone. The Commission concluded that

> The additional gas would reduce the concentration of sulfur dioxide somewhat but there is no showing that using only gas in power plant boilers would have any beneficial effect on the health of the people of Los Angeles.
>
> We are fully conscious that we are here dealing with an issue of public health which does not lend itself to absolute proof and should not be thought of exclusively in economic terms. Obviously, a showing that additional natural gas for boiler use would reduce air pollution in any significant manner would merit the most serious attention, for this Commission, like the general public, is increasingly concerned about the environment in which we live. Not only has there been no such showing, but under the broad public convenience and necessity requirement of the Natural Gas Act, this factor, as important as it is, cannot be considered in isolation. . . . [W]e conceive our responsibilities to be broader and to require a more analytical review of all relevant factors including alternate means of reducing air pollution.[32]

Commissioner O'Connor dissented on the "conventional" ground that the majority decision failed to take into consideration the long-term natural gas needs of the market. His dissent agreed with the majority conclusion that the evidence was insufficient to establish levels at which the various contaminants can be said to be either safe or harmful, but noted that

> it did establish that existing levels of air pollution are deleterious to the health of the people of the Los Angeles area. Furthermore, I am convinced that although the reduction in contaminants emitted as a result of the substitution of natural gas for fuel oil will not completely solve the overall air pollution problem, it will, nevertheless, bring about a reasonable reduction and be in consonance with the overall desires and plans of the people of Los Angeles and the Los Angeles APCD.[33]

Just how extensive a reduction must be brought about in order to warrant certification is a question which the Commission has not yet completely answered.

B. The *Florida Gas* Case

The Commission's next hearing on air pollution occurred the following year in *Florida Gas*, in which the petitioner urged that its "primary reason for entering

---

[32] 36 F.P.C. at 189-90.

[33] *Id.* at 228, 256 (dissent). Additionally, with respect to air pollution, Commissioner O'Connor stated,

> "When the vast sums of money which have been expended by the taxpayers of southern California for the elimination of the air pollution problem are taken into consideration, it becomes self-evident that their desire for more gas is not so much founded on economic considerations as how to get the greatest supply for the longest period of time. . . . These vast expenditures can only be interpreted as indicating an intense desire of the people of Los Angeles towards curbing the amounts of contaminants emitted daily into the atmosphere regardless of the percentage of the total air pollution problem the offending industries or machines contribute."

Id. at 254.

into a contract for additional supplies of natural gas was its desire to alleviate a serious air pollution problem on Florida's lower east coast, which is caused by the burning of high sulfur fuel oil in its electric generating plants."[34]   Both the presiding examiner and the Commission found deficient the air pollution evidence of record, which consisted largely of theoretical computations of atmospheric sulfur dioxide concentration.   The Commission concluded,

> While the calculations show that ground level concentrations of SO_2 in the vicinity of the Port Everglades, Riviera and Cape-Kennedy plants could exceed one part per million, these studies were theoretical, based upon the burning of fuel and assumptions as to atmospheric conditions, not on actual measurement of SO_2 concentrations in the vicinity of the power plants.   It seems significant that HEW did not file exceptions [to the Examiner's initial decision].[35]

The balance of the evidence as to air pollution consisted of complaints, which were almost entirely directed to visible emissions from boiler stacks, and of testimony that certain of the polluting plants were in tourist areas and areas inhabited by elderly and especially sensitive retirees.

Unconvinced by the air pollution evidence, the Commission nevertheless approved the proposal based largely upon its conclusion that the unique nature of the Florida fuel market made it desirable to favor increased industrial consumption of gas.[36] Whereas the Commission usually viewed the use of natural gas for boiler fuel as an inferior end use, in this case the use was found not to be inferior, based on the nature of the market.   In this respect, *Florida Gas* is exemplary of the Commission's flexibility in analyzing in each case whether, in the particular circumstances present, the use is in the public interest.   Unfortunately for advocates of boiler fuel gas as a partial solution to urban air pollution, this flexibility seems to extend only to "conventional" touchstones of public convenience and necessity, stopping short of air pollution.   An additional (and "conventional") factor in the Commission's decision was the approximately $400,000 net savings to resale customers in Florida.

C. The *"Transco"* Case

The Commission's most recent exposure to arguments based on air pollution was in the *Transco* case, late in 1967.   At issue was an application to substitute demand service (gas taken directly from the pipeline) for storage service (gas injected into

---

[34] 37 F.P.C. 466, 475 (Initial Decision of the Presiding Examiner, 1966).

[35] *Id.* at 446.

[36] "An important consideration in our decision here flows from the nature of Florida gas operations which we believe is dictated largely by the unique conditions which prevail in the Florida fuel market. As the Commission recognized in 1956, Florida is a fuel deficiency area and must depend almost entirely on imported fuels. This factor, plus the ease of transporting natural gas, makes this particular type of arrangement more important there than elsewhere in the country. Because of the mild climate which prevails and the low degree-day deficiency the load factor of any pipeline supplying Florida would be relatively low if it were not for the firm industrial consumption and transportation of gas such as is contemplated here."
Id. at 439.

underground storage tanks at a constant rate and withdrawn as needed) currently being rendered to Con Ed of New York by Transcontinental Gas Pipe Line Corporation. Approval of the application would have resulted in making increased quantities of natural gas available to Con Ed for power generation in New York City.

Transco was severed from a larger proceeding for the express purpose of permitting a full hearing on the effect of the proposed service on air pollution in New York City.[37] It resulted in over a week of hearings, ten witnesses, and over 1,000 pages of transcript devoted to the question of the air pollution abatement to be derived from the proposed service. Based upon this evidence, the examiner concluded that New York City's air pollution problem was of "massive proportions";[38] that the sixteen million people in the greater New York area endure the "greatest concentration of sulfur dioxide of any major city in the country";[39] that Con Ed contributed substantially to that concentration;[40] that the evidence showed a causal relationship between exposure to atmospheric sulfur dioxide and certain serious, sometimes fatal diseases;[41] and that the proposed service would reduce Con Ed's annual sulfur dioxide emissions by between 22,800 and 25,500 tons, amounting to about four per cent of the city's total emissions.[42] Despite these findings the examiner denied certification of the proposed service.

At that time New York City was in the initial planning stages of an extensive program to substantially reduce air pollution. As a part of that program the city had recently enacted Local Law 14-1966, which required, among other things, a gradual reduction in the sulfur content of fuel burned for power generation down to one per cent sulfur fuel by May 1971. After the record was closed, Con Ed publicly announced that it had made arrangements to obtain by October 1, 1967 (four and a half years earlier than required) enough one per cent sulfur-content fuel oil for all of its generating needs, enabling it to halve its sulfur dioxide emissions. Based largely upon this announcement, the examiner denied certification, finding that the use of this newly available low-sulfur fuel would

> eliminate the contribution Con Ed has made to New York City sulfur dioxide problem . . . [and, therefore,] that no showing has been made that the substitution of natural gas for high-sulfur content oil and coal is required by public convenience and necessity.[43]

---

[37] Aligned in favor of the proposed service were the applicant (Transco) and intervenors Con Ed, the U.S. Department of Health, Education and Welfare, and Citizens for Clean Air, Inc. Against the service were Fuels Research Council, Inc., National Coal Association, United Mine Workers of America, and the Commission staff.

[38] Presiding Examiner's Initial Decision, Transcontinental Gas Pipe Line Corp. (Phase II), No. CP65-181 (F.P.C., April 11, 1967) (mimeo. at 24).

[39] *Id.*

[40] *Id.*

[41] *Id.* (mimeo. at 42, 43).

[42] *Id.* (mimeo. at 42).

[43] *Id.* (mimeo. at 41). In fact, substitution of the gas for 1% sulfur-content oil and coal would have resulted in the further elimination of between 14,500 and 11,100 tons of sulfur dioxide. Transco, 71 P.U.R.3d at 167.

The Commission reversed, approving the requested service largely because of "substantial annual savings to Con Ed Company and its customers"[44] of approximately $850,000 and $230,758, compared to the use of oil and coal respectively. The Commission concluded,

> We have found Transcontinental Gas Pipe Line Corporation's application to be in the public interest. It has proposed a comparatively modest increase in its firm gas deliveries to Consolidated Edison Company. It has the supplies; there is no question of the market; and the economic feasibility of the transaction is assured."[45]

The air pollution arguments, to which substantial hearing time and large portions of the briefs were devoted, were treated in the Commission's opinion as establishing a convenient but nonetheless superfluous reason for its conclusion.[46] Specifically addressing itself to the severity of sulfur dioxide levels in New York City, the Commission found,

> Both the witnesses for Citizens for Clean Air, Inc. and the Department of Health, Education and Welfare were of the opinion that there is no safe level of sulfur dioxide pollution although the Department of Health, Education and Welfare suggests that the 24-hour concentration in community atmosphere be maintained below 10 parts per 100,000,000 i.e., 0.1 ppm and that this concentration should not be exceeded more than one per cent of the time. Although there is some controversy regarding the adequacy of the SO_2 recording stations, the record clearly shows that the atmosphere in New York does not conform to this standard.[47]

D. Air Pollution Abatement as a Factor in Public Convenience and Necessity

The cases discussed above—*Gulf Pacific*, *Florida Gas*, and *Transco*—reveal a trend toward increasingly lengthy assaults upon the Commission to obtain boiler fuel gas for reasons of air pollution abatement. Nevertheless, the FPC has not admitted air pollution to the list of "conventional" criteria which determine public convenience and necessity. This is not to say that the individual commissioners have not given some weight to air pollution abatement in deciding particular cases. It is difficult, for example, after reading the briefs in *Transco*—all of which were overwhelmingly weighted with air pollution arguments—to accept at face value the Commission's assertion in that case that its decision is based solely on conventional factors. What is clear is that the Commission is highly reluctant to create a

---

[44] 71 P.U.R.3d at 165.

[45] *Id.* at 166.

[46] The opinion was subdivided under such headings as "The Conventional Certificate Requirements," and "The New York Air Pollution Problem." Under the latter heading the Commission stated, "Since . . . [Transco's proposal] is otherwise supported by the record . . . , the effect of this sale on the New York air pollution problem is not controlling. Nevertheless, the serious air pollution in New York may be alleviated slightly by the proposal, and to that extent furnishes an additional benefit." *Id.*

[47] *Id.* at 166-67.

precedent by expressly resting a decision granting boiler fuel gas on air pollution benefits. Several factors seem to underlie this reluctance. The prospect of a precedent which opens the door to unknown numbers of applications from communities besieged by real or imagined air pollution may disturb the Commission somewhat. Further, it may be felt that sufficient numbers of these applications would have to be granted once a precedent was set, thus uncomfortably accelerating the rate of gas consumption. And the commissioners may believe that air pollution is a problem which is well on its way to solution by other means and needs no help from them.[48] Finally, the commissioners may be unwilling to base decisions on scientific facts in unfamiliar fields such as meteorology, public health, medicine, and the chemistry of pollutant compounds.

The Commission's reluctance to rest a decision granting boiler fuel gas on grounds of air pollution abatement has been expressed as an especially high standard (which has never been met) for obtaining boiler fuel gas for that purpose. This standard derives in part from the rebuttable presumption evolved in the 1953 decision in *Mississippi River Fuel Corp.*[49] for determining in any case whether to grant natural gas for boiler fuel:

> [T]he use of natural gas as boiler fuel is an inferior usage and that, while it is not to be denied in all situations, it should be permitted only on a positive showing that it is required by public convenience and necessity.

The degree of "positiveness" required when the use is justified on air pollution grounds, however, seems to be greater than that required when the justification is on grounds more closely related to the so-called "conventional factors."

Somewhat paradoxically, opinions of FPC examiners have advanced as one reason for denying boiler fuel gas the too-small improvement in pollutant levels to be brought about by the particular quantity of gas requested. Yet if larger quantities of gas are sought for greater impact on pollution, denial based on too rapidly depleting gas reserves is surely to be expected.

The examiner recognized in *Transco* that "the Commission's boiler fuel policy is not rigid or unyielding. Air pollution, for example, can be an issue of decisive importance if the use of other fuels creates special dangers for a community."[50] Yet the Commission's refusal to recognize that pollution in New York City (concededly the nation's worst area in this regard) warranted granting boiler fuel gas may indicate that, at least in the commissioners' minds, such a "community" does not really exist.

---

[48] This view was reflected in a 1966 speech by FPC Chairman Lee C. White. *Development of National Policy with Respect to Natural Gas*, in PROCEEDINGS: THE THIRD NATIONAL CONFERENCE ON AIR POLLUTION 137 (Public Health Service Pub. No. 1649, 1967).

[49] 12 F.P.C. 109, 112 (1953).

[50] Examiner's Opinion, *supra* note 38 (mimeo. at 30).

IV

FUTURE PROSPECTS FOR OBTAINING BOILER FUEL GAS

FOR AIR POLLUTION ABATEMENT

Given the existing severity of the air pollution problem and the present attitude of the FPC toward allocation of natural gas in its solution, can we expect a change in the availability of boiler fuel gas in the near to medium term? The answer depends largely upon the extent to which power generation from the polluting fossil fuels (*i.e.*, coal and oil) remains a significant part of the total power generation picture. If the economic facts of life tempt the utilities away from the use of coal and oil for boiler fuel either to less polluting fuels or possibly to methods of power production which bypass steam generation altogether, then natural gas will no longer be necessary to displace those fuels. On the other hand, if coal and oil continue to play a significant role in power generation, then worsening atmospheric pollution over metropolitan areas will give rise to increasing pressures on the Commission to channel more gas to boiler fuel use.

Whether or not the Commission can be expected to yield to these pressures will depend in large measure on the gas expenditures likely to be required for air pollution abatement. If the total expenditure is foreseeable and is not overly large in relation to reserves, the Commission is more likely to loosen the reins on boiler fuel gas than if such a move would rapidly or unpredictably accelerate the present rate of increase in gas consumption. Another factor to be considered is whether in the foreseeable future technology will provide economically feasible methods of removing pollutants from stack emissions rendering coal and oil nonpolluting.

Incentives to technological solution of the pollution problem have been considered by the Commission from a different point of view, namely whether granting natural gas in order to abate pollution will remove existing incentives to find other solutions to the problem. In *Transco*, the hearing examiner speculated,

> If more natural gas is used under boilers to aid in licking the air pollution problem, and if as a result natural gas reserves are depleted, what means will later be used to lick the air pollution problem insofar as stack emissions are concerned? Would it be advances in technology?
> If necessity is still the mother of invention, would use of more natural gas now as boiler fuel necessarily delay the development of needed additional mechanical devices?[51]

To attempt to answer these questions and to discern what can be expected from the Commission in the way of future allocations of boiler fuel gas, consider the probable medium-term trend of electrical generation. Recent studies indicate that electric power generation will increase about 200 per cent between 1960 and 1980, and

---

[51] Initial Decision of the Presiding Examiner, Columbia Gulf Transmission Co., Docket No. CP65-102 (F.P.C., June 13, 1966) (mimeo. at 22).

TABLE 1

ACTUAL AND PROJECTED ELECTRICITY GENERATION BY ENERGY SOURCE, 1960-2000
(Low, Medium, and High Projections)

TOTAL GENERATION:	1960 (*actual*)		1980 (*projected*)		2000 (*projected*)
Hydroelectric (bil. kwh)...................	149		283		363
Nuclear (bil. kwh)......................	3 (1963)	L M H	220 400 580	L M H	1,230 2,400 3,480
Conventional thermal (bil. kwh) (nat. gas, oil, coal)......................................	696	L M H	1,203 1,546 2,225	L M H	1,381 1,948 3,924
Total (bil. kwh)........................	845	L M H	1,706 2,229 3,088	L M H	2,974 4,711 7,767
NATURAL GAS DATA:					
Gas-based generation (bil. kwh)................	181	L M H	313 402 578	L M H	304 429 863
% of conventional thermal......................	26%		26%		22%
% of total generation........................	21%		18%		9%
Fuel rate (cu. ft./net kwh)....................	10,910		9,300		7,875
Amount consumed (bil. cu. ft.).................	2,034	L M H	2,998 3,851 5,536	L M H	2,466 3,479 7,000

Source: H. LANDSBERG, L. FISCHMAN, & J. FISHER, RESOURCES IN AMERICA'S FUTURE, table A15-10 (1963).

then approximately double between 1980 and 2000.[52] The corresponding projections for the use of natural gas in electric power generation do not, however, reflect proportional growth. Table 1 (the medium projections) indicates that consumption of natural gas in electric generation will increase from 2,034 to 3,851 billion cubic feet between 1960 and 1980 and then fall off to 3,479 billion cubic feet by 2000.[53] The primary reason for this drop is the expected increase in nuclear generating capacity. Nuclear power costs have come down more rapidly than was projected a few years ago; between fifty and sixty per cent of all electrical power produced is expected to be generated in nuclear installations by the year 2000. Because the bulk of the increase in nuclear generating capacity is expected to occur after 1980, the demand for all fossil fuels will continue to grow through 1980, though not as rapidly as the growth of total electric production, since nuclear and hydroelectric

[52] FEDERAL POWER COMM'N, NATIONAL POWER SURVEY 39, 349 (1964); H. LANDSBERG, L. FISCHMANN & J. FISHER, RESOURCES IN AMERICA'S FUTURE 844 (1963).

[53] "Out of such conflicting data one cannot fashion directly any projection of the share that gas is likely to hold of the future utility fuel market. On balance, the use of gas as utility fuel may well be reaching its peak, but its eventual decline, for the reasons cited, is likely to be slow. The development of percentage shares [in Table 1] reflects this view."

H. LANDSBERG, L. FISCHMANN, & J. FISHER, *supra* note 52, at 287. The difficulties involved in making projections for gas use are discussed in *id.* at 285-88.

power output are growing even more rapidly. At any rate, there will be a continuing increase during at least the next decade in the quantities of coal and oil burned to generate electricity.

However, the growth of pollution from utilities is not likely to be proportional to the increase in coal and oil consumed by them. Technological progress is being made in solving the emissions problem both (a) by treating the fuel itself to lower its sulfur content, and (b) by cleaning the gases emitted at the stack. In the area of fuel treatment, requirements are being written into state and local air pollution codes which limit the sulfur content of the coal or oil burned. Con Ed, cooperating with New York's Air Pollution Control Department, recently shifted to oil containing a maximum of one per cent sulfur, effecting a reduction of about fifty per cent in the sulfur compounds emitted by it.[54] The burning in New York City of coal or oil having greater than one per cent sulfur content will be prohibited after May 20, 1971, by existing law.[55]

These factors seemingly presage a significant reduction in sulfur emissons. However, such reduction is largely illusory. For example, no attempts are being made to effect a reduction to one per cent sulfur fuels in the private sector earlier than the 1971 deadline because of fears that low sulfur oil would not be available to fill the resultant demand. Oil which can be processed to lower its sulfur content is presently being imported from South America in limited quantities. Until additional desulfurization equipment is designed and installed at South American refineries, no substantial increase in the availability of one per cent (or lower) sulfur content fuel oil can be expected. And the federal government has been most reluctant to increase import quotas for naturally low-sulfur Arabian crude oil,[56] which (unlike the South American crude oil) requires no desulfurization processing for this application. Further, implementation of air pollution control laws have been beset by endless delays, and it may be longer than expected before they are effective in significantly reducing sulfur emissions.

Emission controls—devices which extract sulfur compounds from the effluent in the stack—are technologically feasible but not yet sufficiently attractive economically to provide a solution. Testifying on this point in *Transco*, Vernon G. MacKenzie, Chief of the Division of Air Pollution of the U.S. Public Health Service, expressed the opinion that although a number of technologically feasible processes existed for

---

[54] The change in fuel sulfur content and the resulting change in sulfur oxide emissions are approximately linearly related. In connection with this discussion of low sulfur oil it is interesting to note the recent discovery of extensive oil fields in northern Alaska. N.Y. Times, July 28, 1968, § 3, at 1F, col. 1. Preliminary reports suggest that the crude is very high in quality, indicating a low sulfur content. *Id.*, col. 2. If these reports are correct, then the quantity of acceptable low sulfur oil available for use as boiler fuel in metropolitan areas should increase significantly toward the end of the next decade. (Reports indicate that commercial exploitation of these fields is "several years away" pending development of pipeline facilities. *Id.* at 14F, col. 8.)

[55] Local Law No. 14, May 20, 1966, N.Y. CITY ADMIN. CODE §§ 892-2.0 to 897-2.0 (Supp. 1967). Section 893-1.0 restricts fuel sulfur content and establishes the timetable.

[56] Such a quota increase was recently obtained by Los Angeles for air pollution control.

removing sulfur from combustion gases, it is impossible to predict when (and indeed if) any of those processes would become commercially available. Other witnesses agreed with Dr. MacKenzie that certain existing devices were not suitable for reasons such as lack of space, which apply to any urban center.

In addition to sulfur compound emissions, particulates from utilities' stacks are a serious problem. The technology to solve this problem, however, is largely a reality. Electrostatic precipitators exist which are capable of eliminating over 99.5 per cent of the particulates coming through the stack. The problem is largely one of getting the utilities to install such devices. Con Ed has assertedly found it impossible to upgrade control equipment at many of its plants simply because it lacks sufficient reserve equipment to take the stations off line for upgrading.[57] This situation is likely to occur in any number of urban areas as, in the immediate future, increasing population densities bring about more severe pollution problems before the public alarm necessary to reverse the trend can be aroused.

An additional factor tending to postpone the demise of pollutant generation in densely populated areas is associated with the economics of nuclear power plant location. The refusal of the Atomic Energy Commission to approve nuclear generating stations in densely populated urban areas means higher costs for switching to nuclear power in such areas, due to the cost of transmitting the power into the city. It is precisely the large, densely populated urban area in which air pollution is at its worst. This kind of area therefore has the greatest need for nuclear generation; yet the costs for rights-of-way over which power from remote nuclear plants may be supplied to it are extraordinarily high.

Any attempt to project accurately the future contribution to air pollution of fossil fuel power generation based on factors such as those described above must necessarily be imprecise. Further clouding the picture is a startling lack of understanding on how much a utility's emissions, usually sent aloft through high stacks, contribute to ground level pollutant concentration.[58] It is probably safe to predict, however, that generating utilities will continue to be a major factor in polluting urban atmospheres for five years at the very least, and probably for ten to twenty years to come. The Commission will, therefore, most likely be faced with additional requests for boiler fuel gas over the next several years.

The Commission's fears that in granting such requests it might remove incentives toward technological solutions to the problem seem groundless. The cost of gas to the utility and to the consumer is higher, on a firm basis, than the cost

---

[57] TASK FORCE REPORT 102, 108.

[58] In New York, Con Ed's 500-foot-high stacks, with still higher "effective stack heights" (an engineering concept which takes into effect the velocity and temperature of the stack gases) may send pollutants up through the inversion layer which ordinarily acts as an atmospheric lid on an urban area. A utility which contributes 50% of a city's pollutant emissions thus does not necessarily contribute 50% of its pollutant concentrations. No means is known for quantitatively translating per cent of emission into per cent of concentration. And no one can guess the effect of the emission which "punches through" the inversion layer on the municipalities downwind.

of coal or oil. To continue to purchase these lower cost fuels,[59] as well as to avoid dependence on any single fuel, it will be necessary to engage in research to learn how to burn coal and oil without polluting the environment. Attempts to recover sulfur from stack gases will continue so long as there exists the economic incentive of a valuable sulfur yield. Solutions which envisage refining oil to a lower sulfur content are being explored by oil companies, whose market for the low sulfur product will be much broader than the utilities. This market will no doubt be largely enhanced, if not created, by legislation to limit the sulfur content of fuels.

Returning to the question of whether the Commission is likely to reverse its stand on boiler fuel gas, it is informative to inquire how adequate are our natural gas resources and what impact on them such a reversal might have. During the last ten years,[60] net gas reserves have continued to increase at an average rate of roughly five billion Mcf. (thousand cubic feet) annually (Table 2). Since 1945, newly discovered reserves have been greater each year than net gas production. From 1945 to 1966 new reserves have exceeded net production by over 13.9 trillion cubic feet—equal to eight years' supply at the present rate of consumption.[61] In 1966 proven recoverable reserves—an accepted measure of available gas—stood at a high of 289.3 trillion cubic feet,[62] leaving more than 16.5 years of proven reserves

TABLE 2

SUMMARY OF ANNUAL ESTIMATES OF NATURAL GAS RESERVES, 1945-1966

Note: Volumes are calculated at a pressure base of 14.73 psi, absolute, and at a standard temperature of 60°F.

(Millions of cubic feet)

Year	Natural Gas added during year			Net Change in Underground Storage	Preliminary Net Production during Year	Estimated Proved Reserve as of End of Year	Increase over Previous Year
	Extensions and Revisions	Discoveries of New Fields and New Pools in Old Fields	Total of Discoveries, Revisions and Extensions				
1945............	—	—	—	—	—	146,986,723	
1950............	9,122,566	2,861,724	11,984,290	54,006	6,855,244	184,584,745	5,183,05
1955............	16,209,610	5,688,009	21,897,619	87,161	10,063,167	222,482,544	11,921,613
1956............	19,110,250	5,605,864	24,716,114	133,242	10,848,685	236,483,215	14,000,671
1957............	11,057,936	8,950,119	20,008,055	178,757	11,439,890	245,230,137	8,746,922
1958............	13,316,094	5,580,624	18,896,718	57,588	11,422,651	252,761,792	7,531,655
1959............	14,852,007	5,769,245	20,621,252	160,450	12,373,063	261,170,431	8,408,639
1960............	7,293,016	6,600,963	13,893,979	281,272	13,019,356	262,326,326	1,155,895
1961............	10,258,693	6,907,729	17,166,422	159,543	13,378,649	266,273,642	3,947,316
1962............	13,184,795	6,299,164	19,483,959	159,230	13,637,973	272,278,858	6,005,216
1963............	12,586,733	5,577,934	18,164,667	253,733	14,546,025	276,151,233	3,872,375
1964............	13,342,837	6,909,301	20,252,138	195,111	15,347,028	281,251,454	5,100,221
1965............	14,775,570	6,543,709	21,319,279	150,483	16,252,293	286,468,923	5,217,469
1966............	14,162,707	6,057,725	20,220,432	134,523	17,491,073	289,332,805	2,863,882

Source: COMMITTEE ON NATURAL GAS RESERVES, AMERICAN GAS ASS'N, GAS FACTS 13 (1966).
Note: For intervening years, refer to AMERICAN GAS ASS'N, HISTORICAL STATISTICS OF THE GAS INDUSTRY (1956).

[59] FPC Chairman Lee C. White stated recently, "In the absence of end-use controls or other restrictions, it may be presumed that utilities and other firms which choose to use coal or oil rather than gas when it is available do so because these fuels are less expensive or otherwise preferable." White, *supra* note 48, at 140.

[60] Statistics are not available later than 1966; all data on gas reserves and usage are taken from AMERICAN GAS ASS'N GAS FACTS (1966) (published annually).

[61] *Id.* at 12.

[62] *Id.* at 5.

at the present rate of production even if no additional reserves are found. It has been estimated[63] that the total recoverable gas reserves in the United States are in the neighborhood of 1,400-1,700 trillion cubic feet, enough to last more than eighty years at the 1966 consumption rate and more than fifty years at the rate projected for the year 2000.[64]

Given the rate of technological progress during the last several decades, it is probable that radically new energy sources will be developed to the point of economic feasibility well within the next few decades. The members of the FPC are not unaware of this fact. The Commission's Chairman, Lee C. White, stated in 1966,

> History has shown the remarkable success of science in avoiding resource scarcities by discovering new products and production techniques. There are numerous examples of resources which were replaced by better products long before they were exhausted, and therefore, "saving for the future need" can mean sacrificing for a contingency which never arrives. One of the saddest imaginable prospects for our civilization would be to succumb to pollution while "saving" our natural gas for a future generation that would never be born. Examples of resource waste by too rapid consumption (gas flaring, or wildlife and redwood destruction, for example) are also obvious, and perhaps emotionally more striking. History, then, gives us no clear guide. The "best" rate of gas consumption is an elusive target, but one society must consider when it contemplates large shifts in use among the fossil fuels.[65]

There would seem to be little cause, then, to fear that a change in the Commission's policy regarding boiler fuel gas for air pollution abatement could seriously threaten this country's gas reserves.[66] Even more imminent than the development of new energy sources is the virtual certainty in the author's opinion that, at least within a twenty-year period, adequate methods of cleaning up the effluents from coal and oil thermoelectric generation will have become commercially feasible. Thus, the Commission has no cause to fear that by changing its policy on boiler fuel gas for air pollution abatement it will expose our gas reserves to a never-ending, ever-growing drain. On the contrary, the demand for boiler fuel gas for this purpose should be self-limiting as other nonpolluting methods of obtaining electricity are introduced.

CONCLUSION

The nonexistence of any real threat to reserves from allocations of gas to boiler fuel use, together with the continuing need for gas for this purpose over the next ten

---

[63] *Id.*

[64] Total annual gas production in the United States in 2000 is estimated at 26.6 trillion cubic feet.

[65] White, *supra* note 48, at 141.

[66] In *Transco*, the Commission staff introduced evidence showing the potential expansion in the natural gas market if end use restrictions were eliminated. It showed a potential increase of 17%, assuming the admittedly improbable switchover of all significant steam-electric generating plants in "major metropolitan areas"—areas having either populations of over 500,000 or in excess of 40,000 employees in manufacturing industries—to natural gas.

years, indicate at least the possibility that the Commission can be persuaded to view requests for such gas more charitably than it has in the past. A shift in attitude of this nature could occur with no change whatsoever in the legal rhetoric presently employed by the Commission in its opinions. All that is necessary is to find in any given case "a positive showing" that public convenience and necessity would be served by certification of the proposed service, as required by *Mississippi River Fuel Corp.*[67] Any thoughts presently held by members of the Commission that power generation will soon cease to contribute to air pollution, without action on its part, must be dismissed as utopian. As research leads to more accurate ways of measuring the effects of utilities on atmospheric pollutant concentration (as opposed to emission levels) and to more complete data on the social, medical, and economic costs of air pollution, it will become increasingly difficult for the Commission to overlook the need for boiler fuel gas in alleviating pollution. It will also become increasingly difficult to justify granting boiler fuel gas on economic grounds, as the Commission did in *Transco*, where it found that savings to Con Ed and its customers of between \$230,000 and \$850,000 justified approval of the proposed services. The reason for this is that a party seeking boiler fuel gas in the future will be able to argue more convincingly than is now possible that the direct economic savings from the reduction in pollution to be achieved matches the dollar savings generally considered by the Commission to justify allocating gas to an inferior end use. Short of this degree of economic preciseness, however, as the need for boiler fuel gas for air pollution abatement becomes more pronounced and as scientific data continues to document the effects of the utilities' emissions on health and property, there is reason to believe that the Commission may look with greater favor on expending limited quantities of natural gas as a partial interim solution to the self-made ecological disturbances that man is only beginning to understand.

---

[67] 12 F.P.C. 109 (1953); *see* text accompanying note 49 *supra*.

FIRST STEPS TOWARD EUROPEAN COOPERATION IN REDUCING AIR POLLUTION—ACTIVITIES OF THE COUNCIL OF EUROPE

G. ADINOLFI*

When the Consultative Assembly of the Council of Europe, which is composed of parliamentary delegations appointed by the national parliaments of the eighteen member countries,[1] was confronted with the problem of air pollution, it immediately realized the complexity and urgency of this problem. The Assembly decided to convene an international conference to which specialists in the different fields would be invited. Mr. Radius, who was then Chairman of the Social Committee and Rapporteur of the Assembly, prepared a Recommendation defining the aims and methods of this Conference. This Recommendation was adopted by the Consultative Assembly on September 23, 1961 (Recommendation 290).

The Committee of Ministers of the Council of Europe, which is the executive body of the organization, and is composed of the Ministers for Foreign Affairs of the member States, implemented this Recommendation and convened the European Conference on Air Pollution, which took place in Strasbourg from June 24 to July 1, 1964.

Some 350 persons participated in this Conference: personalities in the fields of science, technology, medicine, industry, law, economics and journalism; representatives of local authorities, administrations, international organizations; and a number of political figures, many of them members of governments.

The agenda comprised the following fourteen items:

(1) effects of pollution on human health;

(2) effects of pollution on animals and plants;

(3) economic aspects of air pollution;

(4) danger thresholds;

(5) terminology and units of measure;

(6) standardization of measuring and control apparatus and of methods of measuring;

(7) meteorological, topographical, and geographical factors influencing air pollution;

(8) methods of reducing pollution caused by combustion (domestic and industrial);

(9) methods of reducing pollution caused by internal combustion engines (motor vehicles);

---

* Dr. iur. 1949, University of Milan. Head of the Private Office of the President of the Consultative Assembly of the Council of Europe.

[1] Austria, Belgium, Cyprus, Denmark, France, Federal Republic of Germany, Greece, Iceland, Ireland, Italy, Luxembourg, Malta, Netherlands, Norway, Sweden, Switzerland, Turkey, United Kingdom.

(10) methods of reducing pollution caused by specific industries;

(11) town and country planning;

(12) organization or development of European cooperation in research, standardization, and documentation concerning the campaign against air pollution;

(13) methods of informing and educating the public on the different ways of combatting air pollution; and

(14) comparisons of national laws and regulations and the possibility of standardizing these and drawing up technical and legislative agreements and European conventions on air pollution.

On each of these items government experts from the different European countries prepared a report. On the basis of these reports fourteen general reports were drawn up—one on each point of the agenda.[2] It is important to note that experts from the United States were invited to prepare information reports on each point of the agenda. This invitation was accepted.[3] Dr. John T. Middleton, Director of the Air Pollution Research Center at the University of California, and Arthur C. Stern, from the Division of Air Pollution of the U.S. Department of Health, Education, and Welfare, were present at the Conference and their participation in the debates was greatly appreciated.

A Committee of Experts on Air Pollution was duly set up and held its first session in October 1966, followed by a second session in October 1967. The major task of this Committee is to draft recommendations and conventions to be submitted to the governments of member countries. In fact, the activities of this Committee are more of a legal and administrative nature than of a technical one, although, of course, their proposals to the governments are based on technical information.

From the outset it seemed important, in order to avoid any duplication of work, that technical or scientific organizations such as the World Health Organization, the Economic Commission for Europe, the World Meteorological Organization, and the Organization for Economic Co-operation and Development should continue work in their own fields of activity, while the Council of Europe would use the relevant scientific information obtained to draw up conventions and recommendations. In consequence, the Committee does not intend to undertake technical studies, but to make use of those carried out by the above-mentioned international organizations. This is a good example of cooperation and distribution of work among the inter-

---

[2] A complete record of the proceedings of the Conference including the 14 general reports, the record of the debates and the proposals submitted by the participants at the Conference, may be obtained in English and in French from the Secretariat of the Council of Europe in Strasbourg.

[3] The following reports were submitted by experts from the United States:
Agenda *Item 1*—report by *Mr. Spicer*; *Item 2*—*Mr. Middleton* and *Mr. Otis Emik*; *Item 3*—*Mr. Smith Griswold*; *Item 5*—*Mr. Rossano*; *Item 6*—*Mr. Thomas*; *Item 7*—*Mr. McCormick*; *Item 8*—*Mr. C. W. Gruber*; *Item 9*—*Mr. Jensen* and *Mr. Scanlin*; *Item 10*—*Mr. Faith*; *Item 10/I*—*Mr. Brandt*; *Item 10/II*—*Mr. Cralley, Mr. Olson* and *Mr. Donaldson*; *Item 10/III*—*Mr. Doherty*; *Item 10/V*—*Mr. Burhouse*; *Item 11*—*Mr. Sutermeister*; *Item 12*—*Mr. Stern*; *Item 14*—*Mr. Edelman*.

governmental organizations. It is worth noting that representatives from these organizations take part in the meetings of the Council of Europe's Air Pollution Committee as observers. Officials of the Council of Europe Secretariat are also invited to meetings organized by these organizations.

The results of the Conference were examined by the Social Committee of the Consultative Assembly which presented concrete proposals to the Committee of Ministers. This organ appointed an ad hoc committee of experts in order to examine the results of the Conference as well as the proposals of the Assembly. In response to the proposals of the ad hoc committee the Committee of Ministers adopted the following Resolution on March 28, 1966:[4]

RESOLUTION (66) 23

AIR POLLUTION

The Committee of Ministers,
Having regard to Article 17 of the Statute;
Having regard to the report of the *ad hoc* Committee on Air Pollution (Doc. CM(65)151),
Decides:

1. A Committee of Experts on Air Pollution shall be set up:

(*a*) to implement the programme of work on air pollution approved by the Committee of Ministers on the basis of the report of the *ad hoc* Committee;

(*b*) to define and follow the work of consultant experts to be appointed and to examine their report;

(*c*) to examine reports communicated to it by the different international organisations;

(*d*) to convene in due course a second European Conference on Air Pollution.

2. The Committee shall consist of two experts per member country appointed by Governments.

3. The Rules of Procedure of Council of Europe Committees of Experts shall apply to this Committee.

The Committee's first aim—and we shall see later why—was to define in general terms the principles to be followed by member governments in order to combat air pollution. These governments should bear in mind these principles when introducing legislation and when formulating administrative regulations. At a meeting of the Deputies of the Committee of Ministers, held in Strasbourg from March 4 to 8, 1968, a resolution was adopted which approved the following declaration of principles on air pollution control:

PART I

Preamble

As air is essential to life, its natural quality must be maintained in order to safeguard man's health and well-being and to protect his environment.

---

[4] Adopted by the Ministers' Deputies on 28th March 1966.

This natural quality of air may be affected by the introduction of a foreign substance or by a significant variation in the proportion of its components.

Air is deemed to be polluted when the presence of a foreign substance or a variation in the proportion of its components is liable to have a harmful effect or to cause nuisance.

The member States of the Council of Europe will take the necessary legislative and administrative action to prevent or abate air pollution from all sources in accordance with the principles set out below.

PART II

Principles

1. *Liability of those causing pollution*

Legislation should provide that whoever causes or adds to air pollution must, even where there is no proof of damage, keep such pollution to a minimum and ensure that impurities emitted are properly dispersed.

2. *Basis of regulations*

Legislation on air pollution control must be based on the principle of prevention.

In each particular case where the circumstances so require, the competent authorities should be in a position to enforce appropriate practicable technical measures, having due regard to the degree and frequency of pollution, the geographical situation, present and future population density and all other relevant factors.

Prevention may be regulated differently according to the nature of the source of the pollution:

(a) where the setting up of new installations or the alteration of old installations is likely to contribute significantly to air pollution, they should be subject to individual authorisation laying down specifications for siting, construction and operation designed to limit emissions; special regulations might be issued for existing installations;

(b) installations which individually contribute less significantly to air pollution may nevertheless be subject to general operating specifications if, for example, their proximity to each other might lead to a significant concentration of pollutants in the neighbourhood;

(c) motor vehicles and mass-produced fuel-burning appliances should be subject to general provisions; since motor vehicles circulate across frontiers, uniform European standards for their construction and operation should be established as soon as possible; such standards might also be envisaged for mass-produced fuel-burning appliances which are the subject of international trade.

3. *Supervision and implementation*

Member States should set up or cause to be set up administrative machinery:

(a) to ascertain the nature and extent of pollution;

(b) to check compliance with regulations governing installations, motor vehicles, and fuel-burning appliances;

(c) to take such action as may be required to bring about the necessary improvements.

4. *Adjustment to technical and scientific progress*

Legislation should be so conceived that due account can be taken of new processes, technical improvements and scientific advances.

5. *Special measures*

Apart from measures applicable to all areas, there should be legislative provision for special measures to be applied to zones requiring special protection, to heavily polluted areas and in cases of emergency.

6. *Financing*

The cost incurred in preventing or abating pollution should be borne by whoever causes the pollution. This does not preclude aid from Public Authorities.

7. *Pollution in frontier areas*

Pollution in frontier areas should be the subject of joint study by the countries concerned, in accordance with a procedure to be laid down.

8. *Town and country planning*

The planning of urban and industrial development should take into account the effects of such development on air pollution; adequate consideration should be given by Planning Authorities to the maintenance and creation of green spaces.

PART III

Government aid for research

In order to make air pollution control more effective, Governments must encourage study and research, at national and international level, on the technical means of preventing or abating air pollution, on the dispersal of pollutants and on their effects on man and his environment.

This declaration having been adopted, the Committee of Experts on Air Pollution will now concentrate on the following problems which take priority on their agenda:

—heating appliances
—limitation of emissions
—correlation between pollution and town planning
—trans-frontier pollution problems
—installations important from the point of view of air pollution
—the right of neighbouring inhabitants to make objections and complaints.

At the moment it is not possible to say what stage has been reached in the above-mentioned activities as the work of the Committee is confidential.

Another of the tasks of this Committee is to collect information from different sources and distribute it to the national administrations which are represented on the Committee. This information would concern, in particular, changes made in the laws and regulations and new developments in the legislation of member States, as well as lists of scientific, technical or administrative bodies, public or private, permanently engaged in the campaign against air pollution.

CONCLUSION

It is difficult to judge the results of the work undertaken if one does not bear in mind that these activities are just beginning. The first aim of the Council of Europe was to find the appropriate ground for European cooperation, taking into account the activities of other intergovernmental organizations. The Council of Europe also intended to facilitate national activities by establishing personal and working contacts among national experts. This aim was achieved by the Conference and its follow-up.

Now a second stage has been reached, and the experts are making the first steps towards cooperation, mainly in the fields of legislation, administration, and information. One must also remember that among the member countries of the Council of Europe only a few have special legislation regarding air pollution and that, apart from the United Kingdom, these countries adopted such legislation in recent years. This is both an advantage and a disadvantage. It is an advantage because as many member countries have not yet adopted special legislation it will be easier to establish it on a common basis, which will make cooperation much simpler in the future. This explains why the first aim of the experts was to establish general principles on the matter. It is a disadvantage because the experience of the member countries in this field is not yet extensive enough, and therefore the experts have to proceed slowly and cautiously when dealing with legislative problems.

Multilateral work in an intergovernmental organization is always extremely difficult and lengthy since one must take into account different customs and sometimes conflicting interests. However, everybody is convinced that in a technical field, such as that of air pollution control, each country has something to gain through a collective analysis of the problems and through collective decisions. Therefore, although the results are not yet spectacular, the governments seem to attach great importance to the work of this Committee.

DATE DUE

MY 22 '73		
MY 30 '73		
MY 26 '74		
NO 13 '78		
JUN 1 1981		
JUN 2 1984		
MAY 2 6 '86		
FEB 22 '91		
MAR 1 2 '91		
JAN 0 8 2002		
		PRINTED IN U.S.A.